2010 SCIENCE YEAR

The World Book Annual Science Supplement

A review of science
and technology
during the
2009 school year

World Book, Inc.

a Scott Fetzer company
Chicago

www.worldbook.com

World Book, Inc.
233 N. Michigan Ave.
Chicago, IL 60601

ISBN: 978-0-7166-0563-8
ISSN: 0080-7621
Library of Congress Control Number: 65-21776
Printed in the United States of America.

STAFF

Andrews, Peter, B.A., M.S.
Free-Lance Writer. *[Computers and electronics]*

Barker, David, B.S., M.S., Ph.D.
Project Manager, Publishers Resource Group.
[Conservation]

Bernick, Jeanne, B.S.
Crops and Issues Editor,
Farm Journal Media. *[Agriculture]*

Brett, Carlton E., M.S., Ph.D.
Professor, Department of Geology,
University of Cincinnati.
[Fossil studies]

Bruce, Timothy J., B.S., Ph.D.
Professor and Associate Chair, Department of
Psychiatry and Behavioral Medicine, University of
Illinois College of Medicine at Peoria. *[Psychology]*

Chiras, Daniel, B.A., Ph.D.
Visiting Professor, Colorado College
at Colorado Springs.
[Environmental pollution]

Despres, Renée, Ph.D.
Free-Lance Writer. *[Medical research]*

Dreier, David L., B.S.
Free-Lance Science Writer and Editor.
[Science Studies, Plastic Planet]

Finger, Brad, B.A.
Free-Lance Science Writer. *[Consumer Science,
How to "Green" Your Lawn; Vitamin D: Is It a
Miracle Vitamin?]*

Graff, Gordon, B.S., M.S., Ph.D.
Free-Lance Science Writer.
[Chemistry]

Hay, William W., B.S., M.S., Ph.D.
Professor Emeritus, Geological Sciences,
University of Colorado at Boulder. *[Geology]*

Haymer, David S., M.S., Ph.D.
Professor, Department of Cell and Molecular
Biology, John A. Burns School of Medicine,
University of Hawaii at Manoa. *[Genetics]*

Hester, Thomas R., B.A., Ph.D.
Professor Emeritus of Anthropology,
University of Texas at Austin. *[Archaeology]*

Johnson, Christina S., B.A., M.S.
Science Writer and Editor,
California Sea Grant, Scripps Institution
of Oceanography. *[Oceanography]*

Johnson, John, Jr.
Science Staff Writer, *Los Angeles Times.*
*[Special Report, Methane: Another Greenhouse
Troublemaker]*

Klein, Catherine J., Ph.D., R.D.
Director, Bionutrition Research, Children's
National Medical Center. *[Nutrition]*

Kowal, Deborah, M.A., P.A.
President, CTC Communications. *[Public health]*

Lunine, Jonathan I., B.S., M.S., Ph.D.
Professor of Planetary Science and Physics,
University of Arizona Lunar and Planetary
Laboratory. *[Consultant–Special Report, The
Search for Water on Mars; Astronomy]*

March, Robert H., A.B., M.S., Ph.D.
Professor Emeritus of Physics and Liberal Studies,
University of Wisconsin at Madison. *[Physics]*

Marschall, Laurence A., B.S., Ph.D.
W.K.T. Sahm Professor of Physics,
Gettysburg College. *[Books about science]*

Mastrandrea, Michael D., B.S., Ph.D.
Research Associate, Woods Institute
for the Environment, Stanford University.
[Climate change]

Milo, Richard G., B.A., M.A., Ph.D.
Professor of Anthropology,
Chicago State University. *[Anthropology]*

Morring, Frank, Jr., A.B.
Senior Space Technology Editor,
Aviation Week & Space Technology.
[Space technology]

Palmer, Todd, B.A., M.S., Ph.D.
Assistant Professor, Department of Biology,
University of Florida. *[Consultant–Mutualism:
The Pleasure of Your Company]*

Peres, Judy, B.A., M.S.L.
Free-Lance Writer.
[Drugs]

Phelan, Carolyn, B.A., M.Ln.
Reviewer, *Booklist,* and Librarian,
Northbrook Public Library. *[Books about science
for younger readers]*

Ricciuti, Edward, B.A.
Free-Lance Writer. *[Special Report,
The Timeless Scourge of Malaria; Biology]*

Schweitzer, Amy, B.S., M.S.
Bionutritionist, Children's National
Medical Center. *[Nutrition]*

Snow, John T., B.S.E.E., M.S.E.E., Ph.D.
Dean, College of Geosciences,
Professor of Meteorology, University of Oklahoma.
[Atmospheric science]

Snow, Theodore P., B.A., M.S., Ph.D.
Professor of Astrophysics,
University of Colorado at Boulder. *[Astronomy]*

Stille, Darlene R., B.A.
Free-Lance Science Writer. **[Special Report,**
Telescopes: 400 Years of Stargazing]

Tamarin, Robert H., B.S., Ph.D.
Dean of Sciences, University of Massachusetts
Lowell. *[Ecology]*

Teich, Albert H., B.S., Ph.D.
Director, Science and Policy Programs,
American Association for the
Advancement of Science. *[Science and society]*

Tsai, Irene, B.S., M.S., Ph.D.
Free-Lance Writer. *[Engineering]*

White-Fournier, Melissa A.
Free-Lance Writer.
[**Consumer Science,** *Distributed Computing:
Supercomputing@home; Bamboo—The New
"Wood";* **Close-Up,** *Energy—and Controversy—
from Canadian Sands]*

Mary Alice Anderson, B.S., M.A.
Lead Media Specialist, Winona
Area Public Schools, Winona,
Minnesota, United States

Ali Banuazizi, B.S., M.A., Ph.D.
Professor of Political Science and
Codirector of Middle Eastern &
Islamic Studies Program, Boston
College, Chestnut Hill,
Massachusetts, United States

David J. Bercuson, O.C., B.A.,
M.A., Ph.D. Professor of History
and Director, Centre for Military
and Strategic Studies, University
of Calgary, Calgary, Alberta,
Canada

Marianna Anderson Busch, B.A.,
Ph.D. Professor, Department of
Chemistry and Biochemistry,
Baylor University, Waco, Texas,
United States

Jesus Garcia, M.A., Ed.D. Professor
of Curriculum and Instruction,
University of Nevada, Las Vegas,
Las Vegas, Nevada, United States

Marc B. Garnick, M.D. Professor
of Medicine, Harvard Medical
School, Harvard University;
Physician, Beth Israel Deaconess
Medical Center, Boston,
Massachusetts, United States

Michael F. Graves, B.A., M.A.,
Ph.D. Professor Emeritus of
Literacy Education, University of
Minnesota, Twin Cities Campus,
Minneapolis, Minnesota, United
States

John T. Greene, B.A., M.A., Ph.D.
Professor Emeritus of Religious
Studies, Michigan State
University, East Lansing,
Michigan, United States

Robert Hodierne, B.A.
Associate Professor of Journalism
University of Richmond
Richmond, Virginia, United States

Alan E. Mann, B.A., M.A., Ph.D.
Professor of Anthropology,
Princeton University, Princeton,
New Jersey, United States

William McKeen, B.A., M.A.,
Ph.D. Professor and Chair,
Department of Journalism,
College of Journalism and
Communication, University of
Florida, Gainesville, Florida,
United States

Jay M. Pasachoff, A.B., A.M.,
Ph.D. Field Memorial Professor of
Astronomy and Director, Hopkins
Observatory of Williams College,
Williamstown, Massachusetts,
United States

Michael Plante, B.A., M.A., Ph.D.
Jessie J. Poesch Professor in Art,
Newcomb Art Department,
Tulane University, New Orleans,
Louisiana, United States

Robert B. Prigo, B.S., M.S., Ph.D.
Director of Teacher Education
and Professor of Physics,
Middlebury College, Middlebury,
Vermont, United States

Michael Seidel, B.A., M.A., Ph.D.
Jesse and George Siegel Professor
of Humanities, Columbia
University, New York City, New
York, United States

Whitney Smith, A.B., A.M., Ph.D.
Director, The Flag Research
Center, Winchester,
Massachusetts, United States

Scott L. Waugh, B.A., Ph.D.
Executive Vice Chancellor and
Provost, University of California,
Los Angeles, United States

CONTENTS

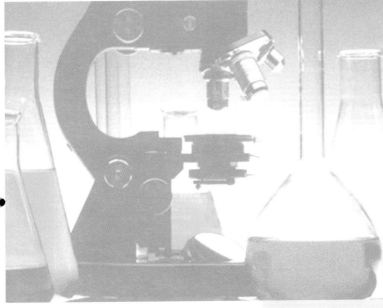

MAJOR SCIENCE STORIES

A worldwide influenza scare and discoveries about water on Mars, planets around distant stars, and Neandertal genetics were among the many developments that made the year eventful in science and technology. These two pages present highlights of stories chosen by the editors of *Science Year* as among the most memorable or important of the year, along with page references for the complete articles.

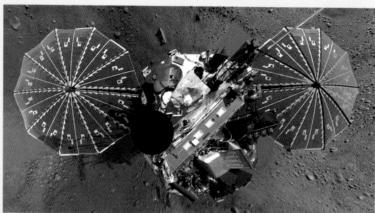

PLANETARY PORTRAITS

Astronomers produced the first photographs of extrasolar planets—planets orbiting stars other than the sun—in 2008 and 2009. Some of these planets were detected using a new technique that images the *infrared* (heat) radiation they emit. In the Special Reports section, see **TELESCOPES: 400 YEARS OF STARGAZING**, page 24; in the Science News Update section, see **ASTRONOMY**, page 164.

EARLIEST HUMAN FOOTPRINTS

Footprints made 1.5 million years ago in what is now Kenya are the earliest preserved tracks left by human beings—that is, members of the genus *Homo*. In February 2009, an international group of scientists announced that the tracks were left by individuals who had feet similar to those of modern human beings. In the Science News Update section, see **ANTHROPOLOGY**, page 155.

PHOENIX "TASTES" WATER ON MARS

NASA's Phoenix Mars Lander made important discoveries about water on Mars from May to November 2008. Instruments on the lander "tasted" ice uncovered just below the surface, providing scientists with the first direct evidence of water on Mars, and detected falling snow. In the Special Reports section, see **THE SEARCH FOR WATER ON MARS**, page 100; in the Science News Update section, see **SPACE TECHNOLOGY**, page 262.

SWINE FLU SCARE

A new strain of influenza—popularly called "swine flu" but officially designated as H1N1—emerged in Mexico in early 2009. By June, the World Health Organization documented at least 18,000 cases and 120 deaths caused by the viral infection worldwide—including at least 17 deaths in the United States. In the Science News Update section, see **PUBLIC HEALTH**, page 254.

ANALYSIS OF NEANDERTAL GENETICS

The first rough draft of the *genome* (set of genetic information) of Neandertals was announced in February 2009 by an international team of scientists. A report on the genetic information, extracted from fossils of the extinct prehistoric human beings, suggested that little interbreeding occurred between Neandertals and modern-type human beings. In the Science News Update section, see **GENETICS**, page 226.

GOOD GORILLA NEWS

In August 2008, conservationists announced the results of a detailed census of western lowland gorillas in Congo (Brazzaville). The census revealed 125,000 gorillas that were previously not counted—boosting estimates of the world gorilla population to perhaps 175,000. In the Science News Update section, see **CONSERVATION**, page 197.

STEM CELL RESEARCH ADVANCES

In March 2009, United States President Barack Obama issued an executive order that allowed new cell lines to be used in federally funded medical research on embryonic stem cells. In addition, a number of research findings involving adult stem cells were announced in 2008. In the Science News Update section, see **GENETICS**, page 226; **MEDICAL RESEARCH**, page 232; and **SCIENCE AND SOCIETY**, page 256.

BISPHENOL A HEALTH RISKS

Possible health risks associated with the chemical bisphenol A (BPA), used to make plastic bottles and various other plastic products, attracted public attention in 2008 and 2009. Studies released in September 2008 described these health risks, and six companies announced in March 2009 that they would no longer sell infant nursing bottles made with BPA. In the Science Studies section, see **PLASTIC PLANET**, page 114.

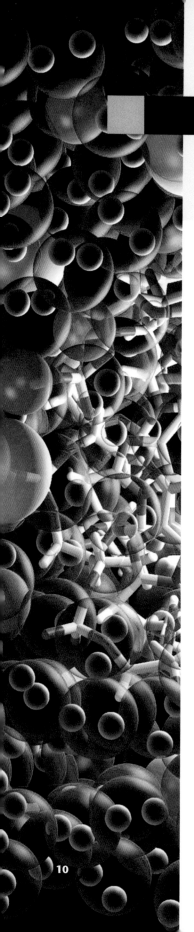

SPECIAL REPORTS

These feature articles take an in-depth look at significant and timely subjects in science and technology.

Fascinating Facts about Fossil Feces

By Alfred J. Smuskiewicz

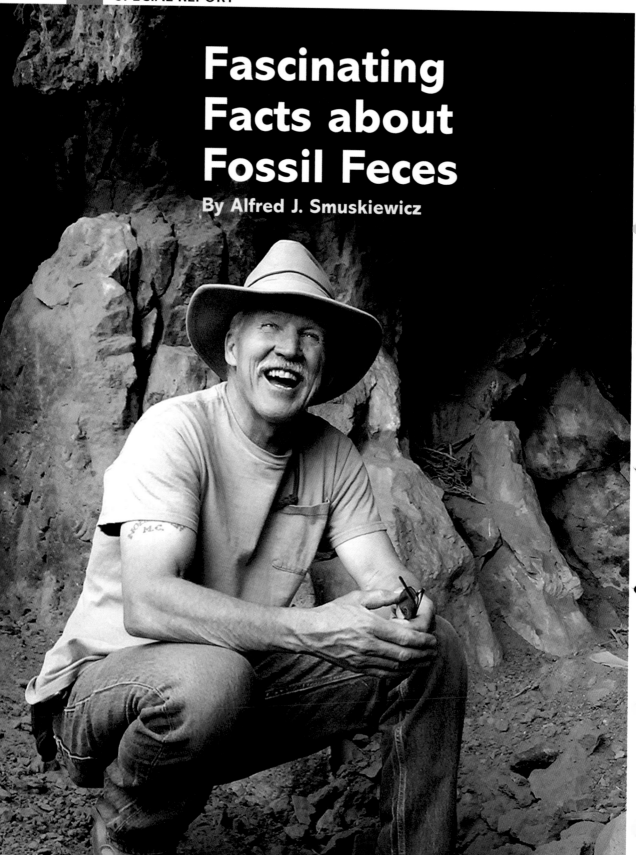

Coprolites, or fossilized feces, are providing important clues about early human and animal life.

Archaeologist Dennis Jenkins poses at the mouth of an Oregon cave where he and colleagues from the University of Oregon discovered a human coprolite containing 14,300-year-old human DNA. The DNA provides some of the earliest direct evidence for the presence of people in North America.

TERMS AND CONCEPTS

Carnivorous: Describes animals that feed primarily on other animals.

Coprolite: A fossilized segment of feces. Over time, minerals dissolved in water largely replace the organic material in the original feces.

Gas chromatography: A scientific technique by which substances in a sample are chemically separated for easy identification.

Herbivorous: Describes animals that feed primarily on plant material.

Phytolith: A calcium- or silicon-based crystal that forms inside a plant cell.

Radioisotope dating: A method for determining the date of rock or rock-like material by assessing the ratio of uranium-235 to lead-207.

Scanning electron microscopy (SEM): A technology for viewing extremely small particles. SEM devices use streams of electrons instead of light beams.

Some scientists make great discoveries by looking into the vast, starry sky, the microscopic nuclei of atoms, or the complex tissues of the human body. Other scientists prefer to look into old latrines and trash dumps. In 2008, scientists investigating a 14,300-year-old latrine in an Oregon cave made a major discovery about one of the most important and highly debated questions in archaeology—when people first arrived in North America. That discovery came in the form of human coprolites, which is the scientific term for fossilized feces. The coprolites—the oldest human evidence of this sort ever found in North America—strongly suggested that the first Americans were living on the continent more than 1,000 years earlier than many scientists had believed.

Coprolites—from both people and other animals—give scientists a unique way to study the past. For example, findings in this fossilized waste have provided exciting information about the eating habits of dinosaurs, the behaviors and health status of prehistoric people, and past changes in environmental conditions and climate.

Most coprolites are composed mainly of calcium compounds, which form into the shape of the feces and its contents through mineralization. In this process, the organic material decays and is replaced by minerals seeping in from the surrounding environment. Many coprolites also contain *desiccated* (dried) bits of undigested material eaten by the animal that left the coprolite. These telltale remains may include pieces of bone or shellfish shell, feathers, scales, eggshells, insect *exoskeletons* (the hard outer covering of insects), seeds, pollen, leaves, and even undigested muscle tissue.

Coprolite fossils range in age from hundreds to millions of years old. They vary widely in size and in shape, from spiral or cylindrical to cone-like or flat. The particular characteristics of a coprolite depend upon the species of animal that left it and the nature of the environment in which it was left. In some cases, scientists can easily determine the species of animal that deposited the coprolite, particularly when other fossils of the animal are found nearby. In other cases,

A coprolite protrudes from a chalk cliff in Kansas. Feces are sometimes buried in mud soon after being deposited. Over time, the mud forms a layer in sedimentary rock. Weather conditions may eventually erode fossils such as this coprolite out of the rock.

INSIDE AND OUTSIDE A COPROLITE

The coprolites on the left illustrate the variety of shapes that fossilized feces can take. Despite their different appearances, all of these coprolites share approximately the same calcified mineral composition.

The inset (right) shows a tiny bit of *dessicated* (dried) organic matter in the open palm of a scientist. The material, which includes bits of feathers from a sage grouse, was extracted from a coprolite. The animal depositing the feces evidently dined on fowl.

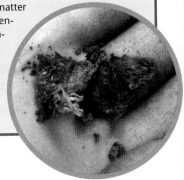

the producer of the coprolite is more of a mystery. Since the English geologist William Buckland published the first study of coprolites in 1829, researchers have collected coprolites from a wide variety of animals. Among them are dinosaurs; ichthyosaurs and plesiosaurs (extinct marine reptiles); prehistoric sharks, birds, and mammals; and modern-type people and human ancestors.

Because fecal matter deteriorates rapidly, coprolites are fairly rare. In order for fecal matter to become fossilized as a coprolite, it must be rapidly buried in sediment and protected from rain, flooding, and other conditions that would break it down. Archaeologists, paleontologists, and other coprolite hunters often search for coprolites in cliffs and chalk formations where sedimentary rock layers have became exposed due to erosion by water or wind. Archaeological sites that are thought to be locations of ancient latrines or *middens* (trash dumps) are often rich sources of human coprolites. Coprolites have also been found inside the intestines of mummies in Egypt, South America, and elsewhere.

How scientists analyze coprolites

After a coprolite is uncovered in the field, it is usually taken to a laboratory, where a technician carefully breaks it open to study its contents. Often, the next step is to soak the fossil in a special rehydration solution made of a chemical called trisodium phosphate. This treatment softens any desiccated organic material in the fossil and makes it pliable. The process may also provide clues as to the identity of the coprolite-producing species. For example, human coprolites typically turn brown or black when exposed to trisodium phosphate.

The author:

Alfred J. Smuskiewicz is a free-lance writer specializing in science and medicine.

One of the chief methods used to examine coprolites is scanning electron microscopy (SEM). In this type of microscopy, a beam of *electrons* (negatively charged particles) strikes the specimen, causing the specimen to give off other electrons in particular patterns. A collecting device counts these "secondary" electrons, and a computer converts the numerical data into images, which are displayed on a monitor at magnifications of several hundred thousand times.

Researchers have used SEM and other laboratory imaging procedures to identify many kinds of biological material in coprolites. For example, they have found certain types of microbes and fungi that reproduced inside the feces after it was deposited by the animal. Various kinds of pollen, which either was eaten by the animal or became attached to the expelled feces, have also been identified. In addition, SEM imaging may reveal plant phytoliths, calcium- or silicon-based crystals that form inside certain plant cells. These crystals, which pass through animals' digestive systems intact, have distinctive shapes that help identify plant species eaten by the animals.

Laboratory analyses of chemical compounds in coprolites provide additional clues about the animals that left the feces. One of the main methods of analysis is gas chromatography, in which substances in a sample are chemically separated for easy identification. The detection of relative levels

RESEARCHER EXAMINES COPROLITES

A researcher (right) carefully examines a coprolite from a *T. rex* dinosaur—one of the largest land predators ever to inhabit Earth. The fearsomely toothed carnivore powerfully chomped its victims' bodies, crushing bone.

A close-up view of the coprolite (below) reveals undigested bone fragments from the *T. rex* meal. The bones are the darker, ridged areas.

of the male hormone testosterone and the female hormone estrogen, for example, suggests the sex of the individual producing the feces. The presence or excess of a particular mineral may provide evidence of disease.

One of the most advanced laboratory methods used to examine coprolites is an analysis of the deoxyribonucleic acid (DNA) in the samples. DNA is the molecule that makes up genes. It consists of thousands of tiny chemical units called nucleotides, the specific sequence of which is unique to each species. Thus, the DNA detected in a coprolite may suggest the animal species that made the feces—assuming the DNA comes from shed intestinal cells. Alternatively, the DNA may suggest the species of the plants or prey consumed by the animal. In cases in which such DNA evidence is unclear, scientists may be able to identify the coprolite producer by examining other contents or evidence found with the fossil.

An important part of any study of coprolites is determining the time when the coprolite was produced. As with other fossils, researchers use several methods to arrive at ages for coprolites, including chemical analyses of the coprolites and of the rock surrounding the coprolites. One method, called radioisotope dating, is based on measurements of a radioactive element in rock called uranium-235 that decays over time at a known rate to form lead-207. By comparing the amount of uranium-235 with that of lead-207, the age of the sample can be estimated.

Coprolites unlock dinosaur secrets

Some of the oldest known coprolites have given scientists fascinating insights into dinosaur behavior. For example, in 1998, paleobiologist Karen Chin of the United States Geological Survey described a large coprolite, 43 centimeters (17 inches) long by 15 centimeters (6 inches) wide, found in southwestern Saskatchewan. Chin dated the coprolite to between 70 million and 66 million years ago. Based on the age and extraordinary size of the coprolite and its location in sediments rich in dinosaur fossils, Chin proposed that it was produced by the large *carnivorous* (meat-eating) dinosaur, *Tyrannosaurus rex,* or *T. rex.*

SEM examination of the *T. rex* coprolite contents revealed crushed bones of *herbivorous* (plant-eating) dinosaurs, the prey of *T. rex.* The pulverized condition of the bones suggested to Chin that *T. rex* may have chewed its food considerably before swallowing, rather than simply gulping it, as some experts had previously proposed.

Chin and her colleagues reported on an even larger dinosaur coprolite in 2003. This 75-million-year-old feces fossil, discovered in southeastern Alberta, was 64 centimeters (25 inches) long and 17 centimeters (7 inches) wide. Based upon dinosaur fossils unearthed in the same sedimentary layer nearby, the researchers theorized that the coprolite had been produced by a close relative of *T. rex*—ironically, a smaller species.

The ultimate importance of the coprolite find was that it contained the oldest known impressions of dinosaur flesh, identified as undigested muscle tissue from a duck-billed dinosaur, a favorite prey of large, carnivorous dinosaurs.

In 2005, paleobotanist Vandana Prasad of the Birbal Sahni Institute in India described a 70-million-year-old coprolite left by a titanosaur, a giant herbivorous dinosaur. An examination of the coprolite revealed phytoliths of many species of grass, palm, *conifer* (cone-bearing plants), and other plants. According to Prasad, the fossil proved that titanosaurs fed on an extensive variety of plants. It also showed that grasses were abundant and diverse and had a widespread range earlier than previously thought. In addition, Prasad reported that distinctive burrows seen inside the coprolite revealed that several species of dung beetle helped recycle the dinosaur feces.

Coprolites and the human story

Scientists are finding that the analysis of very ancient coprolites—not necessarily human—can open a window on human origins. In February 2009, researchers with the University of the Witwatersrand in Johannesburg, South Africa, announced the discovery of human hairs in a hyena coprolite unearthed from a South African cave. The researchers dated the coprolite to from 257,000 to 195,000 years ago. Prior to this find, the oldest known human hairs were from a 9,000-year-old mummy. The hairs in the hyena coprolite did not retain any DNA or protein-rich compounds. But their clear form and structure when viewed under high magnification closely resembled the hair structure in modern humans. Experts speculated that the hairs were either from anatomically modern *Homo sapiens,* which began to appear sometime after 200,000 years ago, or from another hominid species, *H. heidelbergensis,* which appeared roughly 1 million years ago and later died out. The discovery, researchers noted, emphasizes that early humans were part of the food chain, subject to being eaten by other animals. Researchers hoped to find DNA-containing human hairs in other hyena coprolites yet to be unearthed from the South African cave.

Coprolites can also provide information about the activities and behaviors of human beings who lived in prehistoric times or early historic times. (The invention of writing around 3500 B.C. separates prehistoric from historic times.)

The arrival of the first human beings in the Americas has long kindled scholarly debate. The debate centers on the date at which people initially arrived and where they came from. In April 2008, archaeologist Dennis Jenkins of the University of Oregon in Eugene reported the discovery of hundreds of human coprolites in caves near Paisley, Oregon. Radioactive dating of the coprolites revealed an age of approximately

CLUES TO ANCIENT DIETS

Coprolites can provide important information about the diet of the person or animal that deposited them. A human coprolite (right) found in the United Kingdom at a Viking settlement dating from the A.D. 800's revealed that the individual ate mostly meat and bread. A dinosaur coprolite (below) found in Saskatchewan, Canada, probably from a tyrannosaur, contains the remains of what appears to be a juvenile plant-eating dinosaur. The remains suggested that the tyrannosaur chewed its food rather than simply gulping it, as scientists had believed. Both coprolites are shown to scale, though not to actual size.

14,300 years. In a few of the coprolites, the researchers found intestinal cells from which they were able to extract DNA. Comparisons of this genetic material with DNA from modern American Indians and from certain population groups in northeastern Asia revealed important similarities. According to Jenkins, this provides strong support for the theory of Asian ancestry for American Indians.

The Paisley coprolites were the earliest known direct evidence of a human presence in North America—about 1,500 years earlier than the oldest known "Clovis" stone spear points. (For much of the 1900's, scientists regarded the Clovis artifacts, unearthed near Clovis, New Mexico, as the earliest evidence of a human presence in the Americas.) In recent years, other archaeological finds in North and South America have suggested earlier dates than Clovis for the arrival of people in the New World, but the Paisley coprolites were unique in providing direct human evidence through extracted DNA.

Evidence of diet

Human coprolites typically offer clues about diet. For example, seeds of such crops as maize, wheat, squash, tomatoes, grapes, and melons are signs of agricultural activity. From such evidence, scientists often are able to infer the availability of food and the relative well-being of a population in a particular time and place.

An 87-million-year-old fossil that was excavated from the Smoky Hill chalk formation of western Kansas has provided a fascinating snapshot of prehistoric animal behavior. The specimen contains the fossilized intestines of a large fish known as *Cimolichthys* within which is a piece of fossilized feces about to be passed. The coprolite contains a piece of the skull of a fish (outlined in white) known as *Enchodus*. The fossil shows that *Cimolichthys* died before passing the *Enchodus* remains from its body.

The oldest known human coprolites come from caves in southern France that were inhabited by a variety of prehistoric peoples, among them evolutionary ancestors of modern human beings, *H. sapiens*. Evidence from radioactive dating suggests that the oldest of these coprolites date to 300,000 years ago. Researchers have identified numerous coprolites left between that early date and about 50,000 years ago by Neandertals (classified as either *H. neanderthalensis* or a subspecies of *H. sapiens*) and *H. erectus* in the caves. The coprolites contain numerous phytoliths representing many species of plants. The phytoliths reveal the importance of foraging for plant-based foods in these early human cultures.

Plant material extracted from numerous human coprolites discovered in southwestern Texas and dating from about 7,000 to 1,000 years ago suggests that the climate there remained fairly constant over a long period and supported a relatively stable society among the resident hunter-gatherer tribes. Throughout the period, these people consumed yucca, agave, sotol (a relative of agave), cactus, and mesquite. In Utah, scientists have used spores from a certain fungus found in ancient human coprolites as evidence that American Indians in that area consumed rabbits and small rodents. Their conclusion is based on the fact that rabbits and small rodents feed on grasses that are commonly tainted with the fungus.

Some of the coprolites found in the southwestern United States have led to surprising discoveries. In 2000, archaeological excavations of a previously inhabited site in southwestern Colorado uncovered human coprolites and butchered human remains. The scientists attributed the site to Ancestral Puebloans, an American Indian culture that had thrived in what is now the southwestern United States before about A.D. 1300, and dated the find to 850 years ago. An analysis of the coprolites revealed residues of myoglobin proteins that are found only in human muscle tissue. To Brian R. Billman, the anthropologist who led the team investigating the remains, this evidence indicated that there was an outbreak of cannibalism among the Ancestral Puebloans during a period of regional warfare. Contemporary Hopi and Zuni people, who are descendants of this group, reject allegations of cannibalism in previous American Indian societies, and the issue continues to be highly controversial.

A coprolite discovered during the 1970's on the site of a Viking settlement of the A.D. 800's in York, England, revealed that the individual who deposited it consumed mainly a diet of meat and bread. In addition, researchers found hundreds of eggs of parasitic intestinal worms in the coprolite. Other investigators have found clear evidence of parasitic infestation in coprolites within the intestines of ancient human mummies in Egypt and South and North America. Remains of eggs and larvae of intestinal parasites, which are often well preserved in coprolites, are important indications of the relative health of populations. Some of the parasites link people to domesticated animals and are, therefore, markers of agricultural societies rather than hunter-gatherer societies. The findings are also a reminder that for most of human history, people have suffered from an array of parasitic diseases that modern medicine and sanitation have greatly reduced or eliminated in developed countries.

Evidence of technology

Coprolites also provide intriguing clues about the ways people collected, prepared, and preserved food. High levels of carbon in coprolites indicate that people ate charred meat—sure evidence of cooking. Other technologies can be inferred from coprolites as well. Coprolites uncovered from the intestines of naturally occurring mummies in ancient caves in the Ozark Mountains of Arkansas contain fragments of acorn shells—proof that midcontinent American Indians of pre-Columbian times learned how to remove the bitter tannin found in acorns to make these nuts edible.

At archaeological sites in the Pecos Valley of southwestern Texas, investigators found human coprolites containing the remains of fish so tiny that they could not have been caught with a net or a line and hook. At the same site, they found Mexican buckeye seeds, a toxic botanical that humans would not have eaten but that could have poisoned fish. The researchers theorize that the prehistoric Indians living in the region put ground-up Mexican buckeye seeds into rivers or lakes to poison the tiny fish and then skimmed their floating bodies off the water surface.

Evidence about climate

Besides providing information about animal and human diet and behavior, coprolites also contain clues about ancient physical environments. Pollen from tree species suggests the presence of a forest; pollen

MOA COPROLITES

The moa (right) was a flightless bird that once inhabited the islands that are now New Zealand. Several species flourished, ranging from turkey-sized to a 3-meter (10-foot) giant. All species of moa were extinct by the 1700's, though the larger-sized species had disappeared centuries earlier. Paleontologists have unearthed and studied a number of moa fossils, including coprolites.

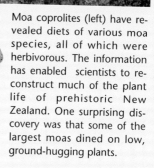

A team of paleontologists, sponsored by South Australia's Adelaide University and New Zealand's Department of Conservation and University of Otago, retrieve moa fossils, including coprolites, from beneath a mound of rocks in the Dart River Valley on New Zealand's South Island.

Moa coprolites (left) have revealed diets of various moa species, all of which were herbivorous. The information has enabled scientists to reconstruct much of the plant life of prehistoric New Zealand. One surprising discovery was that some of the largest moas dined on low, ground-hugging plants.

from cactuses indicates an arid region; and fish or waterfowl bones reveal an aquatic environment.

Evolutionary biologists Jose S. Carrion of the University of Murcia in Spain and Louis Scott of the University of the Free State in South Africa have extensively investigated coprolites left by hyenas in a wide variety of Mediterranean and African locales to document changes in climate during the last glacial epoch (2 million to 11,500 years ago). Hyena coprolites are an excellent resource for this purpose because hyenas are *omnivores* (animals that eat almost anything), and they range widely in their search for food. Using data from these coprolites, the researchers were able to open a window into climates of the times. They concluded, for example, that the climate of the Cape coast of South Africa was cooler and more like inland conditions early in the glacial epoch than it is today.

Molecular biologist Hendrik Poinar of the Max Plank Institute for Evolutionary Anthropology in Germany and colleagues investigated plant remains and DNA in coprolites deposited from 28,500 to 11,000 years ago by giant ground sloths (now extinct) in present-day Nevada. From these analyses, they concluded that the climate of the Great Basin region of North America became increasingly drier during that period.

Coprolites will surely continue to provide scientists with new insights. Just as the household waste that people toss out every day can tell us much about their behaviors and habits, the waste produced by animal and human bodies long ago can tell scientists a great deal about past life and past conditions on Earth.

■ FOR ADDITIONAL INFORMATION

Web sites

ArchNet, the World Wide Web Virtual Library of Archaeology, maintained by the Archaeological Research Institute of Arizona State University—
http://archnet.asu.edu
Minnesota State University (Mankato) EMuseum of Archaeology—
http://www.mnsu.edu/emuseum/archaeology
"When Dinosaurs Roamed North America": Discovery Channel online exhibit—
http://dsc.discovery.com/convergence/dinos/dinos.html

Periodicals

Cury, Andrew. "Pre-Clovis Breakthrough." *Archaeology.* April 3, 2008—
http://www.archaeology.org/online/features/coprolites
Jenkins, Dennis. "Oregon Discovery Challenges Beliefs about First Humans."
WTTW11: The Online News Hour. June 30, 2008—
http://pbs.org/newshour/bb/science/jan-june08/firstamerican_06-30.html

Telescopes: 400 Years of Stargazing

by Darlene R. Stille

Although people have been studying the skies for centuries, only since the mid-1900's have astronomers been able to "see" the stars in more than visible light.

Long before the dawn of history, people gazed at the nighttime sky and wondered: What were the pinpoints of light that dotted the heavens? What was the milky-white band that stretched across the horizon? What meaning did these objects have for those who lived on Earth? Ancient astronomers tracked the movements of the sun, moon, and stars across the sky. They used their observations to create the first calendars and to develop theories about Earth and its place in the universe.

For thousands of years, all the discoveries made about the heavens were limited to what people could see with the unaided eye. Then, in 1609, astronomy changed forever. An Italian mathematician and astronomer, Galileo, used a telescope to study the sky. Galileo did not invent the telescope. That honor probably goes to Dutch lens makers, who made a handheld telescope in 1608. But Galileo was the first to use a telescope in the practical service of astronomy. From then on, the telescope became the astronomer's most important tool.

Like all telescopes, these first instruments magnified objects that are far away. Through a telescope, Galileo and later astronomers made out previously unobserved details on the moon and planets. Galileo sketched and mapped the surface of the moon. He found moons orbiting Jupiter and discovered that the white band in the sky—the Milky Way—contains individual stars. His observations of Venus supported a new theory that the sun, not Earth, is the center of our solar system.

At first, telescopes were used mainly to observe planets in the solar system. As telescopes became bigger and more powerful, astronomers turned their attention to the Milky Way. They found that it is shaped like a spiral. They found that our solar system lies far out on one of the galaxy's spiral arms and that our sun, with all the other stars, orbits the galactic center. More shocking still was the discovery that our galaxy is but one of many in a vast universe.

By the mid-1900's, astronomers were using telescopes that can "see" in more than visible light. Visible light is part of a "rainbow" of radiant energy called the electromagnetic spectrum. All objects in space give off electromagnetic rays that travel as waves. Different kinds of electromagnetic waves vary in wavelength, the distance between the crests of the waves. By detecting other types of electromagnetic rays, these new telescopes revealed such previously unknown objects as quasars, pulsars, and black holes.

Using these evolving telescopes, astronomers probed the farthest reaches of space. They calculated how large and how old the universe is. They questioned how the universe began and how—or if—it might end. Thanks to the telescope, astronomers were able to develop not only a better understanding of the universe, but also of our place within it.

In 1609, Italian astronomer Galileo, depicted in an engraving from the 1800's, became the first scientist to use the telescope in the practical service of astronomy.

The Horsehead Nebula (opposite page, far left inset) appears in far greater detail in an image made by an optical telescope in 2008 than it does in the first photograph ever taken of the massive cloud of gas and dust (left inset) in 1888. The William Herschel Telescope (bottom), named in honor of British astronomer Sir William Herschel, sits atop a mountain in the Canary Islands.

Land-based Optical Telescopes

Professional and amateur astronomers alike use optical telescopes. These telescopes "see" in the visible part of the electromagnetic spectrum, just as human eyes do. There are three basic types of optical telescopes—refracting, reflecting, and refracting-reflecting. They produce an image by directing light to an eyepiece, photographic film, or a digital camera with a computer chip called a charge-coupled device (CCD).

Galileo's telescopes were refractors. Refracting telescopes use glass lenses in long tubes to collect and focus visible light. It is important for a telescope to produce a clear, sharp image. The larger the diameter of the lens, the clearer the image it can produce. Through refracting telescopes, astronomers could make out details on the moon and planets that were otherwise impossible to see.

Reflecting telescopes use mirrors to collect light. English physicist Sir Isaac Newton invented the reflecting telescope in 1668. Most optical telescopes today use mirrors.

The refracting-reflecting telescope, invented in 1930, uses lenses and mirrors. These telescopes provide wide views of the sky.

From 1948 to 1993, the 5-meter (200-inch) Hale reflector at Mt. Palomar Observatory in California was the largest operating telescope in the world. Astronomers used it to make important discoveries about galaxies. Different kinds of optical telescopes then came into use, including the Keck I telescope on Mauna Kea in Hawaii. The Keck I has 36 mirrors that work as one mirror 10 meters (33 feet) in diameter.

The author:
Darlene R. Stille is a free-lance science writer.

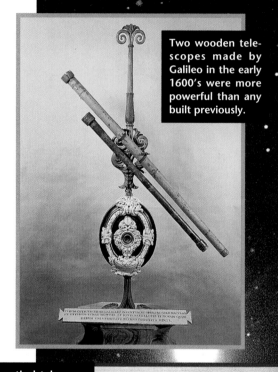

Two wooden telescopes made by Galileo in the early 1600's were more powerful than any built previously.

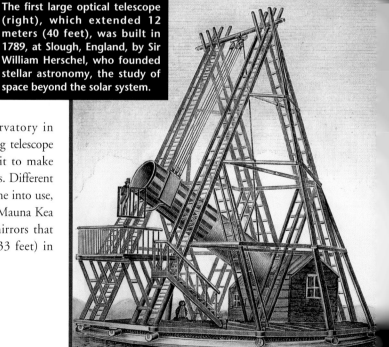

The first large optical telescope (right), which extended 12 meters (40 feet), was built in 1789, at Slough, England, by Sir William Herschel, who founded stellar astronomy, the study of space beyond the solar system.

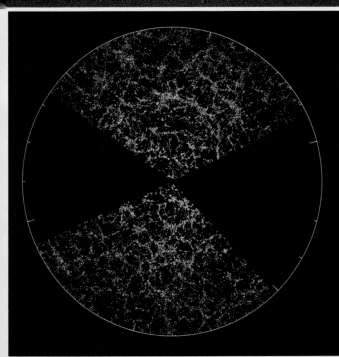

The spiral galaxy NG 7217 (left), which lie about 40 million light-year from Earth in the constella tion Pegasus, is captured i amazing detail in an imag made by the Willia Herschel Telescope (WHT (A light-year is the distanc light travels in a yea about 9.46 trillion kilome ters [5.88 trillion miles] The WHT is the thir largest single-mirror tel scope in the world and ca collect visible light as we as several other types electromagnetic radiation

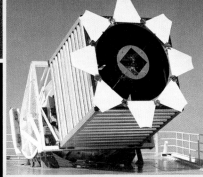

A 2.5-meter (100-inch) optical telescope at Apache Point Observatory in New Mexico (above) is used to conduct the Sloan Digital Sky Survey (SDSS), an ambi-tious census of the night sky. By 2009, SDSS scientists had cataloged more than 230 million celestial objects. They also produced a 3-dimensional map (left) showing the distribution of nearly 1 million galaxies, with Earth at the center. The colors of the galaxies indicate the ages of their stars, with red representing those with the oldest stars. (The dark wedges represent areas in which dust in the Milky Way obscures the view.)

Hubble Space Telescope

Some of the most amazing images, from planets in our solar system to objects in deepest space, were taken in the 1990's and 2000's by the Hubble Space Telescope. Launched by the space shuttle Discovery in 1990, the Hubble orbits about 610 kilometers (380 miles) above Earth, to eliminate distortions caused by the atmosphere.

The movement of air in Earth's atmosphere makes stars appear to twinkle and causes images from even the largest telescopes on Earth to blur. Many telescope observatories, therefore, are built on high mountaintops, where the atmosphere is thinner. The best way to escape atmospheric blurring, however, is to place a telescope in orbit around Earth where there is no atmosphere at all.

The Hubble telescope is a reflecting optical telescope with a mirror that is 240 centimeters (94 inches) in diameter. The mirror collects infrared and ultraviolet as well as visible light. The light can be directed to CCD's, which send digital images to Earth. The light can also be sent to an instrument called a spectrometer, which analyzes light from stars and other objects. Spectrometer analysis can provide scientists with such information as which elements stars contain, whether stars are moving toward Earth or away from it, and the temperature of objects in space.

A loosely bound collection of stars called an open star cluster surrounds a vivid planetary nebula known as NGC 2818 about 10,000 light-years from Earth, in a colorized image from Hubble. The colors of the nebula represent emissions from various elements—blue for oxygen, red for sulfur and nitrogen, and green for hydrogen. The nebula is the shell of a star from the cluster that collapsed and threw off the outer layers of its atmosphere. Few nebulae exist within open star clusters in the Milky Way. Stars usually collapse and create planetary nebulae only after existing for billions of years. Open star clusters rarely remain together long enough for a member to collapse.

A system of three galaxies called Arp 274 (above), about 400 million light-years from Earth, appears in a colorized image made by the Hubble Space Telescope in 2009 to celebrate the International Year of Astronomy (IYA). The IYA marks the 400th anniversary of Galileo's observations of the sky with a telescope. All three galaxies show evidence of new star formation (blue clusters). Although the galaxies appear to partially overlap, they are actually some distance apart.

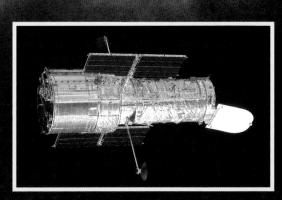

The Hubble Space Telescope (left) orbits about 610 kilometers (380 miles) above Earth, where it can create images free from the distortion caused by Earth's atmosphere. Launched in 1990, the telescope was named in honor of American astronomer Edwin P. Hubble, whose work revolutionized our understanding of the size and structure of the universe. In 2009, the Hubble received new parts and equipment upgrades that were expected to keep the telescope operational until at least 2014.

The magnificient images of celestial bodies taken by Hubble and other modern telescopes are highly popular with the public. These beauti- fully colored images, however, are created to reveal scientific information as well as to showcase the majesty of the cosmos.

How telescopes see

Telescopes detect visible light and other forms of electromagnetic radiation moving through space as waves of electricity and magnetism. They differ in wavelength, the distance from the crest of one wave to that of the next. The forms of electromagnetic radiation are—from shortest to longest wavelength—gamma rays, X rays, ultraviolet rays, visible light, infrared waves, microwaves, and radio waves. Some radio waves can be longer than a football field. Gamma-ray waves can be as short as the *nucleus* (core) of an atom. Visible light is the only part of the electromagnetic spectrum human eyes can see. We see waves of visible light as colors of the rainbow. Each color has a different wavelength, with blue being the shortest and red the longest.

In addition to moving waves, electromagnetic radiation can be thought of as tiny, traveling particles called photons. Photons are packets of energy. Those of ultraviolet light have more energy than those of infrared light.

Spectrum

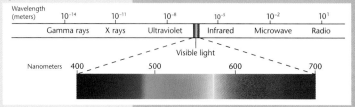

Wavelength (meters): 10^{-14} 10^{-11} 10^{-8} 10^{-5} 10^{-2} 10^{1}

Gamma rays X rays Ultraviolet Infrared Microwave Radio

Visible light

Nanometers 400 500 600 700

What radiation reveals

Name	Sources
Gamma waves	Collapsed stars; matter-antimatter annihilations
X rays	The sun's corona; disks of material around black holes; quasars
Ultraviolet rays	Hydrogen gas between the stars; the sun
Visible light	Planets; stars; galaxies; asteroids; comets
Infrared waves	Stars in the process of forming; relatively cool stars; planets
Microwaves	Radiation left over from the early universe
Radio waves	Pulsars; quasars; gas clouds orbiting the center of the Milky Way

Composite images

Composite images, such as that of the Pinwheel Galaxy (right), combine views from two or more telescopes. They allow scientists to compare various aspects of a celestial body in one image. To create this image, NASA specialists combined photographs of the galaxy made by the the Chandra X-ray Observatory, the Hubble Space Telescope, and the Spitzer Space Telescope. X-ray emissions from exploded stars, fantastically hot gases, and energy near black holes, registered by Chandra (opposite page, left), appear blue. The visible light emitted by stars in the galaxy, captured by Hubble, shines brightly in yellow (opposite page, center). Red areas represent heat emissions from dusty areas where stars may form, collected by Spitzer (opposite page, right).

Composite of images at right

Ultraviolet light	Visible light	Infrared light
◄ Shorter wavelength		Longer wavelength ►

Black-and-white images taken of filtered light

Color assigned to black-and-white images

Final image after combining the color images

Colorizing Images

Creating images of astronomical information requires artistry as well as technological expertise. Most telescopic photographs of planets, nebulae, stars, and other celestial bodies begin as black-and-white images. These images are made using filters that allow certain wavelengths to pass through but screen out others. Red, green, and blue—the primary colors of light—are added to the photographs using additional filters. Because of the way the human eye works, combining these three colors produces almost every color we can see.

Telescopic photographs are colorized to achieve various effects. Color is added to some photographs to emphasize subtle details for study, such as the towering clouds of gas and dust in the Eagle Nebula (left). For this image, blue represents light from a form of oxygen; green, from hydrogen; and red, from sulfur.

Other photographs are colorized to represent in a more vivid way the actual appearance of objects in space, such as the reddish color of Mars. Still others are colorized to create images of objects that would normally be invisible to human eyes, such as pulsars, which emit radio waves.

Chandra X-ray Observatory
X rays

Hubble Space Telescope
visible light

Spitzer Space Telescope
infrared light

Gamma-ray and X-ray Telescopes

The shortest wavelengths of electromagnetic radiation belong to gamma rays, which are given off when matter and antimatter annihilate one another. Matter and antimatter differ in such properties as electric charge. The Compton Gamma Ray Observatory, operating from 1991 to 2000, found gamma-ray bursts all over the sky. The telescopes on the Swift Gamma-Ray Burst Mission, launched in 2004, and the Fermi Gamma-ray Space Telescope, which followed in 2008, look for gamma rays coming from black holes, neutron stars, and other strange objects in the universe.

X rays have very short wavelengths and can go right through most kinds of material. They are used to make images of the inside of the body. Because X rays can also go through ordinary telescope mirrors, most X-ray telescopes have slats made of iron or lead—instead of mirrors—through which the X rays pass to a detector.

X rays come from the hottest places in space, such as the sun's corona and material spiraling into black holes. In such places, the force of gravity is so strong that not even light can escape. These X rays cannot pass through Earth's atmosphere. They must be studied with instruments on satellites. The first X-ray satellite was launched from Kenya in 1970 and named Uhuru—the Swahili word for *freedom*. The X-ray telescope that produces the clearest images is the Chandra X-ray Observatory, launched in 1999.

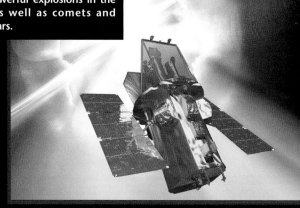

Telescopes on the Swift Gamma-Ray Burst Mission register a burst in an artist's rendering (below). Swift was launched in 2004 to detect and observe gamma-ray bursts, currently the most powerful explosions in the universe, as well as comets and exploding stars.

Comet 8P/Tuttle (above, center), which passed through the inner solar system in 2008, is captured in a composite image of ultraviolet and visible light by the Swift Mission. Data about the comet's frozen gas and dust enabled scientists to determine the makeup of the comet.

Electromagnetic energy shooting from a pulsar (arrow) has created a nebula resembling a large hand in a colorized image from the Chandra X-ray Observatory. Pulsars are believed to be dying stars that rotate up to hundreds of times per second. This pulsar, called B1509, is only 19 kilometers (12 miles) in diameter but is radiating energy over a span 150 light-years across. The blue parts of the nebula represent the most energetic X rays, while green areas indicate X rays in the medium range. The lowest-energy X rays, shown in orange and red (upper right), are part of a neighboring gas cloud into which some of the energy from the pulsar has flowed.

Ultraviolet Telescopes

A segment of the Milky Way, viewed by an ultraviolet telescope (above).

To study the ultraviolet sky, astronomers use mainly telescopes mounted on satellites. A part of Earth's atmosphere called the ozone layer blocks most ultraviolet light coming from objects in space. Like optical telescopes, ultraviolet telescopes use mirrors to collect and reflect the ultraviolet rays. Some mirrors have special coatings that better reflect the short wavelengths of ultraviolet light. The ultraviolet rays that the telescopes collect are used to create images or are analyzed for information about the temperature and chemical makeup of the objects giving off the rays.

The Andromeda Galaxy, the Milky Way's nearest galactic neighbor, is captured in a composite image (above) of both ultraviolet and infrared light by the Galaxy Evolution Explorer (GALEX) and the Spitzer Space Telescope, respectively. Astronomers use GALEX, which was launched in 2003, to study the evolution of galaxies and the origins of stars. GALEX records the hotter regions of space, including those with young, high-mass stars, depicted in blue, and old stars, shown in green. Spitzer records the cooler, dusty areas where stars are forming amid clouds of dust and gas in red.

Several orbiting ultraviolet telescopes, including the International Ultraviolet Explorer, which operated from 1978 until 1996, have collected information from ultraviolet rays given off by hot gases around stars and in the space between the stars. The Extreme Ultraviolet Explorer, launched in 1992, collected very short wavelength ultraviolet rays until 2001. The Far Ultraviolet Spectroscopic Explorer, in use from 1999 to 2007, collected information about hot hydrogen gas that helps astronomers learn about the early universe. The Hubble Space Telescope also collects data about ultraviolet rays from hot gases in space.

The Solar and Heliospheric Observatory (SOHO), launched in 1995, carries instruments that study our sun in both visible and ultraviolet light. Astronomers use the information to learn more about the corona, the solar wind, and the makeup of the sun's interior.

A huge eruption of the sun called a solar prominence (right) dominates an image made using the Solar and Heliospheric Observatory (SOHO). A prominence, which consists of particles with electric charges, may be thousands of kilometers long. Hotter areas of the sun appear white, while cooler areas appear red.

SOHO, designed to help scientists study the atmosphere and interior of the sun and the solar wind, appears in an artist's rendering (above). The observatory, which was launched in 1995, orbits the sun at a point about 1.5 million kilometers (932,000 miles) from Earth.

Approximate size of Earth relative to the sun (not actual position of Earth).

Infrared Telescopes

Infrared rays are rays of heat. All objects, even cold ones, give off infrared rays. Infrared telescopes must be kept very cold because any heat given off by the device could interfere with the images.

Earth's atmosphere is also a problem for infrared telescopes. Water vapor and molecules of carbon dioxide gas in the atmosphere block out infrared rays. As a result, infrared telescopes must be built on high mountains, flown aboard special research airplanes, or orbited on satellites in space.

Infrared telescopes have mirrors like those of optical telescopes. In fact, some optical telescopes, such as the Hubble Space Telescope, also collect infrared rays. The mirror reflects the infrared rays to a heat detector. The Spitzer Space Telescope, designed to observe in the nfrared part of the electromagnetic spectrum, was launched in 2003. Rather than orbit Earth, it orbits the sun at the same distance as Earth. This orbit positions it farther away from the heat given off by our planet.

Astronomers have used infrared telescopes to detect new stars arising in clouds of gas and dust. They have also used these telescopes to examine rings of dust around distant stars for signs that planets might be forming.

A segment of the Milky Way, v
by an infrared telescope (above)

Light from more than 300 new
stars blazes through a blanke
dust and gas in the central clou
the Rho Ophiuchus nebula (righ
a false-color image taken with
Spitzer Space Telescope. One o
closest star-forming regions to
solar system, Rho Ophiuchus is a
407 light-years from Earth. The
ors represent the wavelength
infrared energy emitted by objec
the nebula and so depict the s
relative temperatures and ages.
surrounded by red disks are
youngest, only about 300,000 y
old. These disks contain mat
from which planetary systems
form. Older stars, which have
their disks, are blue.

NASA's Spitzer Space Telescope is shown against the glowing infrared emissions of the Milky Way in an artist's rendering. Launched in 2003, the telescope was named after American asronomer Lyman Spitzer, Jr., who pioneered the use of telescopes in space.

About 1,000 young stars (shown in blue) illuminate the Orion nebula (below left), in an image taken by Spitzer's infrared camera. The nebula, about 1,450 light-years from Earth, appears at the center of the image, surrounded by dust that has been heated by the stars to a red and orange glow. Massive stars just below and to the left of the bright white center are creating a cavity as they blast away gas and dust. Dark veins near the top of the dust cloud (arrow) contain new stars in the earliest stages of development.

Microwave Telescopes

Microwave telescopes take scientists nearly as far back in time as the beginning of time itself. The telescopes detect cosmic microwave background (CMB) radiation, the afterglow of the big bang, the cosmic explosion that started the expansion of the universe. The CMB radiation formed in the tremendous heat of the early universe and then cooled as the universe expanded. Because the radiation displays a pattern from the time it formed, scientists recognize it as a fundamental measuring stick for the universe.

The American physicists Arno Penzias and Robert W. Wilson of Bell Labs in New Jersey shared half of the 1978 Nobel Prize in physics for their discovery of the CMB radiation in the 1960's. Their work convinced most scientists that the big bang theory was correct. It confirmed that the universe is *homogeneous* (having the same properties in all locations, when averaged over great volumes) and *isotropic* (the same in all directions).

Two of the most important microwave telescopes have been NASA's Cosmic Background Explorer (COBE), launched in 1989, and the Wilkinson Microwave Anistrophy Probe (WMAP), launched in 2001 by NASA and Princeton University in New Jersey. These and other microwave telescopes have produced significant finds about the age, shape, and structure of the universe as well as evidence explaining how galaxies, stars, and planets formed from a hot, dense "soup" of subatomic particles.

A segment of the Milky Way, viewed with a microwave telescope (above).

The Planck mission, launched in May 2009 by the European Space Agency, was designed to map the CMB radiation in unprecedented detail. The microwave satellite was named for the Nobel Prize-winning German scientist Max Planck.

Tiny temperature fluctuations in the CMB radiation collected by the COBE satellite (above) revealed the long-sought "seeds" around which, astronomers had predicted, the first galaxies formed. As the universe expanded, the denser areas (shown in blue), which had a stronger gravitational pull, formed clumps that evolved into stars and other large structures.

WMAP data showed variations in CMB radiation in astonishing detail (right). These data provided the first direct evidence for the theory of inflation, the idea that the universe expanded at an accelerated rate for the first fraction of a second after the big bang.

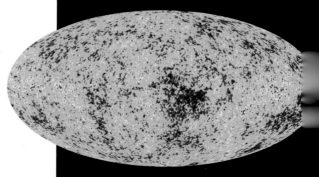

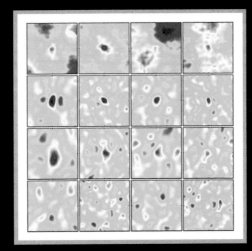

Previously unknown galaxy clusters (shown in blue) in the early universe appear in an image of CMB radiation distortions (left) captured by the South Pole Telescope. The telescope, which is operated by a consortium of North American universities, was located in Antarctica because of the region's clear atmosphere.

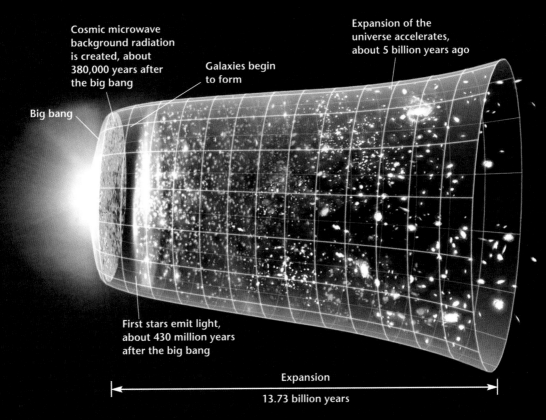

Cosmic microwave background radiation is created, about 380,000 years after the big bang

Galaxies begin to form

Expansion of the universe accelerates, about 5 billion years ago

Big bang

First stars emit light, about 430 million years after the big bang

Expansion
13.73 billion years

Data from WMAP enabled scientists to calculate the age of the universe with unprecedented accuracy, dramatically increase the number of known galaxies in the early universe, and determine that the universe appears to be slightly elliptical rather than spherical. Using WMAP data, scientists have also worked out that the universe is about 4.6 percent ordinary matter, 23.3 percent dark matter, and 72.1 percent dark energy. Dark matter is an invisible substance that reveals itself only through its gravitational pull on visible objects. Dark energy is the force that accelerates the expansion of the universe against gravitational forces.

A segment of the Milky Way, viewed with a radio telescope (above).

Radio Telescopes

Like gigantic ears, radio telescopes "listen" for radio signals from deep space. Instead of a polished mirror or lens, a bowl-shaped dish antenna collects the radio waves. The dish is like a satellite television dish, except much bigger. Astronomers call the dish a reflector because it focuses and reflects the radio waves to a radio receiver.

Grote Reber, a ham radio operator and engineer, built the first radio telescope in 1937 in the backyard of his home in Wheaton, Illinois, a Chicago suburb. He used his telescope to confirm the 1932 discovery by Bell Labs (now Lucent Technologies) physicist Karl Jansky that radio waves were reaching Earth from somewhere in our galaxy.

Astronomers have learned that many objects give off radio waves, including planets and hot gases in interstellar space. Using radio telescopes, astronomers can detect galaxies otherwise hidden by clouds of gas and dust and quasars, the brightly glowing centers of galaxies far off in the universe. Astronomers using a radio telescope discovered pulsars, the rapidly spinning remains of huge exploded stars. The Search for Extraterrestrial Intelligence (SETI) uses radio telescopes in an effort to detect radio signals that may be coming from intelligent life forms on other worlds.

A colorized image of the sun captured with the Very Large Array (VLA) radiotelescope in New Mexico allows astronomers to "see" temperatures on our nearest star based on an analysis of radio waves. The waves indicate that the average temperature of the sun is about 16,650 °C (30,000 °F). Areas in red have a temperature of 555,000 °C (1 million °F) and pinpoint the location of strong magnetic fields. Green indicates cooler regions where the sun's atmosphere is very dense. Dark blue features are even cooler. Near the bottom of the image, a dark blue line marks the boundary of the sun's south pole, an area where the atmosphere is thin. The locations of the north and south poles change from day to day, as variations in the sun's temperature affect its magnetic fields.

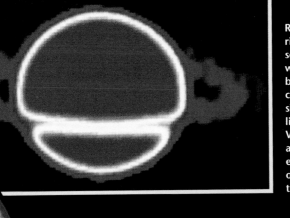

Radio-telescope images of Saturn and its rings, such as one taken by the VLA telescope (left), have revealed that the planet is warmer than predicted. Many astronomers believe that much of Saturn's internal heat comes from energy generated by the slow sinking of helium through the liquid metallic hydrogen in the planet's interior. The VLA telescope image also shows that the atmosphere (yellow) is cooler than the planet itself. The line cutting across the bottom of the disk represents emissions from rings that have absorbed energy from the planet.

The transformation of a dying star into a planetary nebula is captured clearly for the first time in an image made by the VLA radio telescope. A ring of gas (right, in green)—whose radius measures about twice the distance from the sun to Pluto—surrounds the collapsing star. Two "arms" (also green) contain energy streaming from the star. Water molecules in the ring and the arms emitted the radio waves picked up by the VLA. The image captured a rare event, because scientists believe the water is destroyed within 100 years after the transition to a nebula begins.

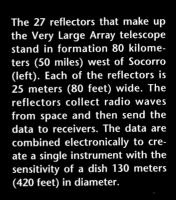

The 27 reflectors that make up the Very Large Array telescope stand in formation 80 kilometers (50 miles) west of Socorro (left). Each of the reflectors is 25 meters (80 feet) wide. The reflectors collect radio waves from space and then send the data to receivers. The data are combined electronically to create a single instrument with the sensitivity of a dish 130 meters (420 feet) in diameter.

Methane is becoming more abundant in the atmosphere. Like another greenhouse gas, carbon dioxide, it traps heat in the atmosphere and threatens to spur further global warming.

Methane escaping from an ice hole in a frozen lake burns with a bright blue flame (below). The photographer lit the gas with a match before taking this picture.

At first glance, cows grazing peacefully on the lush grass of a mountain valley would appear to have little to do with environmental pollution and global warming. Cows, however, belch continuously, and with each belch, the animals exhale methane gas. Cows aren't doing anything new. They have been exhaling methane, a by-product of digestion in their multichambered stomachs, for thousands of years. The problem is the huge increase in their numbers—and emissions—because of modern livestock farming. On average, a domestic cow releases enough methane each day to fill 300 2-liter soda bottles.

Like carbon dioxide (CO_2), methane is a greenhouse gas. Such gases cause Earth's atmosphere to retain a substantial amount of the sun's heat rather than radiating most of it back out into space. Climate scientists have determined that, since the

Methane

Another Greenhouse Troublemaker

By John Johnson, Jr.

Methane gas bubbles up from the La Brea Tar Pits in Los Angeles (above).

TERMS AND CONCEPTS

Anaerobic bacteria: Species of bacteria that flourish in low-oxygen conditions; some anaerobic bacteria give off methane.

Gas hydrate: A chemical compound in which a methane molecule is entrapped within a crystal formed by water molecules.

Greenhouse gas: A gas, such as carbon dioxide or methane, which traps the sun's heat within Earth's atmosphere.

Hydrocarbon: A family of chemicals based on hydrogen and carbon; methane and all fossil fuels are hydrocarbons.

Methane sink: A natural system, such as communities of methane-consuming organisms, that breaks down methane.

Permafrost: Ground that remains frozen for at least several years.

Ruminants: Species of mammals that possess a specialized, multichambered stomach for digesting cellulose, plant tissues consisting of tough fibers. Examples include cows and sheep.

mid-1800's, the average surface temperature of the Earth has risen by about 0.76 Celsius degrees (1.4 Fahrenheit degrees). Most of this increase has occurred in the period between the mid-1900's and the 2000's. Strong scientific evidence links human activities to most of this warming.

Methane versus carbon dioxide

Although CO_2 is more notorious, methane is actually a more potent greenhouse gas. Molecule for molecule, methane traps about 25 times as much atmospheric heat as does CO_2. Since the mid-1800's, atmospheric methane levels have increased by about 250 percent, according to a 2007 report by the Intergovernmental Panel on Climate Change (IPCC), a United Nations group that monitors Earth's climate. Scientific studies of air bubbles trapped in polar ice sheets have revealed that methane is now more abundant in Earth's atmosphere than at any time in the last 400,000 years. Scientists have calculated that methane accounts for about 20 percent of the total modern heating effect caused by all greenhouse gases.

Belching cows are only one factor contributing to rising levels of atmospheric methane. About 40 percent of the methane entering the atmosphere comes from natural sources, including wetlands and the oceans. Scientists are more concerned about the 60 percent coming from human-related sources, including agriculture and the mining and distribution of fossil fuels.

Although methane is more potent than carbon dioxide, it has a shorter lifespan. According to the Environmental Protection Agency (EPA), a methane molecule lasts in the atmosphere for only about 12 years. In that length of time, methane typically breaks down into other compounds. Although scientists disagree on how long CO_2 lingers in the atmosphere, many climate experts believe that a substantial proportion of the gas introduced into the atmosphere by human activity persists for hundreds or even thousands of years.

Because human activity is responsible for significant methane emissions, efforts to reduce excess methane could theoretically produce significant results relatively quickly. A number of experts on climate

The author:

John Johnson, Jr., is a staff writer who specializes in science for the *Los Angeles Times*.

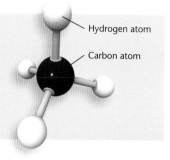

Methane (CH_4) is the simplest of all hydrocarbons, the most important class of *organic* (carbon-containing) compounds. A methane molecule consists of four hydrogen atoms bonded to a single carbon atom. Hydrocarbons can also be found in coal, natural gas, and petroleum.

Hydrogen atom

Carbon atom

HOW METHANE IS PRODUCED IN WETLANDS

Wetlands are the largest source of naturally produced methane gas. Dead plant material continually sinks to the bottoms of pools in marshes and swamps. There, bacteria in oxygen-depleted environments break down the dead organic material into nutrients. In the process, they give off gaseous methane, which bubbles up to the water's surface and enters the atmosphere.

Methane gas bubbles

Microbes decomposing dead plant material

change believe that solving the problem of methane build-up could prove easier and less expensive than the related problem of CO_2 build-up.

Natural sources of methane

Methane is a gaseous hydrocarbon and belongs to the same class of chemical compounds found in coal, natural gas, and petroleum. Natural gas is about 95 percent methane. Methane gas is colorless, odorless, and nontoxic, though breathing air with a high proportion of methane deprives the lungs of needed oxygen and thus can kill.

The largest single natural source of atmospheric methane is the world's wetlands, which account for 76 percent of all natural methane production. Wetlands produce so much methane because the combination of standing water and decaying vegetable matter creates an *anaerobic* (oxygen-deficient) environment favored by methane-producing bacteria. Controlling these emissions is not on anyone's agenda be-

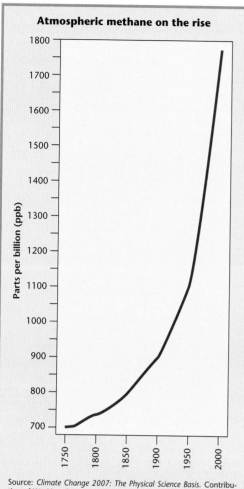

Atmospheric methane on the rise

Parts per billion (ppb)

Source: *Climate Change 2007: The Physical Science Basis.* Contribution of Working Group I to the Fourth Assessment Report of the Intergovernmental Panel on Climate Change.

The concentration of methane in Earth's atmosphere has risen dramatically since 1750. Methane, a greenhouse gas, is about 25 times as efficient at trapping heat in the atmosphere as is carbon dioxide, the most abundant greenhouse gas.

cause wetlands provide important environmental benefits. They teem with plants, animals, and other organisms, some of which exist nowhere else. They also absorb floodwaters and replenish *ground water* (water held underground in cavities or porous rocks). Governments around the world devote tremendous resources to preserving wetlands from development.

The termite, one of the world's most widely distributed insect pests, also plays an important role in methane emissions. Approximately 11 percent of all naturally generated methane results from the termite's digestive process. Like cow stomachs, termite stomachs host populations of microbes that break down cellulose—tough fibers in plants' cell walls—into usable sugars. These microbes give off methane as a by-product of their activity.

The world's oceans continuously produce methane, but the gas comes from several unrelated sources. Ocean-living organisms release about 8 percent of the methane produced naturally on Earth. Most of this gas comes from the digestive systems of fish and tiny animals floating in plankton, masses of tiny organisms drifting on or near the ocean surface.

Troublesome crystals

Gas hydrates from the ocean depths are another natural source of methane. They form under low-temperature, high-pressure conditions. Geologists have found vast deposits of gas hydrate crystals in ocean sediments, mainly at depths greater than 450 meters (1,476 feet). In some places, the sea floor is paved with lumps of hydrate like cobblestones on an undersea highway. Methane hydrates are believed to form when methane gas escapes from cracks along fault lines in sedimentary rock on the sea floor and makes contact with the highly pressurized cold water along ocean bottoms.

At the molecular level, gas hydrates consist of a methane molecule trapped in a "cage" fashioned of chemically bonded water molecules.

NATURAL SOURCES OF METHANE

Methane occurs naturally on Earth and comes from a number of sources. The most important source is wetlands. In these watery environments, bacteria feeding on rotting vegetation give off methane. Termite stomachs harbor microorganisms that aid in digestion and release methane in the process. Fish and other marine creatures produce methane as part of their digestive processes. Gas hydrates are complex crystals on ocean floors that trap methane. When heated, the crystals release their methane, which bubbles up to the ocean surface and enters the atmosphere.

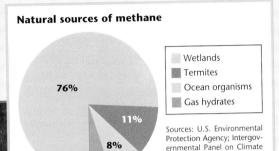

Natural sources of methane

- Wetlands
- Termites
- Ocean organisms
- Gas hydrates

76%

11%

8%

5%

Sources: U.S. Environmental Protection Agency; Intergovernmental Panel on Climate Change.

The cypress swamp in South Carolina's Congaree Swamp National Park naturally contributes methane to the atmosphere. In a swamp, such plant material as leaves, stems, and fruits constantly drop into the water. Bacteria in the airless environment of the muddy bottom assist in the rotting of the material and give off methane.

Termites (left) are able to feed on and digest wood because of highly adapted microorganisms in their stomachs. These organisms produce methane as a by-product.

A lump of ice-like gas hydrate on the seabed of the Gulf of Mexico gives off methane bubbles. The gas hydrate, formed under great pressure at cold temperatures, locks methane molecules within its crystalline structure. A warm-up of deep ocean currents could thaw gas hydrate deposits, releasing vast quantities of methane into ocean waters and, ultimately, into the atmosphere.

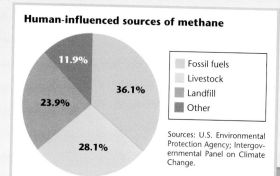

Human-influenced sources of methane

- 36.1% Fossil fuels
- 28.1% Livestock
- 23.9% Landfill
- 11.9% Other

Sources: U.S. Environmental Protection Agency; Intergovernmental Panel on Climate Change.

Human activities are responsible for well over half of the total amount of methane emitted annually into the atmosphere. In the United States, the production, transport, and burning of petroleum and other fossil fuels accounts for the release of more methane than any other human-influenced activity. Livestock and landfills are also major contributors. The "Other" category includes such human-conducted activities as rice farming and the treatment of human waste in sewage plants.

A bulldozer compresses garbage in a landfill. Garbage consists of a variety of material, but there is typically enough organic material— such as paper, food remnants, and pet waste—for microorganisms to generate methane as they decompose the waste. Gases seeping from open landfills produce bad odors and can pose a fire hazard.

This feedlot in the Texas Panhandle packs hundreds of cattle into a small area. The cattle contribute methane to the atmosphere by burping up the gas from their stomachs. The manure they deposit contributes yet more methane as it decomposes.

Workers tend rice plants in a rice paddy in Southeast Asia. Rice cultivation requires flooding of fields, creating an ideal environment for anaerobic bacteria to feed on rotting vegetation. The bacteria give off methane, which bubbles up into the air. In some Asian countries, rice cultivation is the largest contributor of methane to the atmosphere.

Gas hydrates are sensitive to heat, which breaks down the molecular "cages" and releases the methane. Currently, methane seeping from natural gas hydrates on the ocean floors, bubbling up to the ocean surface and escaping into the atmosphere, contributes about 5 percent of the world's naturally produced atmospheric methane.

Hidden danger

Because just one cubic meter (35 cubic feet) of gas hydrate yields 164 cubic meters (5,792 cubic feet) of methane, these deep-ocean deposits represent a hidden danger. If accelerated global warming were to heat the oceans significantly, the gas hydrates could break down and liberate vast quantities of methane gas to bubble up into the atmosphere.

A similar threat exists on the Earth's land surface. In places like Siberia in Russia, Arctic Canada, and northern Alaska in the United States, large amounts of dead vegetation have been locked up for thousands of years in permafrost, ground that remains frozen for at least several years. Some scientists predict that continued global warming is likely to thaw vast expanses of permafrost, discharging huge quantities of methane gas into the atmosphere.

Of particular concern to climate scientists is the West Siberian Bog, a largely frozen wetland in Russia equivalent in size to France and Germany combined. In 2005, hydrologist Larry Smith of the University of California-Los Angeles estimated that the bog contains more than 70 billion metric tons (77 billion tons) of methane gas, perhaps one-quarter of the planet's land-based methane. Global warming threatens to release much of this methane reservoir into the atmosphere.

Human-influenced sources of methane

More than 60 percent of Earth's total annual methane production is linked to human activity. The largest source of human-produced methane comes from the mining and the distribution of fossil fuels, particularly through natural gas pipelines. The decomposition of organic material by bacteria inevitably produces methane, whether that proc-ess is taking place today—or took place millions of years ago. Together, the fossil fuel industries—natural gas, coal, and petroleum—contribute about 36 percent of the atmospheric methane produced by human activity in the United States, according to figures published in 2003 by the EPA.

Cows and other *ruminants* (a family of grazing mammals with split hooves) contribute significantly to methane volume in the atmosphere. Ruminants include many domesticated animals, including sheep, cows, oxen, buffalo, camels, and llamas. Ruminant stomachs host a variety of methane-producing microbes, which help in digesting cellulose. Ruminants release methane as their stomachs do the work of digestion, and particularly as they chew their cud.

If the populations of the world's ruminants were wild, their methane output might be relatively insignificant. According to agriculture experts, however, the global population of domestic cattle topped 1.3 billion in 2009, more than double the animals' population in the mid-1900's. Because of the factor of domestication in agriculture, livestock-produced methane is generally considered a human-influenced source of methane, rather than a purely natural source. EPA scientists estimate that digestion in cattle and other ruminants contributes about 21 percent of the human-related methane released annually in the United States. If methane produced by the decomposition of the animals' manure is factored in, the percentage attributed to livestock rises to 28 percent or more.

Landfills are another major source of methane. The 2,300 landfills in the United States account for 24 percent of human-linked methane emissions in the United States, according to the EPA. As with other methane sources, the process involves decomposing waste matter under low-oxygen conditions.

Other important methane contributors include sewage treatment plants, iron and steel manufacturing, and rice cultivation. Cultivating rice requires flooding fields, which initiates a process of anaerobic decay of inundated vegetation. In the United States, rice cultivation is a minor factor in the release of methane. However, it is highly significant in vast regions of eastern and southern Asia. Some experts estimate that rice paddies could be responsible for up to one-quarter of all the methane produced by people worldwide.

Methane sinks—nature's way

Until the mid-1800's, certain natural processes kept atmospheric methane levels relatively low. Scientists refer to these self-regulating processes as "sinks," suggesting a metaphor of washing waste "down the drain."

Earth's most effective sink for methane is in the atmosphere itself. This atmospheric sink is actually a chemical called the hydroxyl radical (OH) that forms continually as a result of the action of sunlight on ozone (O_3) and water vapor. Ozone is a gas consisting of three oxygen molecules. Hydroxyl, unlike stable compounds, carries an electric charge and reacts very easily with other chemicals. In the atmosphere, the OH radical changes methane to water (H_2O) and the methyl radical (CH_3). Because this second chemical is also unstable, it undergoes a further chain of reactions. The outcome of this process is the production of substances that are harmless to the atmosphere. Scientists estimate that about 500 million metric tons (551 million tons) of methane are neutralized by the OH sink each year.

Another natural methane sink consists of populations of bacteria in the soil. Although some bacteria, like those in the digestive systems of

Studies of atmospheric methane have turned up some surprising sources for this greenhouse gas. For many years, hydropower—energy produced by falling water—was considered an environmentally friendly alternative to power plants that burn fossil fuels. More recently, however, scientific findings have begun to tarnish hydro's "green" image.

The falling water itself is not to blame; instead, the culprit is the reservoir of water behind the dam. Submerged plant matter in the flooded land plus new plant material that steadily washes into the reservoir decay under *anaerobic* (low-oxygen) conditions. This process produces methane. When the methane-rich water is pumped from this high-pressure environment to the power plant's turbines, most of the methane gas is liberated and released into the atmosphere. In addition, a 2007 study by Brazilian and American scientists found significant methane emissions downstream from a dam in the Amazon basin.

Just how much methane the world's dams produce is a matter of controversy. Scientists with Brazil's National Institute for Space Research (INPE) estimated in 2007 that the world's 52,000 large dams contribute more methane to the atmosphere than does the entire United Kingdom. Critics, however, said the study did not take into account the methane that would have been produced by a comparable area of unflooded land.

Nevertheless, researchers are beginning to tackle the problem of methane emissions from

The Three Gorges Dam—the world's largest—spans the Yangtze River in central China. In late 2008, engineers brought the last of the dam's 26 electrical generators on line. The dam failed to fulfill its promise of "clean" power, however. Its huge reservoir has disrupted the ecology of a wide area, and submerged vegetation creates ideal conditions for anaerobic bacteria to thrive and release vast quantities of methane gas.

dam reservoirs. INPE scientists have proposed moving a plant's intake pipes from the methane-rich lower levels of the reservoir to higher levels, where methane levels are low. They also suggest capturing methane from lower levels of the reservoir and burning it to produce additional power.

cows and termites, produce methane, others "eat" it. The producers are called methanogens, and the eaters, methanotrophs. The methanotroph "eaters" consume methane as a source of carbon, breaking down the greenhouse gas into harmless substances in the process. These types of bacteria thrive mainly in forest soil where deep tree roots keep the water table low. (Water-logged soil, on the other hand, favors anaerobic bacteria, which tend to be methanogens.) Methanotrophs neutralize an estimated 30 million to 40 million metric tons (33 million to 44 million tons) of methane each year.

Reducing methane

One of the chief sources of human-caused atmospheric methane emissions—the mining and distribution of fossil fuels—presents one of the best opportunities for reducing methane emissions. Scientists and engineers are working together to develop technologies to reduce methane emissions by the oil, coal, and natural gas industries. According to the EPA, such efforts within the coal industry have already begun to show results. From 1994 to 2006, coal mine operators, using new equipment for recovering methane, prevented about 15.1 billion cubic meters (535 billion cubic feet) of the gas from escaping into the atmosphere. This volume of methane is equivalent to the greenhouse-gas emissions that 39 million cars would produce in one year. (There are more than 600 million cars in operation in the world.)

Pipelines

Preventing leaks in gas pipeline systems presents a greater challenge. According to the Energy Information Administration of the U.S. Department of Energy, there are more than 486,000 kilometers (302,000 miles) of transmission pipelines in the U.S. national gas network. The system also includes thousands of compressor stations and underground storage facilities, all of which can and do malfunction and leak. To address this potential for widespread leakage, the EPA in 1993 began the Natural Gas STAR program, a voluntary partnership with natural gas companies to reduce gas leaks from distribution systems.

A map displays methane leaks in a natural gas pipeline. To generate the map, a helicopter equipped with satellite-imaged maps and a computerized laser leak detector flies over the pipeline route. The device samples air below the helicopter for methane molecules. It compiles the data and outputs video and maps.

Helicopter flight path

Methane leak of from 4.5 parts per million (ppm) to 6 ppm

Methane leak greater than 6 ppm

Thanks to technological advances, companies can now monitor patterns of heat and radiation clustered around their pipeline networks—indicating leaks—through satellite imagery. Engineers also use a variety of tools, including lasers and *acoustical* (sound) detectors, to search for leaks. New technologies are also being developed to minimize or eliminate emissions when repairs must be made to pipes. In some circumstances, replacing old, leaky cast iron pipes, which tend over time to develop gaps and holes at joints, can significantly reduce pipeline leakage. According to the EPA, in 2007 alone, participants in the STAR program prevented the release of a volume of methane equivalent to the annual emissions of 6.8 million cars.

Landfills

In response to the environmental dangers posed by landfill emissions, EPA officials launched the Landfill Methane Outreach Program (LMOP) in 1994. LMOP is a voluntary program that provides incentives to landfill operators to capture their methane releases and use the gas to generate energy.

Landfill gas is an efficient source of energy, consisting largely of methane. With specialized equipment, including liners to keep landfill waste from migrating off site, operators can capture between 60 and 90 percent of all the methane emitted from a landfill. The captured gas can be sold to natural gas users or burned directly to drive electric-power generators. Since LMOP began, nearly 500 landfills in the United States have installed the equipment necessary to capture the methane. The EPA estimates that another 500 or so municipal landfills could install methane-capturing equipment at their dump sites. According to EPA statistics, landfill gas recapture projects have, since 1994, diverted from the atmosphere the greenhouse-gas equivalent of yearly emissions from 14 million cars.

A high school in Missouri has taken advantage of this "green" landfill management. Officials at Pattonville High School in Maryland Heights installed a 1,097-meter (3,600-foot) pipeline from a nearby landfill to fuel the school's heat-producing boilers with methane. The pipeline saves the school $40,000 per year in commercial natural gas purchases. Annual savings of that magnitude justify the initial investment of $175,000, school officials believe. However, school administrators are not taking all of the credit; students in Pattonville High School's energy club first proposed the idea of using landfill gas to heat their school.

Cows and termites

Reducing methane produced by termites and cows presents another kind of challenge. Termites contribute more methane to Earth's atmosphere than all ocean-living organisms combined. It is unlikely that scien-

Termites are known mainly for their voracious appetite for cellulose-rich wood. Homeowners in the United States alone spend more than $2 billion per year for extermination and wood-repair services. Perhaps even more troubling is the substantial volume of heat-trapping methane gas the insects collectively contribute to the atmosphere. Ironically, the insect's remarkably complex digestive system may actually provide scientists with a way to reduce global greenhouse-gas emissions.

The wood tissue that termites consume contains chains of thousands of complex sugar-based molecules that can be made into a biofuel called cellulosic ethanol. Biofuels are made directly from plant materials or biomass, rather than from fossil fuels, which formed in underground deposits in the geological past.

Cellulosic ethanol offers several advantages over gasoline and corn ethanol, the most widely used biofuel in the United States. Cellulosic ethanol can be fermented from plant scraps and grasses, whereas corn ethanol production consumes crops that could be used to feed hungry people. Moreover, cellulosic ethanol is distinctly "greener" than corn ethanol—that is, it produces just 15 percent of the greenhouse gas emissions produced by gasoline and substantially less than corn ethanol.

One of the problems with producing cellulosic ethanol, however, is piercing the defenses that plants have evolved to protect the sugars in their cellulose-rich tissues. The cellulose *polymers* (long chain-like molecules) strongly resist decomposition into simpler sugar molecules. Despite decades of research, chemists have not yet developed cost-effective technologies for extracting cellulosic sugars from plants for fermentation.

But where people have failed, the termite has succeeded. In the termite's stomach, 300 different types of microbe work to strip sugars from their cellulosic straightjackets with an efficiency approaching 90 percent.

In 2007, the U.S. Department of Energy launched a research initiative to reveal the termite's digestive secrets. The initiative set a five-year goal for developing technology that would make cellulosic ethanol cost-competitive with gasoline.

Much of the new research is focusing on the microbes that breach wood's defenses to liberate the valuable sugars inside. For example, geneticists are sequencing the DNA of these microbes, attempting to find the key that enables the organisms to unlock cellulose's defenses.

Dried-mud termite mounds dot an African landscape of savanna, or grassland. Many termite species have specially adapted stomachs that enable them, with the help of microorganisms, to digest tough cellulose. The microorganisms give off methane as a by-product of this digestive activity.

tists will find ways to reduce termite-discharged methane, because these insect species are widely dispersed and well integrated into numerous Earth ecologies.

Cows may be an easier fix. Scientists around the world are investigating ways to change or supplement diets of domesticated cattle to reduce the amount of methane they produce. British researchers, funded by a government grant, are feeding cattle grasses rich in sugar. They theorize that the higher sugar levels will assist digestion and reduce the action of methane-producing organisms in cows' stomachs. This change, in turn, should result in a reduction of cows' exhalation of methane. Researchers at the Institute of Animal Nutrition in Hohenheim, Germany, are developing a slow-release pill for cows that would neutralize some of the methane produced in their stomachs by breaking it down into simpler compounds.

Researchers in Australia have suggested a novel approach to the cow-belching problem: widespread domestication of kangaroos to replace cattle stocks. Kangaroos do not burp up methane; the microbes in their stomachs break down cellulose in a different way. Advocates of this approach point out that kangaroo meat is already available in Australian meat markets.

To develop a more generally applicable solution, genetic researchers in Australia are working to isolate kangaroo genes that control digestion. Such genes might be transferred to cows to transform their stomachs from methane factories into more kangaroo-like digestive systems.

Pipes and storage towers are part of a heating system that uses methane produced by a landfill in Missouri as fuel. The methane is piped from the landfill to boilers at nearby Pattonville High School in Maryland Heights, saving the school thousands of dollars per year in heating costs.

Livestock manure

Methane-rich livestock manure presents different challenges and opportunities. Highly industrialized modern agriculture features densely concentrated livestock operations that produce vast amounts of manure. This amassed manure potentially fouls air, soil, and waterways with methane and other contaminants. To address this growing problem, some farms are installing anaerobic manure digesters (AMD), systems that harvest methane from decomposing manure and use the gas to generate electric power.

Farm operators using an AMD system collect livestock manure and

ANAEROBIC MANURE DIGESTER

An anaerobic manure digester produces fuel for an electric generator by harnessing the power of methane-producing bacteria. As the bacteria decompose manure delivered to the digester, they give off gases rich in methane. The methane is then piped to an electric generator. The solids that remain after treatment can be used as fertilizer.

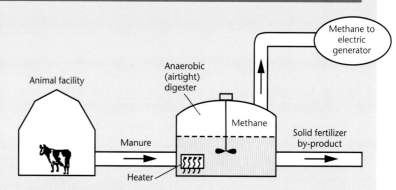

Sources: Colorado State University Extension; Penn State College of Agricultural Sciences Cooperative Extension; U.S. Department of Agriculture.

An anaerobic digester system on a dairy farm includes a collecting bin for manure (foreground) and a digester enclosure (circular tank in the background). Bacteria work on the manure in the airless, heat-controlled interior of the digester. The methane they give off is channeled to an electric generator, where it is burned to drive the generator's turbine.

load it into a large, airtight tank that maintains a constant temperature of 38 °C (100 °F). At this temperature and in the absence of oxygen, anaerobic bacteria thrive. These microscopic organisms—numbering in the billions—function as tiny factories, feeding on the raw manure and giving off gases consisting of 55 to 70 percent methane and 30 to 45 percent CO_2 as well as other trace gases. The AMD system siphons off the methane and pipes it to a gas-fired electric generator, which releases the CO_2 and trace gases into the air. The discharge of CO_2, the number-one greenhouse gas, is a drawback to the system. However, AMD proponents point out that manure rotting naturally in pools or piles releases far more CO_2 as well as methane that is not tapped and put to good use.

The AMD systems have side benefits, too. They greatly reduce odors associated with massed livestock manure. The solids remaining after treatment are far less odorous than untreated manure. Because the solids have been cleansed of most disease-causing bacteria, they can be used for fertilizer.

An AMD system is not cheap. An installation appropriate for a dairy farm can cost $300,000 or more, limiting the technology's applicability to large farming operations. According to the U.S. Department of Agriculture (USDA), only 111 U.S. farms had AMD systems for methane production in operation around the end of 2007. The technology is more widespread in Germany and some other western European countries. In the United States, the USDA and several state agriculture and energy departments offer loans and grants to defray the costs of investing in AMD technology.

Looking toward the future

The good news about methane is that, even if the more fanciful schemes for trapping and utilizing the gas do not yield immediate success, basic science offers tools to tackle the problem of rising atmospheric levels. Reduction efforts, including improved pipeline technology, landfill methane recovery, and manure digesters are already lowering methane emissions.

In the long term, many scientists warn, the potential for rapid atmospheric methane build-up is linked to the prospect of accelerated global warming. Vulnerable undersea gas hydrates and in-ground permafrost are both fragile systems that might yield their vast burdens of methane in response to excess heating. Many experts believe that the solution to rising atmospheric methane must be twofold—reducing our methane output and restraining global warming.

▨ FOR ADDITIONAL INFORMATION

Periodicals

Gartner, Bettina. "How Better-Fed Cows Could Cool the Planet." *Christian Science Monitor,* Aug. 16, 2007.
Margonelli, Lisa. "Gut Reactions." *Atlantic,* September 2008.

Web sites

Environmental Protection Agency, "Landfill Methane Outreach Program"—http://epa.gov/lmop/
Environmental Protection Agency, "Methane"—http://www.epa.gov/methane/
Greenhouse Gas Online—http://www.ghgonline.org/
Intergovernmental Panel on Climate Change, "IPCC Fourth Assessment Report (2007)"—www.ipcc.ch/ipccreports/ar4-wg3.htm

Mutualism: The Pleasure of Your Company

by Alfred J. Smuskiewicz
and Barbara A. Mayes

Many species exist in mutually beneficial relationships, some of which are far more complex than previously thought.

Swimming near the tentacles of a sea anemone is a perilous undertaking. The tentacles have stinging cells that eject poison or sticky threads that can immobilize prey for capture. For clownfish, however, the sea anemone is an effective bodyguard. Clownfish have a skin barrier that protects them from the anemone's sting and not only live among the tentacles but also build their nests beneath them. In return for the protection—and, perhaps, some leftovers—the clownfish sometimes eat parasites that plague sea anemones.

This beneficial relationship is just one example of a fascinating natural phenomenon called mutualism, which dates back about 100 million years. In mutualism, two or more species interact with one another to the benefit of all parties. In some cases, the species are so dependent on each other that they cannot survive on their own.

In "protection mutualism" relationships—such as those between clownfish and sea anemones—one species gains protection from predators, parasites, or other enemies, while the other receives such benefits as food or a safe place to live. On coral reefs, tiny wrasse fish and some shrimp set up "cleaning stations" where they pick parasites, dead skin, algae, and other unwanted material from sharks, eels, and other marine animals. Scientists have often observed these animals waiting in line for their turn at these stations, which may stay in business for years.

In "dispersal mutualism" relationships—such as those between honey bees and flowering plants—one species gets food in return for spreading another species' seeds or pollen. Termites represent a third form of mutualism. These insects cannot naturally digest cellulose, the primary material in wood. That job is instead done by bacteria and protozoa living in the termites' intestines. In exchange for supplying most of the enzymes needed for cellulose digestion, the microorganisms have a home and a ready supply of food.

Scientists note that mutualistic species are not doing "favors" for each other. Both species are actually being selfish from an evolutionary perspective—that is, they are working to improve their own chances of survival and reproduction. They cooperate with each other but at the lowest possible cost to themselves.

Mutually dependent clownfish and sea anemones

The authors:

Alfred J. Smuskiewicz is a free-lance writer specializing in science and medicine.

Barbara A. Mayes is managing editor of World Book Supplementary Publications.

Pollination

Many flowering plants depend on cross-pollination for reproduction. This method requires an animal or the wind to spread pollen from one flower to another. Animal pollinators include bees, butterflies, moths, beetles, flies, birds, and bats. These animals are attracted to the flowers by strong aromas, bright colors, or special markings. While helping the flowers reproduce, the animals obtain food.

Honey bees carry out more pollination than any other kind of insect. Bees collect nectar and pollen from flowers and carry the food back to their hive. However, some pollen, which contains male sex cells, clings to their bodies and is carried to other flowers, where it fertilizes female sex cells. People benefit from the bees' activities by gaining a delicious sweetener—honey. Bees also pollinate billions of dollars worth of food crops each year. Flowers pollinated by insects and birds generally produce more colorful blossoms and a more fragrant aroma than flowers pollinated by wind.

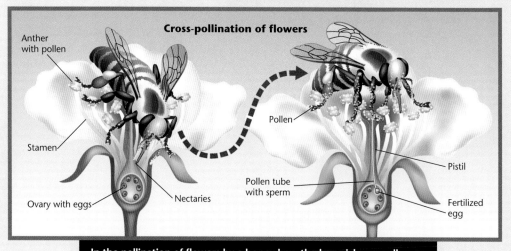

Cross-pollination of flowers

Anther with pollen

Stamen

Ovary with eggs

Nectaries

Pollen

Pollen tube with sperm

Pistil

Fertilized egg

In the pollination of flowers by a honey bee, the bee picks up pollen on its legs from the anthers on a flower's stamens (male parts) as it feeds on the sweet nectar at the bottom of the flower. When the bee visits another flower, it unintentionally deposits some pollen grains carrying sperm (male sex cells) on the flower's pistil (female part). Pollen tubes then grow down the pistil, allowing the sperm to reach the eggs in the flower's ovary, where fertilization and seed development occur.

A long-dash skipper butterfly inserts its sucking proboscis into one of many tiny flowers that make up the composite flower head of a sweet smooth oxeye. The proboscis is a highly specialized body part that butterflies and moths use to feed on nectar. After the proboscis is extended and inserted into a flower, the movement of muscles in the insect's head draws the nectar fluid up the proboscis. When not in use, the proboscis is coiled up under the insect's head. Like bees, butterflies and moths pick up pollen as they feed on a flower and transfer the pollen to other flowers.

Many kinds of flowers have special markings that serve to attract pollinating insects and guide the insects to the flower's nectar and pollen. To human eyes—which can see only visible light—this silverweed appears to be uniformly yellow (left). However, to the eyes of a bee or other pollinating insect—which can see ultraviolet light as well as light visible to human eyes—this flower appears to have bright markings, known as nectar guides (right). The markings increase the chances that the flower will be pollinated.

A golden northern bumble bee, whose body is covered with pollen, collects nectar from a purple coneflower. The long, flexible straw-like "tongue" of these bees allows them to reach the nectar that lies deep inside this and many other kinds of flowers. Along with honey bees, bumble bees are among the most important pollinators of wild flowers, garden flowers, and crops.

Pollination

A cactus wren inserts its head inside a large, white flower of a desert saguaro cactus. While feeding on the flower's nectar, the bird may cross-pollinate the plant with pollen from another flower. After the cactus's seed-rich fruit develops, the wren also feeds on that. Unlike insects, most birds have only a weak sense of smell. Thus, flowers that depend on birds for pollination must attract the birds through their appearance.

A Mexican long-nosed bat hovers as it feeds on nectar and pollen inside the flowers of a century plant, a desert plant in the agave family. As the pollen-dusted bats move from flower to flower, they also cross-pollinate the plants. Some scientists believe that the close dependence between agave plants and the Mexican long-nosed bat, as well as the lesser long-nosed bat, indicates that the plants and bats evolved together.

Seed/Spore Dispersal

Various kinds of plants and fungi are spread from one area to another by the dispersal of their seeds or spores in the excrement of animals. The animals—ranging from insects to birds to mammals—take the seeds or spores into their bodies while feeding on fruits, nuts, or fungal parts. In this kind of mutualism, the animals obtain food while the plants or fungi benefit from dispersal into new habitats.

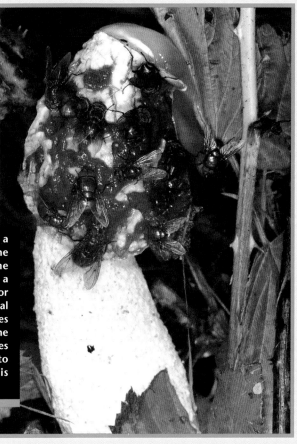

Greenbottle flies crawl over the top of a stinkhorn fungus while feeding on the slimy, gelatinous mass containing the fungus's spores. Stinkhorns exude a strong, foul odor that mimics the odor of *carrion* (decaying flesh)—the typical food of the flies. After feeding, the flies travel to other locations and release the spores in their excrement. If the spores land in a suitable spot, they grow into new fungi. In this way, the fungus is able to exploit new habitats.

Numerous undigested berries can be seen in the large scat (feces) left behind by a grizzly bear in a wet, mossy meadow in Alaska. The feces not only serve as a means of dispersal for the berries and their seeds but also serve as fertilizer for the new plants that will grow from the seeds. The seeds of many kinds of fruits are widely dispersed by mammals, birds, and other animals in forests, meadows, prairies, wetlands, and other ecosystems.

Nutrition

Relationships between animal, plant, algal, or fungal species involving nutrition may be the most common kinds of mutualism. In some of these relationships, both species in the association obtain nutritional benefits. In other cases, one species obtains nutrition while the other obtains such benefits as protection, cultivation, or dispersal.

Nodules, small, knot-like growths containing nitrogen-fixing bacteria, cover the roots of this soybean plant. Nitrogen-fixing bacteria take molecular nitrogen from the atmosphere—which plants cannot use as a nutrient—and combine it with other elements, such as hydrogen and oxygen, to form compounds that plants can use for growth. Because soybeans and other plants in the legume (pea) family have these nitrogen-fixing nodules, farmers often use these plants to add nutrients to the soil. The farmers later grow other crops in the enriched soil.

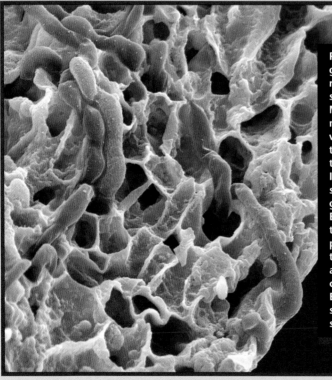

Filaments of a mycorrhizal fungus (orange) entwined in the root of a plant are shown in a scanning electron micrograph. Most kinds of plants have such mycorrhizal associations, in which the fungus gains access to carbohydrates and other nutrients produced by the plant. In turn, water and minerals absorbed from the soil by the fungus are shared with the plant. Ectomycorrhizal fungi live on the outside of roots of woody plants, such as oak and pine trees. Mushrooms are the above-ground fruiting bodies of certain ectomycorrhizal fungi. Endomycorrhizal fungi live inside the roots of certain plants, such as orchids and azaleas.

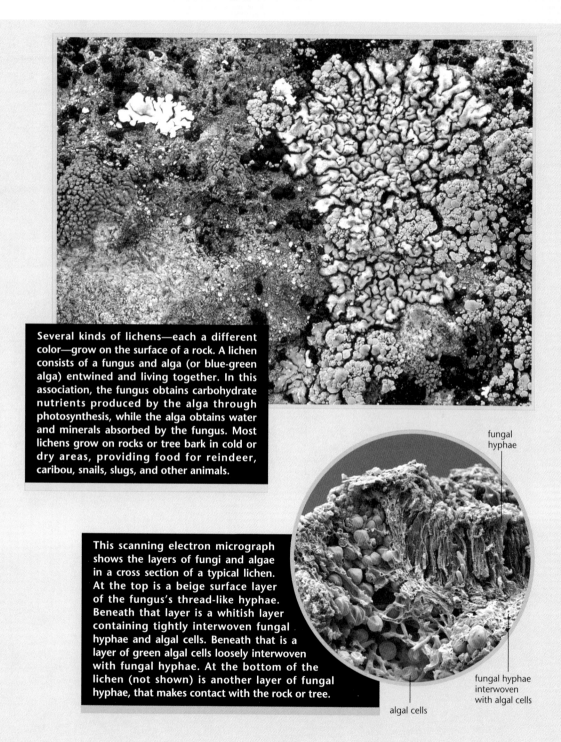

Several kinds of lichens—each a different color—grow on the surface of a rock. A lichen consists of a fungus and alga (or blue-green alga) entwined and living together. In this association, the fungus obtains carbohydrate nutrients produced by the alga through photosynthesis, while the alga obtains water and minerals absorbed by the fungus. Most lichens grow on rocks or tree bark in cold or dry areas, providing food for reindeer, caribou, snails, slugs, and other animals.

This scanning electron micrograph shows the layers of fungi and algae in a cross section of a typical lichen. At the top is a beige surface layer of the fungus's thread-like hyphae. Beneath that layer is a whitish layer containing tightly interwoven fungal hyphae and algal cells. Beneath that is a layer of green algal cells loosely interwoven with fungal hyphae. At the bottom of the lichen (not shown) is another layer of fungal hyphae, that makes contact with the rock or tree.

fungal hyphae

fungal hyphae interwoven with algal cells

algal cells

Nutrition

An ant "milks" aphids, sucking the sweet liquid, called honeydew, that is expelled from the aphid's abdomen. Aphids feed on juices in plant stems, producing honeydew as a by-product. Ants encourage the aphids to expel the honeydew by stroking their abdomens. As the honeydew pours from the rear tip of the aphid, the ant sucks it up. In order to ensure a steady supply of honeydew, ants take care of the aphids, by warding off enemies and carrying the aphids from one plant to another.

A colony of leaf-cutter ants tends its eggs and larvae in a fungus garden that the ants cultivated within their nest. The ants created the garden by cutting pieces of leaves from trees, shrubs, and other plants and carrying the fragments back to their nest. There, they used the leaf pieces as fertilizer for fungi. As the fungi grow, the ants use them for food—both for themselves and for the ant larvae developing in the nest.

The white appearance of some of the polyps in this coral colony appear to be a sign of "bleaching." In bleaching, the single-celled zooxanthellae algae that live inside the polyp tissues and provide the coral with color die or are expelled. Scientists believe bleaching is caused by abnormally high water temperatures and other environmental stresses.

Under normal conditions, the zooxanthellae—seen as tiny dots in the polyp's head (left) and as green circles in the microscope photo (far left)—provide nutrients in the form of carbohydrates from photosynthesis and waste products. In return, the polyps produce waste products that the algae use as nutrients. The algae also have a protective place to live. Once their algal partners are lost, most corals cannot survive.

Protection

Mutualistic associations involving protection are widespread in nature, from the savannas of Africa to the coral reefs of the Pacific Ocean. In some of these associations between species, both species receive protection, such as protection from disease (through the removal of disease-causing organisms or parasites) or protection from predators. In other associations, one species obtains protection while the other species receives some other benefit, such as access to a food source.

An impala drinks at a water hole in a South African wildlife preserve while oxpeckers feed on ticks, fleas, and other parasites living in the impala's hide. Oxpeckers spend most of their life on such large mammals. The removal of parasites protects the mammals from disease caused by infestations. The birds also sometimes warn their hosts of danger, such as approaching predators, by making loud calls when alarmed.

Some oxpeckers go to great lengths to find parasites on their mammal hosts, such as this bird (circled in red) who has plunged its head into the nostril of a Cape buffalo in South Africa. Although impala, buffalo, rhinoceroses, giraffes, and most other mammals do not seem to mind the busy little birds crawling all over their bodies, some mammals, such as elephants and certain species of antelope, typically will not tolerate the oxpeckers and will try to shake or brush them off. Oxpeckers may also feed on wound tissue, blood, and other body secretions of mammals.

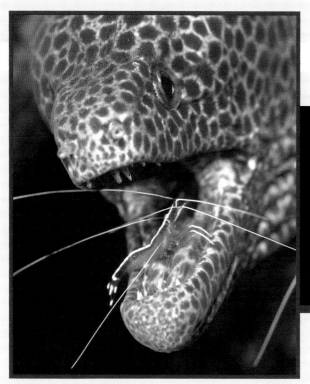

A scarlet cleaner shrimp searches for parasites or other food inside the mouth of a leopard moray eel in the Pacific Ocean. Various species of cleaner shrimp eat parasites, dead tissue, and other particles of food found on or around fish. Cleaner shrimp often group together at "cleaning stations" on coral reefs, where they flag down passing fish by waving their antennae and swaying their bodies. When the fish pause to examine the shrimp, the crustaceans get on board to begin their cleaning activities.

A cleaner wrasse picks off parasites inside the mouth of a yellow goatfish in the ocean waters surrounding Hawaii. Cleaner wrasses perform such cleaning activities on many species of larger fish. When larger fish see these wrasses, they usually open their mouths and gills to allow the wrasses to enter and begin their cleaning work. Owners of aquariums value both cleaner wrasses and cleaner shrimp for their tidy behaviors.

A Breakdown of Mutualism

Mutualistic relationships between plants and animals may be surprisingly complex as well as disturbingly vulnerable to changes caused by human activities. These findings emerged from a casual observation of sickly acacia trees in Kenya by ecologist Todd Palmer of the University of Florida in Gainesville. The trees had been fenced off to protect them from elephants and other browsing mammals that feed voraciously on their leaves. But instead of flourishing, the trees grew weaker than unfenced trees nearby and became infested with a destructive beetle. The problem, Palmer and his colleagues found, was that the browsers were actually key players in a mutualistic relationship between the trees and several species of ant. Keeping the browsers from the trees led to the breakdown of a relationship that has likely existed for thousands of years.

1 Acacia trees grow mainly in tropical and subtropical regions. In Africa, they are a major food source for elephants, giraffes, and many other animals. For protection, some African acacias have evolved bulbous, hollow "swollenthorns." These thorns provide nesting space for four species of stinging ant. The ants ferociously attack any browser or insect that attempts to disturb the trees.

2 Acacia trees "pay" their ant bodyguards by rewarding them with a sugar-rich nectar that is secreted by glands at the base of the leaves. Healthy trees may host more than 100,000 ants.

3 Palmer and his team discovered that when elephants, giraffes, and other large browsers no longer feed on the acacias, the trees have less use for their ant bodyguards. The acacias reduce the amount of sugar-rich nectar they produce. In response, the ant colonies grow smaller, weaker, and less protective of the trees.

4 With their defenses down, the trees come under attack by insects called cerambycid, or longhorn, beetles. These beetles tunnel into the trees and eat away at their woody interiors.

5 Increased beetle attacks cause the trees to grow more slowly and die younger than trees protected by vigorous ant colonies that are still "earning" a lot of nectar in return for protecting the trees against large browsing mammals.

INVASION OF THE JELLYFISH

By Robert N. Knight

I t's another summer day at one of the many popular seaside resorts along Spain's Mediterranean coast in 2008—but this day is not all fun in the sun. The water is dotted with bright-blue flags to warn swimmers to stay away from areas in which swarms of dangerous jellyfish have been spotted. Emergency workers in patrol boats skim the water surface with huge nets to capture as many of the stinging creatures as possible. Other workers cart away mounds of stinking jellyfish carcasses lying on the shore. Even with the precautions, many people may need medical treatment for jellyfish stings, and some may even need to be taken to the hospital to save their lives. The problem is so bad on certain days that Spanish authorities must close the beaches to the public.

Such summer jellyfish "invasions" occurred annually in the early 2000's, prompting the Spanish government to ask citizens to alert authorities at the first sign of any jellyfish *blooms* (sudden population explosions) in order to issue public warnings. Officials also sought help from marine scientists to better understand the phenomenon. Although the sting of this jellyfish is not typically fatal, it can be life threatening to people who are allergic to the toxin in the sting. Another troublesome jellyfish in the Spanish Mediterranean blooms was the fried-egg jellyfish (*Cotylorhiza tuberculata*), a yellow-and-white creature that sometimes became so numerous that it turned the water milky-white. This jellyfish can also deliver unpleasant stings.

Scientists are trying to understand why jellyfish populations are exploding, causing public health hazards and ecological damage.

Spain has not been the only country plagued with jellyfish blooms. In the Mediterranean region, jellyfish blooms were observed from Spain's Costa del Sol to the French Riviera to Sicily. Regions as far-flung as Japan, the United Kingdom, Hawaii, the eastern seaboard of the United States, the Bering Sea off the coast of Alaska, the South Atlantic coast of Africa, and Australia's eastern coast have also experienced massive jellyfish invasions. In Australia, the onslaught was particularly sinister, because one of the proliferating species, a "box" jellyfish named *Chironex fleckeri*, ranks among the most dangerously venomous animals in the world.

Soiled beaches and spoiled seaside vacations were not the only casualties of the jellyfish invasions. The jellyfish have clogged water-intake pipes and other industrial equipment used by such facilities as *desalination plants* (which extract fresh water from seawater) and nuclear power plants. Jellyfish blooms have also interfered with commercial fishing activities by gumming up and tearing nets. In addition, the venom from jellyfish stingers can contaminate fish caught in nets, and jellyfish eat the eggs and young of valuable commercial fish. In the Gulf of Mexico, U.S. shrimpers lost many weeks of trawling time in the early

The author:
Robert N. Knight is a free-lance writer.

TERMS AND CONCEPTS

Bloom: A sudden population explosion of a species.

Cilia: Hair-like projections in comb-like bands on the bodies of comb jellies.

Dead zone: An oceanic area that is mostly devoid of life during parts of the year, typically as a result of the ecological effects of agricultural pollutants.

Invertebrate: An animal without a backbone.

Medusa: The bell-shaped body of an adult "true" jellyfish, in the class Scyphozoa.

Mesogloea: The mucus-like "jelly" that lies between the two cell layers of a jellyfish's body wall.

Nematocysts: Stinging cells on the tentacles of jellyfish that can fire off poisoned barbs.

Phylum: A large, primary group of related animal species.

Polyp: The immature, stationary stage in the life cycle of a "true" jellyfish.

Salinity: The amount of dissolved salt in a volume of water.

Siphonophore: A jellyfish-like animal that has a body consisting of a colony of small individual organisms called hydra.

2000's because of massive jellyfish blooms. Fishing activities were also severely affected in the Bering Sea, where—according to the Alaska Fisheries Science Center—jellyfish were about 40 times as abundant in 2000 as they had been in 1982. Jellyfish became so numerous along one stretch of the Alaskan Peninsula that fishers began calling the area the "Slime Bank." The problematic jellyfish species in the Bering Sea included the highly prolific Pacific sea nettle (*Chrysaora fuscescens*). This species had extended its range northward from its original habitat in coastal waters from California to Oregon. Jellyfish blooms in the Bering Sea were of particular concern to U.S. commercial fishing interests, because more than 50 percent of all fish and shellfish harvested by the United States comes from that body of water.

In the waters of Hawaii—as in Australia—box jellyfish were on the increase in the early 2000's. Marine scientist Jerry Crow of Waikiki Aquarium in Honolulu spoke for many scientists struggling to understand jellyfish blooms around the world when he noted, "The question is, where are all these jellies coming from, and why now?"

Jellyfish are a normal part of the ocean ecosystem. Typically, their populations wax and wane in cycles in response to variations in such ecological factors as the availability of food, predator populations, water temperature, and water *salinity* (amount of dissolved salt). Jellyfish blooms occur naturally, even in healthy marine ecosystems. In addition, a lack of solid data on blooms in previous years is complicating efforts to determine the severity of the current invasions. In fact, many factors may be affecting the current jellyfish invasions. However, many scientists suspect that climate change and rising temperatures in the world's oceans may be increasing the number and severity of blooms.

Simple elegance in the ocean ecosystem

Jellyfish are *invertebrates* (animals without backbones) that scientists classify into two *phyla* (large, primary groups of related species). So-called "true" jellyfish, of which there are more than 200 species, are classified in the phylum Cnidaria, within the class (subgroup in a phylum) Scyphozoa. They have an umbrella-shaped body, called a medusa, from which dangle a whorl of long tentacles equipped with stinging cells, called nematocysts. When the tentacles brush against the jellyfish's prey (such as zooplankton and other small animals), an enemy (such as tuna, mackerel, or other large predatory fish), or a swimming person, the nematocysts explode, launching tiny barbed stingers into the victim. These barbs then release a poison into the victim's body to stun, paralyze, or kill it. If the victim is prey, the jellyfish uses its tentacles and frilly projections called oral arms, which also have nematocysts, to sweep it into its "mouth." The mouth is a

THREE TYPES OF JELLYFISH

Biologists classify jellyfish into three main groups: "true" jellyfish, or medusae, in the class Scyphozoa of the phylum Cnidaria; siphonophores, in the class Hydrozoa of the phylum Cnidaria; and comb jellies, in the phylum Ctenophora.

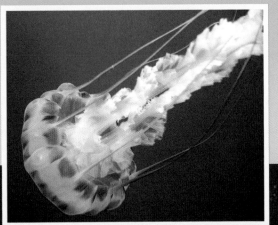

"True" jellyfish

A purple-striped jellyfish (*Chrysaora colorata*) swims off the coast of southern California. Its bell-shaped, or umbrella-shaped, body with a whorl of long tentacles is typical of jellyfish in this class.

Siphonophore

The long, thin body of a giant siphonophore (*Praya dubia*) glows with bluish bioluminescent light as it trails a "curtain" of numerous tentacles. Like all siphonophores, its body consists of a colony of small individual organisms called hydra.

Comb jelly

A winged comb jelly (*Leucothea multicornis*) floats in the waters of Hawaii, displaying just one of many body forms that comb jellies may have. All comb jelly species have bodies with comb-like bands of cilia (hair-like projections), the beating of which aids swimming.

short tube that serves for both digestion and reproduction.

The phylum Cnidaria also consists of more than 150 species of jellyfish-like creatures called siphonophores, which scientists place in the class Hydrozoa. The body of each of these animals is made up of a precisely arranged colony of small individual organisms called hydras. Some siphonophores have tentacles of stinging cells that are as long as 30 meters (98 feet). Perhaps the most familiar siphonophore is the Portuguese man-of-war (*Physalia physalis*), a large, dangerously venomous species that can be recognized by its bright blue, gas-filled float and tentacles of various colors. Stings from the Portuguese man-of-war can cause severe breathing difficulties and even death. Besides true jellyfish and siphonophores, cnidarians also include corals, sea anemones, and solitary hydras.

Comb jellies, classified in the phylum Ctenophora, are gelatinous creatures that are quite different from cnidarian jellyfish. The more than 100 species of comb jellies have various body forms—including balls, cylinders, and ribbons. However, they all have surface bands with *cilia* (hairlike projections) that resemble combs. The beating of these cilia aids in swimming. Comb jellies do not have true stingers. Instead, their tentacles have sticky surfaces that catch tiny drifting plankton for food.

Scyphozoan jellyfish cause most of the problems associated with jellyfish blooms. These jellyfish have a complex life cycle that begins when the male releases sperm into the water. The female takes the sperm into

JELLYFISH LIFE CYCLE

The life cycle of a scyphozoan medusa jellyfish begins when the male releases sperm into the water. The female takes the sperm into her mouth, where they fertilize her eggs, forming tiny, flat larvae called planulae. The planulae sink to the sea bottom, where they attach to hard surfaces and grow into stationary polyps. Eventually, appropriate environmental conditions cause new medusae to bud from the polyps.

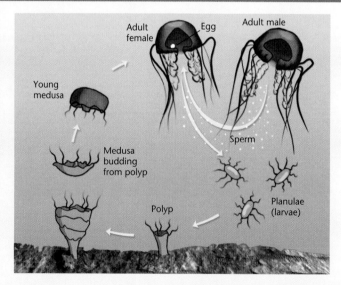

her mouth, where they fertilize her eggs, forming larvae. (In some jellyfish species, a single individual can produce both sperm and eggs.) After the larvae are released, they sink to the sea bottom, where they attach to rocks or other hard surfaces. There, the larvae grow into stationary, tube-like polyps, the immature stage of jellyfish. Polyps can spread into large colonies as new polyps bud *asexually* (without sex) off older individuals. Scientists believe the polyp stage can last many years.

Eventually, the proper combination of water temperature, light level, and food availability is thought to trigger the next life cycle stage, during which many medusae bud off each polyp. These medusae drift away and develop into the familiar bell-shaped, sexually mature jellyfish—and the life cycle begins anew.

Jellyfish bodies have an exceptionally simple structure. The body wall of a jellyfish medusa consists of two thin layers of cells—an outer layer called the ectodermis (or epidermis) and an inner layer called the endodermis (or gastrodermis). These two cell layers are separated by a thick layer of mucus-like material called mesogloea—the "jelly" that gives these animals their name. This body wall surrounds a digestive cavity. A jellyfish has no heart, brain, or other specialized organs, though it does have a primitive network of nerve cells. A jellyfish body consists of at least 95 percent water—substantially more than in complex animals, such as human beings, which are about 65 percent water.

Although a jellyfish typically drifts along with the current, it is capable of weakly propelling itself forward. It does so by expanding and contracting its body in a manner that resembles the opening and closing of an umbrella. In the contraction movement, the animal forces a jet of water out of its mouth, which pushes it forward, bell first. Water then reenters the body, and the contraction movement is repeated.

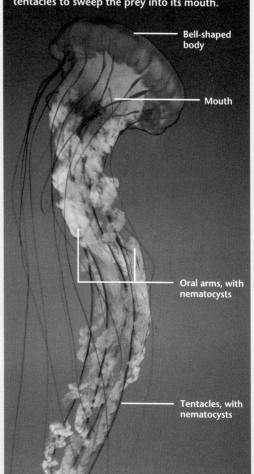

THE BODY OF A TYPICAL JELLYFISH

The bell-shaped body of an adult scyphozoan jellyfish, called a medusa, consists of two layers of cells separated by jelly-like material. A medusa captures its prey using tentacles covered with stinging cells, called nematocysts. When touched, the nematocysts explode, firing off poisoned barbs that can paralyze or kill small animals. The jellyfish then uses its oral arms, which also have nematocysts, and/or its tentacles to sweep the prey into its mouth.

Bell-shaped body

Mouth

Oral arms, with nematocysts

Tentacles, with nematocysts

DEAD ZONES AROUND THE WORLD

Researchers have identified more than 400 oceanic dead zones around the world. Dead zones, which are mostly devoid of life during parts of the year, generally develop in spring and summer, when large amounts of agricultural pollutants are washed into oceans from river systems. The pollution triggers ecological changes that cause oxygen levels in the water to drop dramatically. Dead zones with the best documented loss of oxygen are marked by red dots in the map below.

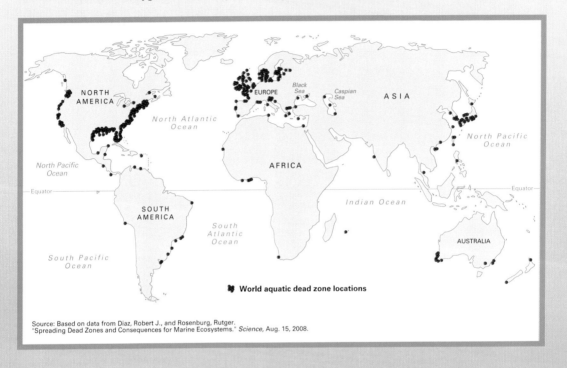

■ World aquatic dead zone locations

Source: Based on data from Diaz, Robert J., and Rosenburg, Rutger. "Spreading Dead Zones and Consequences for Marine Ecosystems." *Science*, Aug. 15, 2008.

Adapting to environmental stresses

Jellyfish are highly opportunistic creatures—meaning that they can readily adapt to changing environmental conditions. Rapidly growing human populations and the highly industrialized global economy have placed severe stresses on the ecological health of the oceans. The opportunistic behaviors of jellyfish, however, have allowed them to flourish in spite of these stresses. By contrast, large fish and other ecologically sensitive species have not been able to adapt as well as jellyfish to changes in the ocean ecosystem.

Foremost among the ecological stresses on oceans is pollution, especially from land-based human activities. Virtually all land is drained by streams that feed into rivers that, in turn, flow into the oceans. Rivers draining highly populated regions carry great quantities of industrial chemical by-products, dissolved agricultural fertilizers, animal wastes from large livestock operations, and other pollutants. As a result, many areas of outflow from large river systems into oceans are marked by dead

BLACK SEA DEAD ZONE
One of the best-documented dead zones is in the northwestern corner of the Black Sea, a large body of water straddling southeastern Europe and the Middle East. This dead zone was first observed in the 1980's and has grown in some years to the size of Switzerland. It is caused by agricultural pollutants flowing from the mouths of the Danube, Dniester, and Dnieper rivers. A nonnative comb jelly—*Mnemiopsis leidyi* (inset), which was probably discharged from a merchant ship—rapidly occupied the dead zone and then spread throughout the Black Sea. The Black Sea population of *M. leidyi* declined after 2000, mainly as a result of invasion by another comb jelly species that preys on *M. leidyi*.

zones, regions that are mostly empty of marine life during parts of the year. Most dead zones develop in spring and summer, when large amounts of agricultural pollutants are washed into the sea.

Researchers have identified more than 400 dead zones around the world, according to data reported in August 2008 by marine biologist Robert Diaz of the Virginia Institute of Marine Science in Gloucester Point. Every spring and summer since the 1980's, scientists have observed the largest dead zone in North America, at the mouth of the Mississippi River in the Gulf of Mexico. In 2008, the Gulf dead zone may have been the biggest one yet, at more than 20,700 square kilometers (8,000 square miles)—approximately the same area as Massachusetts.

A dead zone begins to develop as chemical nutrients in fertilizer runoff promote an explosive growth of algae at the sea surface. As the algae die over time, massive amounts of dead and decaying algae drift downward to the sea floor. This debris is broken down by bacteria that use oxygen from the water for respiration. In the process, oxygen levels crash, killing or driving out much of the animal life in the area.

Jellyfish are among the few animals that can survive in such oxygen-depleted waters, because they carry their own supply of dissolved oxygen inside their watery tissues. This oxygen reservoir keeps the jellyfish "breathing" when external oxygen levels are low. Eventually, jellyfish need to replenish their oxygen supplies, such as by swimming to oxygen-rich waters. When dead zones develop, opportunistic jellyfish are among the first organisms to move into the area to take advantage of the small amount of food resources that may exist there.

One of the world's most degraded dead zones was first observed in the 1980's in the northwestern part of the Black Sea, a major body of water in southeastern Europe and the Middle East. As pollutants poured out from the mouths of the Danube River in Romania and the Dniester and Dnieper rivers in Ukraine, a dead zone the size of Switzerland developed. Then, a nonnative comb jelly, *Mnemiopsis leidyi*, appeared in the zone, probably discharged inadvertently from a ship's *ballast water* (water used to stabilize a ship). This comb jelly rapidly took over the largely vacant dead zone. From there, the opportunistic comb jelly gradually spread throughout the Black Sea, outcompeting many native species. Marine biologists estimated that by 1990, the total mass of comb jellies in the Black Sea exceeded 815 million metric tons (900 million tons)— 10 times as much as the total annual fish catch from all the world's

Workers on a factory fishing ship process bluefin tuna in the eastern Mediterranean Sea near Turkey. Over-fishing with such technologically advanced vessels has led to population declines of tuna, mackerel, and other predators of jellyfish. Some researchers believe that reduced numbers of these predators is one reason behind the population explosions of jellyfish.

A salmon farm off the coast of Northern Ireland (above) was wiped out in November 2007 by a massive invasion of jellyfish called mauve stingers (right). By eating salmon eggs and young, stinging the salmon, and tainting the salmon with venom, the jellyfish caused the loss of more than 100,000 fish.

oceans. The Black Sea population of *M. leidyi* declined substantially after 2000, however—mainly as a result of invasion by another species of comb jelly, a species that preys on *M. leidyi*.

The ever-growing human consumption of fish may also be promoting jellyfish populations. Commercial fishing became highly industrialized in the second half of the 1900's. Factory fishing ships began trawling the oceans with massive nets, sonar equipment, and other devices capable of quickly and efficiently scouring broad areas of seawater and sea floor. Consequently, populations of desirable food fish fell sharply.

Overfishing of many of the world's waters caused population declines of certain large predators of jellyfish, including tuna and mackerel. In addition, the leatherback turtle, one of the main predators of jellyfish, experienced disastrous population losses, especially in the Pacific Ocean, in the second half of the 1900's. The leatherback turtle was threatened mainly by the development of homes and businesses on its beach nesting sites, as well as by disruption of these sites by tourists. Those small fish that compete with jellyfish for food also declined in number. These drops in the number of jellyfish predators and competitors opened up more opportunities for jellyfish numbers to grow.

Many scientists believe that yet another factor that may be promoting jellyfish blooms is global warming. Earth's average surface temperature increased by approximately 0.76 °C (1.4 °F) between the mid-1800's and early 2000's, according to widely accepted scientific data. Most climate scientists believe that human activities, primarily the

Vast numbers of dead Portuguese man-of-war jellyfish litter a beach on the eastern coast of Australia after being washed ashore by tides. Scientists believe that warming water off the Australian coast has contributed to increases in jellyfish populations and an expansion of jellyfish ranges.

burning of *fossil fuels* (coal, oil, natural gas), are contributing to global warming by increasing the concentration of carbon dioxide and other greenhouse gases in the atmosphere. Such gases trap heat near Earth's surface, leading to the warming of the surface.

Shifts in sea currents

Global warming affects Earth's oceans in complex ways. As water temperatures increase, patterns of ocean currents—both at surface and deep-sea levels—change. For example, worldwide patterns of ocean circulation result from cold, dense surface water sinking to ocean depths. The deep cold water then spreads out toward warmer regions, where it becomes warmer and less dense. This water rises again, to form surface currents. However, this temperature-dependent system of circulation and currents is disrupted as the average ocean temperature increases. Temperature measurements made over long periods in a number of locations provide strong evidence that coastal ocean waters have warmed in many places since the early 1900's.

The warming of the ocean favors jellyfish and related sea creatures for several reasons. Warming surface waters contribute to the growth of masses of plankton, which the opportunistic jellyfish are quick to exploit as an abundant food source. Warmer deep currents may promote the growth of jellyfish polyps. In addition, the warming of seawater can lead to shifts in currents in ways that help jellyfish expand their ranges.

Such a change in ocean currents has affected jellyfish populations along the eastern coast of Australia. In 2007, scientists with Australia's Commonwealth Scientific and Industrial Research Organization determined that average water temperature along the coast of Tasmania, the island state off the southeast coast of Australia, had risen 0.8° C (1.4° F) over the past century. According to the scientists, the Tasmanian temperature spike confirmed other data indicating the strengthening of a warm ocean current flowing down the eastern coast of Australia from Queensland. This current strengthening corresponded with substantial increases in jellyfish populations along Australia's eastern coast, including populations of such dangerous box jellyfish as *C. fleckeri* and the Irukandji (*Carukia barnesi*).

In 2007, scientists from the United Kingdom's (U.K.) Marine Climate Change Impacts Partnership, which coordinates the collection of ocean data related to climate change, released a study indicating substantial warming of British coastal surface waters since the mid-1990's. According to the data, 7 of the 10 warmest years on record for U.K. coastal waters occurred between the mid-1990's and 2007. Furthermore, U.K. scientists evaluating water temperature data collected on the Isle of Man, an island in the Irish Sea, detected a rise in average temperature of at least 1.0° C (1.8° F) between the early 1900's and early 2000's. Most of that temperature rise was recorded since the mid-1990's.

The documented increase in sea temperatures in British waters was accompanied by a series of jellyfish blooms, alarming the public and scientists alike. In one of the most intense blooms, millions of mauve stingers proliferated in the Irish Sea along the coast of Northern Ireland in November 2007—later in the year than most other jellyfish blooms.

Japanese fishermen draw up a net packed with Nomura's jellyfish—rather than the fish the men had hoped to catch. From 2002 to 2007, enormous numbers of this giant jellyfish crippled fishing activities in the Sea of Japan by filling, weighing down, and destroying fishing nets. The population of Nomura's jellyfish in the Sea of Japan began to decline in 2008 for unknown reasons—though the animals remained a problem.

People who enjoy beaches are likely to encounter jellyfish—and perhaps get stung. By and large, the experience proves unpleasant, though it is not usually dangerous or life-threatening. Many people describe a jellyfish sting as a sensation rather like touching their skin to a hot stove burner. However, a sting can be much more serious—even fatal—in individuals who have allergic reactions to the venom. For most jellyfish stings, physicians recommend spraying or dousing the affected area of skin with vinegar. The mildly acidic characteristics of vinegar prevent the barbed stingers that the jellyfish shoots into the victim from releasing toxin into the victim's body. Many bodyguards on beaches that tend to have high jellyfish populations keep supplies of vinegar on hand. Victims who have allergic reactions to jellyfish venom need immediate professional medical attention and are usually taken to hospitals. Beach visitors should also learn to identify—and avoid—the most poisonous species of jellyfish that are likely to occur in their areas. Government natural resource departments and university biology departments may have such information available for the public.

Blisters from jellyfish stings cover a woman's knee. In some cases, jellyfish stings can be so serious that victims need to be hospitalized to save their lives.

The jellyfish spread throughout an area of 26 square kilometers (10 square miles) to a depth of 11 meters (35 feet). By eating fish eggs and young, stinging the fish, and contaminating the fish with venom, jellyfish in the bloom destroyed a salmon farm that had been distributed along the seacoast in underwater cages.

Reports of jellyfish invasions of British beaches and seaside resorts became more common after 2000. In August 2008, beachgoers were met by sightings of large numbers of Portuguese men-of-war along the coasts of southern and southwestern England. Blooms of the dangerously venomous lion's mane jellyfish (*Cyanea capillata*) also occurred in this same region. Less dangerous, but still irksome, jellyfish invasions in the British Isles included massings of the by-the-wind-sailor jelly (*Velella velella*) along the Cornwall coast in 2004 and of the moon jelly (*Aurelia aurita*) off the northwest coast of Wales that same year.

Along the western coast of Japan, in the Sea of Japan, spectacular invasions of gigantic Nomura's jellyfish (*Nemopilema nomurai*) were observed each year between 2002 and 2007. This creature, which can grow to the size of a compact car and weigh more than 200 kilograms (440 pounds), wreaked havoc on Japanese commercial fishing fleets by destroying nets. Nomura's jellyfish are native to Korean and Chinese waters, on the opposite side of the Sea of Japan. Scientists suspected that shifts in ocean currents, perhaps caused by global warming, extended the normal range of this jellyfish. Observers reported a reduction in numbers of Nomura's jellyfish inhabiting Japanese waters in 2008—for unknown reasons. Japanese researchers sought to better understand the reasons for both the blooms and the sudden decline of the blooms.

Restoring the ocean to health

By 2009, many marine scientists had linked jellyfish blooms in a number of locales to human-caused stresses on ocean ecosystems. As is the case with many environmentally based problems, there were no quick fixes to the jellyfish difficulties. Nevertheless, scientists recommended a number of measures to help improve the ecological health of the oceans and, perhaps, reduce jellyfish blooms.

Reducing sewage and agricultural runoff into rivers and streams is one of the most important of these recommendations. Because chemical compounds in runoff promote the growth of algae in coastal waters, reducing runoff would help prevent the formation of dead zones. Curtailing agricultural runoff would require that commercial agriculture operations use much less chemical fertilizer to grow crops.

Scientists also recommend that all commercial fishing be restricted or prohibited in ecologically fragile marine regions, including areas in which prized food fish have been largely depleted. In ocean areas that can still sustain commercial fishing, scientists suggest that the most ecologically destructive fishing practices be prohibited. In 2008, several conservation groups in Canada conducted a joint study of commercial fishing methods, ranking them from most to least destructive. Their report identified bottom trawling as the most destructive fishing method. In bottom trawl-

A diving scientist attaches an electronic tag to a Nomura's jellyfish in the Sea of Japan in 2008. The sensor, equipped with a radio transmitter, provides scientists with information on the jellyfish's travel habits, the water temperature and depth, and other factors. Such data can help researchers better understand how to manage jellyfish numbers.

Biologist Andrew Brierley of the University of St. Andrews in Scotland holds a large jellyfish aboard a research vessel off the coast of Namibia in the Atlantic Ocean. Brierley's research focused on the role that depleted stocks of sardines, anchovies, and other small commercial fish have on jellyfish populations. He concluded that overfishing allows more plankton and other food to be available for the jellyfish.

ing, a huge net kept open at one end by metal weights is dragged along the sea bottom. The trawl net captures a great number of aquatic species in addition to food fish. Moreover, trawling severely disrupts the biologically diverse communities of coral reefs.

Marine ecologists note that several populations of natural jellyfish predators need to be restored. In addition to tuna, mackerel, and other large food fish, these predators include the leatherback turtle and other sea turtles. All species of sea turtles were classified as threatened or endangered as of 2009.

Finally, scientists urge the establishment of more protected areas in oceans—places similar to national parks—in which commercial activities are restricted or prohibited. The U.S. government has designated approximately one-third of all U.S. waters as Marine Protected Areas (MPA's), but protection levels vary widely. Only about 3 percent of the total MPA area is classified as "no take"—that is, waters in which no commercial fishing or other commercial activities are allowed.

Marine scientists point out that jellyfish should not be viewed as only culprits in ocean degradation. Like all successful forms of life, jellyfish are merely taking advantage of environmental opportunities. Moreover, jellyfish have important roles to play in healthy marine ecosystems. Their polyps and young medusae serve as food for many sea animals. Other sea creatures prey on adult jellyfish.

Much remained unknown about jellyfish in 2009, including many details about their life cycles. Scientists believe that jellyfish polyps mass together in large "fields" on sea floors. However, researchers have had difficulty locating these tiny, transparent polyps in nature, and they have never actually examined and studied the biological activity in polyp fields.

Based on the increased sightings of jellyfish blooms, marine biologists suspected that the budding rates of polyps and medusae in jellyfish polyp fields were extraordinarily high in the early 2000's. Scientists hoped to eventually measure these rates in various regions of the sea to gain an improved understanding of jellyfish life cycles and population patterns. They expected this knowledge, in turn, to lead to better ways of battling jellyfish blooms.

To meet this challenge, marine biology departments at many universities were increasingly investing in the study of jellyfish and related ocean organisms in the early 2000's. Researchers at some universities also requested that the public assist in the collection of jellyfish specimens and the reporting of jellyfish sightings. The University of the Western Cape in South Africa and James Cook University in Australia are among the institutions most active in jellyfish research.

In the United Kingdom, Swansea University in Wales and University College Cork in Ireland have jointly sponsored the EcoJel project. Funded in part by the European Union, EcoJel researchers were using sophisticated technology to investigate the secrets of jellyfish. This technology included the attachment of electronic tags, or sensors, to captured jellyfish. After tagged jellyfish are released, the tags record water temperature, ocean depth, and other environmental variables in the animals' environment. Then, after the jellyfish die, the tags are washed ashore with the bodies, enabling scientists to retrieve and analyze the electronic data. Some sensors used in such research are equipped with radio transmitters that relay data to scientists in real time.

Scientists had determined by 2009 that Earth's marine ecosystem was undergoing dramatic changes. The jellyfish "invasions" may be disturbing evidence of the worldwide ecological problems caused by ocean pollution, overfishing, and global warming.

■ FOR ADDITIONAL INFORMATION

Books and periodicals

Connor, Judith L., and Deans, Nora L. *Jellies: Living Art.* Monterey Bay Aquarium Press, 2002.

Mee, Laurence. "Reviving Dead Zones." *Scientific American.* November 2006, pp. 79-85.

Nouvian, Claire. *The Deep: The Extraordinary Creatures of the Abyss.* University of Chicago Press, 2007.

Web sites

National Science Foundation: Jellyfish by the Numbers—http://www.nsf.gov/news/special_reports/jellyfish/by_numbers.pdf

South Carolina Department of Natural Resources: Jellyfish—http://www.dnr.sc.gov/marine/pub/seascience/jellyfi.html

University of the Western Cape: SAJellyWatch—http://sajellywatch.uwc.ac.za/

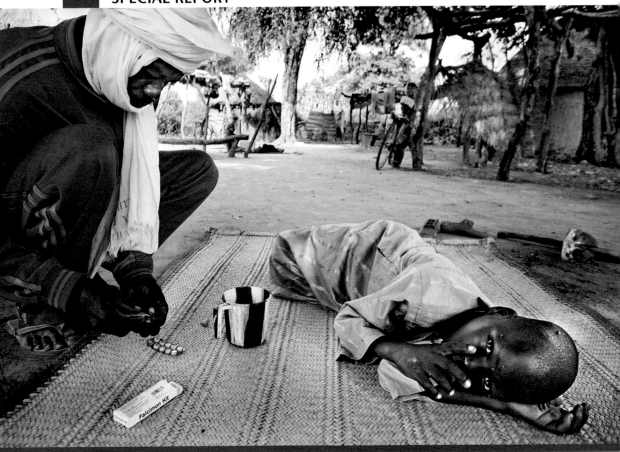

The Timeless
Scourge of Malaria

by Edward R. Riciutti

Malaria has ravaged humankind since the dawn of time, but governments, charitable organizations, and health professionals are fighting back with new weapons.

A young boy with malaria (above) receives treatment at a health center in Chad run by the international organization Doctors Without Borders (Médecins Sans Frontières), based in Brussels, Belgium.

The physician was puzzled. Although his patient had flu-like symptoms, the symptoms had lasted only a few hours, disappeared, then returned a few days later. When questioned, the patient revealed that about a month earlier, she had picked up a friend at an international airport near her home in a northern United States city. Afterward, she had found a mosquito bite on her arm. The physician ordered a blood test, which confirmed his suspicions. His patient had malaria, a disease usually associated with the tropics. A mosquito carrying the disease had hitchhiked on an airliner, flown 11,300 kilometers (7,000 miles), then buzzed into the terminal and bitten her.

A malaria-infected *Anopheles* mosquito (above) engorges itself with blood as it feeds on a human victim. In the process, the insect injects saliva infected with malaria parasites into the human bloodstream. The parasites travel to the human liver, mature there, and then return to the bloodstream. They next infect and feed on human red blood cells (above left), deforming and eventually rupturing them.

The chances of contracting malaria at an airport—outside of malaria-prone areas in the tropics and subtropics—are actually quite low. However, the incident underscores a sobering reality—malaria is widespread and entrenched in many places in the world. Moreover, modern transportation systems and, perhaps, global warming may increase malaria's threat to billions more outside these regions.

Malaria is a serious and, if untreated, sometimes fatal disease caused by tiny parasites carried by mosquitoes. Female mosquitoes, needing protein to produce eggs, feed on the blood of human beings (or animals). Certain species of mosquitoes in the *genus* (group of related species) *Anopheles* may leave something behind besides a bite mark. While they are feeding, they may inject the malaria parasite into the bite victim's bloodstream.

Anopheles mosquitoes live everywhere on Earth except Antarctica. In 2008, malaria was *endemic to* (regularly occurred in) 109 countries and territories, according to the World Health Organization (WHO), an agency of the United Nations (UN). Almost half of these countries were in Africa, with the rest in Asia and tropical America. WHO experts estimate that about 250 million people around the globe become sick from malaria each year and that nearly 1 million die from the disease. In recent years, more than 90 percent of all malaria deaths have occurred among Africans, the vast majority among children under 5 years of age. In fact, according to the UN Children's Fund (UNICEF), malaria kills one child on Earth every 30 seconds and causes one-fifth of all childhood deaths in Africa.

The problem is not confined to tropical and subtropical regions, however. Epidemiologists, or scientists who study patterns of disease

The author:
Edward R. Ricciuti is a free-lance writer based in Killingworth, Connecticut.

TERMS AND CONCEPTS

Anopheles: The *genus* (group of related species) to which all malaria-carrying mosquitoes belong.

Artemisinin: Derived from a Chinese plant, a chemical compound that forms the basis of an antimalarial drug widely used today.

Cerebral malaria: A form of malaria that affects the brain, sometimes leading to permanent brain damage or death, particularly in children.

Endemic: Regularly occurring, in reference to the prevalence of a disease in a human population.

Epidemiologist: A scientist who studies patterns of disease transmission.

Placental malaria: A form of malaria that afflicts pregnant women, greatly increasing health risks for both the mother and the unborn baby.

Plasmodium: The name of the *genus*, or family, of the various species of malaria-causing parasites; for example, *P. falciparum* is of the species *falciparum*, belonging to the genus *Plasmodium*.

Quinine: Derived from the bark of a South American tree, a substance that forms the basis of a long-used family of antimalarial drugs.

Vector control: The practice of isolating disease-carrying organisms, such as *Anopheles* mosquitoes, from human populations.

transmission, estimate that across the globe some 3.3 billion people, or about half of the world's population, are at risk for malaria. Indeed, until the mid-1900's, malaria-carrying mosquitoes infested parts of the United States and western Europe.

Malaria destroys not only individual health but also the social and economic health of entire societies. The economic burden, in particular, is crushing. In some countries, malaria is responsible for half of all hospital admissions and millions of lost workdays. Some African families spend a quarter of their income on malaria control and prevention, including the costs of traveling to clinics and buying drugs. A 2000 study jointly sponsored by WHO and Harvard University in Cambridge, Massachusetts, found that if malaria had been eliminated in 1965, sub-Saharan countries would have added $100 billion to their combined *gross domestic product* (the measure of all goods and services produced in a year) in the intervening 35 years. Some of the world's poorest countries bear the heaviest burden of malaria.

The malaria parasite

The parasites that cause malaria are protozoans, tiny one-celled organisms of the genus *Plasmodium*. Of the more than 200 species of *Plasmodia* (the plural form), some infect such animals as monkeys, mice, and birds. Although five species of *Plasmodia* are known to cause malaria in people, the species known as *P. falciparum* causes the most widespread and serious form of the disease in human populations.

MALARIA HOT SPOTS

Malaria is *endemic to* (regularly occurs in) tropical and subtropical regions of the world. Outbreaks of malaria occasionally occur in other regions.

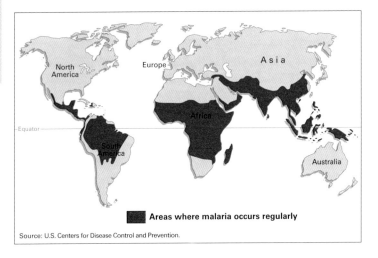

■ **Areas where malaria occurs regularly**

Source: U.S. Centers for Disease Control and Prevention.

THE LIFE CYCLE OF THE MALARIA PARASITE

Malaria is caused by protozoans called *Plasmodia*. These tiny organisms spend part of their life in the bodies of human beings and part in the bodies of *Anopheles* mosquitoes. The disease spreads from person to person through the bite of these mosquitoes.

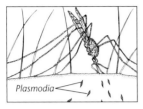

An infected mosquito injects *Plasmodia* when it bites a person.

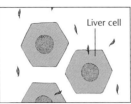

Each *Plasmodium* invades a liver cell and multiplies.

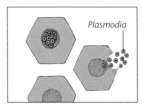

The cell bursts, releasing a new form of *Plasmodium*.

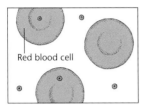

Each *Plasmodium* enters a red blood cell and multiplies again.

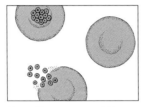

The cell ruptures, and *Plasmodia* are released to invade other red cells.

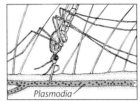

An infected person may transmit *Plasmodia* to a mosquito as it feeds on that person's blood.

Life cycle of the malaria organism

A *Plasmodium* undergoes a complex, multistage life cycle. It begins when a female mosquito whose salivary glands are infected with malaria sporozoites, one form of the organism, bites a person. The sporozoites enter the human bloodstream and migrate to the liver, where they take over certain cells and produce numerous merozoites, the parasitic stage of the organism. The liver cells burst and release the merozoites into the bloodstream, which enter red blood cells (RBC's). There they feed on *hemoglobin* (the iron-based pigment that transports oxygen in blood) and multiply. Eventually, each infected RBC bursts, releasing thousands more merozoites into the bloodstream.

P. falciparum is capable of infecting up to 5 percent of the host's RBC's. It is at this stage of infection—the destruction of thousands of RBC's—that the human host suffers symptoms of malaria.

Plasmodium species that cause malaria in people

P. falciparum	Widespread and dangerous, dominant in Africa; responsible for the most deaths worldwide.
P. vivax	Widely dispersed though not a major factor in Africa; most common type in India and South America. If untreated, it can remain dormant in the liver and reappear to cause disease years later.
P. ovale	Similar in effect to P. vivax.
P. malariae	Causes the mildest form of malaria; can remain in the body for many years or for life.
P. knowlesi	Recently emerged as a common source of infection in Southeast Asia; potentially very dangerous. Easy to confuse with other species: DNA analysis is required to identify the parasite conclusively.*

* According to information released in October 2008 by an international team of researchers funded by the Wellcome Trust Sanger Institute in Cambridge, United Kingdom.

Eventually, some of the merozoites change into *gametocytes* (sex cells), which circulate in the blood, ready for transfer to a mosquito. When an *Anopheles* mosquito bites, it swallows the malarial gametocytes with blood. The gametocytes in its stomach fuse to form eggs, from which sporozoites hatch. The sporozoites migrate to the mosquito's salivary gland—and the entire infection cycle starts over again.

Malaria's disease profile

The symptoms of a malaria attack begin about 10 days to a month after infection. They include fever, headache, muscle pain, chills, and nausea. After a bout, the symptoms disappear, but they often return, sometimes within a few days. Fatalities from malaria occur generally in young children, pregnant women, or people with weakened immune systems. Occasionally, malaria recurs several years after the initial illness.

The major cause of death from *P. falciparum* infection, particularly in children, is cerebral malaria, a condition in which blood flow to the brain is restricted and brain cells die. Inside an infected RBC, the malaria parasites secrete a glue-like protein that forms sticky knobs on the cell's surface. The knobs cause the RBC's to clump and stick to the inner walls of blood vessels, eventually clogging some of them. Cerebral malaria develops when infected RBC's clog blood vessels in the brain, resulting in high fever, convulsions, and coma, followed by death in as many as half of all cases. Survivors may suffer permanent brain damage.

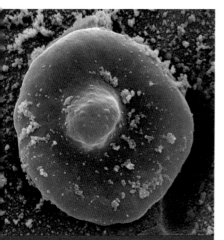

The surface of an infected red blood cell is deformed by malaria parasites active within the cell. Much of the cell's surface is covered by bumps consisting of sticky proteins likely to bind the cell to the wall of a blood vessel.

Placental malaria

Another highly dangerous form of malaria is placental malaria, a condition that occurs in pregnant women. Placental malaria affects only women who live in areas where malaria is endemic—that is, where continual infection and reinfection has created some degree of immunity in human populations. Because of this immunity in the mother, the malaria parasites retreat to the placenta, the disk-shaped organ that links the mother's organ systems with the fetus. The parasites synthesize special proteins that allow them to bind firmly to the placental wall. In the placenta, the parasites escape destruction by the mother's immune system, because her immune response is blunted there to prevent her from rejecting the fetus.

The concentration of malaria parasites in a pregnant woman's placenta interferes with the oxygen supply going to the fetus and increases the danger of serious and even life-threatening complications for both mother and fetus. A doctor's care during pregnancy and preventive treatment with certain medications can reduce these risks. Women who undergo multiple pregnancies naturally build up resistance to

Immunity to malaria can come at a cost. By some estimates, malaria has been infecting people for 100,000 years. During this time, some people in malaria-prone areas have gained resistance to the disease through genetic *mutations* (changes), which have been passed down through generations of descendants. People of African ancestry frequently possess a gene for the so-called sickle-celled trait, inherited from one parent. That trait provides resistance to *P. falciparum* malaria. If the gene is inherited from both parents, however, an often fatal disease, sickle-cell anemia, occurs.

Another type of immunity that comes at a price is that of many Africans to *P. vivax*. Scientists believe that this form of malaria is rare in Africa because most Africans are Duffy-negative—that is,

they lack the Duffy protein, a molecule normally produced on the surface of red blood cells. The downside to the protection afforded by Duffy-negative status is that blood transfusions between Duffy-negative and Duffy-positive individuals can lead to a life-threatening allergic reaction. This condition may also develop between a Duffy-positive mother and her Duffy-negative fetus. To further complicate the Duffy factor, a U.S.-based research team discovered evidence in 2008 that the absence of the Duffy protein in a Duffy-negative individual actually assists HIV, the virus that causes AIDS, in invading blood cells. The research team, drawn from a number of U.S. universities, was led by Sunil Ahuja of the University of Texas Health Science Center in San Antonio.

placental malaria. Over time, their immune systems produce proteins that prevent malaria parasites from attaching to the placental wall. As a result, a woman develops more protection against placental malaria in subsequent pregnancies, though not necessarily against other forms of the disease.

Immunity to malaria

Because young children lack a naturally acquired immunity to *Plasmodia*, they are especially vulnerable to malaria. However, if they survive early infections and bouts of the disease, they typically attain a degree of immunity and experience less serious episodes later in childhood.

Human immunity to *P. falciparum* and other malaria-causing *Plasmodia* is incomplete and transitory, however. Medical experts estimate that adults living in malaria-endemic areas may become relatively immune to malaria over a five-year period of exposure. Such individuals lose their immunity if they live outside of malaria-endemic zones for about the same amount of time, because their bodies' immune response gradually weakens in the absence of exposure to *Plasmodia* organisms.

The difficulty of attaining and keeping a high level of immunity to malaria can best be explained by the genetic sophistication of disease-causing *Plasmodia*, which continually mount defenses against human immune systems. In 2005, Australian-based researchers with the Howard Hughes Medical Institute reported that *P. falciparum* uses a "cloaking" strategy to evade attacks by the host's immune system. As parasites invade RBC's, they attach copies of a protein called PfEMP1 to the surface of each infected cell. PfEMP1 enables infected RBC's to stick to the walls of blood vessels. In the process, it also exposes an "alien" presence for potential identification and attack by the host's immune system. To avoid attack, however, *P. falciparum* has devised 60 variants of PfEMP1. The parasite continually exchanges PfEMP1 "flavors"—thus keeping the host's immune system off balance.

Getting malaria under control

Malaria is an immensely complex disease. Understanding it is like trying to assemble a puzzle with only a few pieces that can fit together in endless ways. The pieces include the mosquitoes and their life cycles and behavior; the life cycle and biology of *Plasmodium* organisms; the behavior, biological condition, and immunity of people in vulnerable populations; the effectiveness of drug treatments; and the tendency of drugs to induce resistance in the malaria parasites.

It might seem as if eradicating all *Anopheles* mosquitoes would put an end to malaria. Not only is this impossible—and even undesirable in terms of ecological stability—but also unnecessary. Instead, many scientists advocate a program of substantially decreasing contacts between people and malarial *Anopheles* mosquitoes. This approach of isolating disease-causing organisms from people as much as possible is referred to as vector control. (Epidemiologists define *vector* as the means by which a disease is transferred to people.)

In the first half of the 1900's, workers dug ditches in southern U.S. locales to drain standing water where malaria-causing mosquitoes breed. Efforts such as these helped eliminate malaria from the South.

Vector control of disease-causing *Anopheles* mosquitoes has been achieved in various places and times. For example, malaria used to be endemic in certain parts of the southeastern United States. These areas have warm climates with mild winters and many natural wetlands—ideal conditions for breeding mosquitoes. In the early to mid-1900's, public health officials carried out large-scale mosquito control programs, particularly targeting problem areas with insecticide spraying. Enough mosquitoes were killed or removed from contact with people to break the *Plasmodium* cycle and eliminate the parasite.

International efforts to control mosquitoes also achieved striking success in the 1950's and 1960's. Disease statistics for malaria in India and Sri Lanka (then called Ceylon) showed dramatic declines during that period. However, both countries suffered resurgences during the 1970's, when antimalaria campaigns were abandoned because of wars, governmental instability, and lack of resources.

Epidemiologists attributed many of the initial successes to spraying with DDT, a powerful insecticide. Unfortunately, DDT is capable of causing considerable ecological and environmental harm. During the

1970's, the United States and most European nations banned DDT. However, some countries continued to use the insecticide. South Africa, for example, launched a new antimalaria campaign in the late 1990's that included spraying with DDT. According to the South African National Institute for Communicable Diseases, South Africa has experienced an 80-percent decline in malaria cases since that time. Results like these have sparked some malaria researchers to rethink restrictions on DDT. In fact, WHO in 2006 endorsed the use of DDT in controlled indoor spraying to combat malaria. However, the policy of using DDT even in carefully controlled applications remains highly controversial. Many environmental organizations continue to strongly oppose any use of DDT.

Some researchers are investigating the possibility of controlling mosquitoes in a different way—by "malaria-proofing" the insects. Geneticists, or scientists who investigate altering organisms by altering genes, are working with *Anopheles* mosquitoes to render them immune to harmful species of *Plasmodium* protozoans. If the number of mosquitoes capable of transmitting malaria parasites to people were greatly reduced, fewer people would become infected. Achieving success with this strategy will involve introducing into the wild hardy *transgenic* (genetically altered) mosquitoes that are capable of surviving and reproducing at higher rates than the wild species.

Boarding students at a school in Zambia sleep under insecticide-treated nets (ITN's) for protection from malaria-carrying mosquitoes. The ITN's greatly reduce malaria transmission, because the disease-causing species of mosquitoes feed mainly at night.

Micromanaged mosquito control

In recent years, epidemiologists and public health experts have learned that the most effective methods of mosquito control are often small-scale measures that individuals and families can take in their own homes. Two widely endorsed control measures include indoor residential spraying (IRS) and sleeping under insecticide-treated nets (ITN's).

Careful spraying of wall surfaces in houses at dusk reduces the activity of mosquitoes indoors during their early-evening feeding times. In many African countries, DDT is used for this purpose, but insecticides with less toxic side effects, including plant-based substances, can also be used. Malaria experts have found that sleeping nets that have been impregnated with long-lasting insecticide are highly effective in reducing mosquito bites and the transmission of the malaria parasite. Medical experts emphasize that it is especially important for children and pregnant women to sleep under protective ITN's. However, the use of the nets is generally advocated for the entire population in malaria-endemic locations.

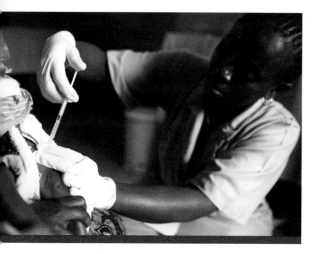

A medical worker in Tanzania injects a child with a trial vaccine for malaria in 2007. Medical researchers evaluating the results of the trial approved a follow-up, large-scale trial, to begin in late 2009.

Treating malaria with drugs

More than 2,000 years ago, the Chinese discovered that an extract of the annual wormwood plant, qinghaosu (CHEENG HOW SOO), effectively treated symptoms of malaria. This substance is the basis of the important modern drug artemisinin. Another modern family of antimalaria drugs is based on quinine, a substance derived from the bark of the South American cinchona tree. Widely used synthetic versions of quinine include chloroquine, mefloquine, and primaquine. A few standard antibiotics have also been used to treat malaria.

The problem with all antimalaria drug treatments, however, is that the *Plasmodium* parasites are extremely adept at mutating new defenses against widely used drugs. Since the mid-1900's, mosquitoes have developed resistance to quinine-based drugs and conventional antibiotics, and in some places even to artemisinin, the most widely effective antimalaria drug today. Drug-resistant parasites pose a serious danger because they tend, over time, to overtake nonresistant strains and can spread globally.

To combat this trend, medical experts and public health officials recommend abandoning single-drug therapy and adopting artemisinin-based combination therapy, or ACT. Essentially, an ACT is a multidrug "cocktail," one of whose components is artemisinin. Artemisinin is included because it disappears from the blood quickly, and the protozoans have less time to adapt to it. Meanwhile, a second, longer-lasting drug in the cocktail continues to weaken and kill parasites.

Even ACT's may not be safe from resistance, however, according to Pascal Ringwald, WHO's malaria coordinator. Ringwald and other scientists recently documented the emergence of artemisinin-resistant strains of *P. falciparum* living along the border between Cambodia and Thailand. If the resistance spreads, it could render ACT drug treatments less effective or even ineffective against malaria.

New approaches to drugs

Recent advances in molecular biology are providing new possibilities for drug development. Molecular biology is the study of the role of complex molecules, including DNA (deoxyribonucleic acid, the molecule from which genes are made), in cellular processes. Whereas traditional malaria drugs aim at killing the parasite, new drug strategies include finding ways to block life processes of the organism to render it harmless.

In 2007, scientists at the United Kingdom's National Institute for Medical Research in London identified an enzyme produced by malaria parasites inside an infected human RBC. (An enzyme is a molecule that assists chemical reactions.) The enzyme, called PfSUB1, triggers the

The interaction between malaria-causing *P. falciparum* and the HIV virus—the cause of AIDS and related HIV disease—may have established a kind of "co-infection partnership," according to researchers with the Fred Hutchinson Cancer Research Center and the University of Washington, both of Seattle, Washington. In 2006, the researchers reported findings from their evaluation of patients in Kisumu, Kenya. The researchers discovered that when *P. falciparum* infects a person already carrying the HIV virus, the blood level of the virus increases by as much as 1,000 percent. On the other hand, people suffering from suppressed immune systems caused by the HIV virus are more susceptible to the effects of malaria if they are exposed to the parasite. The researchers also concluded that malaria infection increases an HIV-positive individual's chances of transmitting HIV infection, because of his or her higher levels of the virus.

bursting of the RBC and the release of infection-spreading merozoites. Later, the researchers identified a plant-based compound that blocks the action of PfSUB1. This substance could form the basis of a new drug.

Scientists at the London School of Hygiene & Tropical Medicine described another possible blocking strategy in 2008. They discovered that an enzyme called kinasea is needed for *Plasmodium* gametocytes to develop into male and female forms inside mosquitoes. Blocking the enzyme would stop gametocytes from reproducing, thus ending the life cycle.

In March 2009, researchers at Virginia Commonwealth University in Richmond reported the discovery of a molecule on the surface of human red blood cells to which invading malarial parasites attach. Biochemical tests conducted by the researchers identified a molecule called EBL-1 as the specific attachment site on the cell membrane. EBL-1 is a component of a protein complex that spans the thickness of the RBC membrane and serves as a gateway into the cell. The researchers speculated that EBL-1 could provide an ideal target for drug or vaccine development.

Researchers at the Eliza Hall Institute of Medical Research in Melbourne, Australia, in 2008 made a discovery that could lead to a new treatment for cerebral malaria. The researchers identified eight proteins in *P. falciparum* that enable infected RBC's to stick to blood vessel walls. Removing just one of these proteins prevents the RBC's from sticking. If the "sticky" factor could be eliminated from the parasites, infected RBC's would not clog blood vessels in the brain, and the train of events leading to cerebral malaria would be disrupted.

Quest for a vaccine

Researchers have been searching for a malaria vaccine for at least 50 years. However, the genetic sophistication and complex life cycle of the malaria-causing parasite species present formidable challenges to developing a truly effective vaccine.

In 2008, researchers reported that a vaccine developed by London-based GlaxoSmithKline showed promise when tested in children in Kenya and Tanzania. In a small-scale trial, funded in part by the Bill and Melinda Gates Foundation and carried out by British, Kenyan, and

A worker in Singapore sprays insecticide as part of a mosquito control campaign. Research shows that spraying helps reduce malaria transmission, but critics charge that many of the insecticides are harmful to wildlife populations.

Tanzanian researchers, slightly more than half of the participants acquired immunity against *P. falciparum*, the parasite targeted by the vaccine. The researchers noted that a malaria vaccine was unlikely to provide the same high level of immunity as vaccines against viruses or bacteria, which are genetically much simpler. Nevertheless, they regarded the trial's outcome as highly positive and began recruiting test subjects in 2009 for a large-scale test of the vaccine.

Antimalaria campaigns

Given the scope of endemic malarial infection and the devastation wrought by the disease across the globe, it should not be surprising that international organizations, governments, and private corporations have in recent years mobilized resources to attack malaria. Fighting malaria is expensive. WHO statisticians calculated that at least $688 million in donor funds was spent in Africa in 2006. WHO officials have estimated the annual global cost of implementing control measures to effectively combat the disease to be about $4.5 billion. Funds have come from a variety of sources, including the UN Global Fund to fight AIDS, Tuberculosis and Malaria; WHO; the World Bank, a UN affiliate; and many donor nations and private foundations and donors.

In 2005, WHO issued a strategic plan to reduce the global incidence of malaria by 75 percent by 2015. WHO recommended combining four strategies to combat malaria in endemic regions:

- distribute insecticide-treated nets (ITN's);
- promote prudent indoor residual spraying (IRS) of insecticide;
- treat malaria with ACT's instead of single-source drugs; and
- provide pregnant women with preventive care to protect them and their fetuses from such complications as placental malaria.

The results of a 2007 WHO-sponsored study, released in 2009, provide evidence that the health organization's antimalaria strategy is working. Researchers focused on selected districts in Ethiopia and Rwanda in which ITN coverage and the distribution and use of ACT's was extensive. All of the districts reported declines of at least 55 percent in the number of malaria cases among children under 5. The death rate among this group fell by at least 60 percent.

Despite this success, conditions "on the ground" in many parts of Africa were far less encouraging several years out from the launch of the WHO campaign. In many countries, little improvement was apparent by 2009. This was especially true in the Congo (Kinshasa), torn by years of civil war, and Zimbabwe, afflicted with internal strife and economic collapse. Medical experts noted, in particular, the unpromising continent-wide statistics on the distribution and use of ACT's. According to the

WHO 2008 Global Malaria Report, only 3 percent of African children suffering from symptoms of malaria received the recommended combination drugs in 2006. Donors had provided funding for the new drugs, but ineffective health care delivery systems complicated their distribution.

Global warming and malaria

Some scientists speculate that malaria may be gaining a new ally in global warming. They wonder if warmer Earth climates would enable malarial mosquitoes to extend their ranges into regions now unaffected by the disease.

The UN's Intergovernmental Panel on Climate Change (IPCC), which assesses the threat of global warming, cites models suggesting that malaria mosquitoes will follow rising temperatures to higher altitudes and higher latitudes. One advocate of this position is Paul R. Epstein, director of the Center for Health and the Global Environment of Harvard Medical School. Epstein has warned that the malaria zone—regions in which malaria is endemic—could expand from 45 percent to 60 percent of the world's population if the current pace of global warming continues.

Other scientists, however, are reluctant to link a potential spread of malaria with climate change. Paul Reiter, director of the Department of Insects and Infectious Diseases at the Pasteur Institute in Paris, rejects the idea that global warming by itself will expand the range of endemic malaria. According to Reiter, such destabilizing factors as poverty, civil unrest and wars, and ecological disruption are far more important factors than climate change in malaria's global profile.

As scientists, public health experts, and donors assessed the global malaria threat in 2009, they had reasons to hope. Various disease treatments and effective methods of mosquito control showed promise of reducing the incidence and severity of malaria. Researchers seemed poised to deliver new drugs and—perhaps—an effective vaccine. On the other hand, progress in many countries—particularly in sub-Saharan Africa—was slow and in some, almost entirely lacking. Whether malaria would continue to find effective allies in difficult living conditions—or perhaps in global warming—remained to be seen.

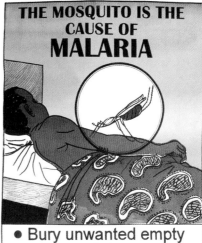

A poster reminding citizens to do their part in controlling mosquito populations is part of a public health campaign in Ghana. Reducing the incidence of malaria in Ghana and other countries where the disease is endemic requires a massive public health effort.

■ FOR ADDITIONAL INFORMATION

Web sites

The Bill and Melinda Gates Foundation—
    http://www.gatesfoundation.org/topics/pages/malaria.aspx
The Carter Center—http://www.cartercenter.org/health/malaria_control/index.html
World Health Organization—http://www.who.int/topics/malaria/en/

The Search for Water on Mars

Possible locations of oceans on Mars more than 3 billion years ago appear in an artist's rendition.

Evidence collected by spacecraft suggests that Mars may once have been a very watery world, expanding the possibility of past—or even present—life on the red planet.

By Michael DuRoss

The appearance of bright white patches excited NASA scientists anxiously watching the robotic arm of the Phoenix Mars Lander dig through the Martian soil in June 2008. The disappearance of some of the patches within only four days positively thrilled project investigators. At first, the scientists were uncertain about the nature of the patches. The bright material could have been salt or solid carbon dioxide (dry ice). Salt, however, would not have disappeared. Solid carbon dioxide would have disappeared in less than a day under the conditions on the Martian surface. Water-ice was the only substance that could have *sublimated* (changed directly from solid to gas) in that time. Although scientists had remote sensing evidence that water-ice existed on the surface of Mars, the vanishing patches gave them close-up photographic evidence of this substance that is so common on Earth.

Rocky debris in craters on Mars (above left) hides large underground glaciers (above right) in an artist's depiction. The depiction is based on ground-penetrating radar data gathered by the Mars Reconnaissance Orbiter in November 2008. Scientists estimated that these glaciers might contain enough water to fill Earth's Great Lakes.

TERMS AND CONCEPTS

Altimeter: An instrument used to measure altitude, typically based on radar, laser, or pressure analyses.

Extremophile: A microorganism that thrives in such extreme environmental conditions as harsh temperatures, great pressures, high radiation levels, or high salt or acid levels.

Hematite: A mineral consisting of iron and oxygen that often forms into small spheres as ground water flows through porous rock.

Maria: Dark regions on Mars that appear to change shape, consisting of dark rock that becomes covered from time to time with lighter soil dispersed by dust storms.

Outflow channels: River-like systems on Mars that formed long ago as water burst from below ground, possibly as a result of volcanic activity.

Spectrometer: Instrument that, based on wavelength, spreads light into a spectrum in which different colors represent different chemical elements and compounds.

Sublimate: To change directly from a solid substance to a gas, with no liquid phase.

"Follow the water" is NASA's strategy for determining whether Mars may have had—or may still have—some form of primitive life associated with water. Acting on the assumption that there can be no life without water, NASA has launched a number of missions to Mars with the capability of detecting existing water or evidence of past water. By the beginning of 2009, after nearly 45 years of exploration, probes launched by NASA and the European Space Agency (ESA) had revealed that the red planet currently has large quantities of water-ice all around its globe. Scientists had also established that Mars had flowing liquid water on its surface in the past—more than 3 billion years ago and perhaps much more recently. The question of whether Mars had—or has—life remained unanswered.

Mysterious Mars

Since early in human civilization, people have viewed Mars as unique among the innumerable points of light in the night sky. In ancient times, the Greeks named it Ares, after their god of war, because of its distinctly reddish, blood-like color. The Romans later followed suit, naming the planet Mars after their war god.

The first practical observations of Mars using a telescope were made in 1609. The Italian scientist Galileo pointed his low-powered instrument at the mysterious red point of light and discovered that Mars was, in fact, a planetary sphere. Surface details remained invisible to Earth-bound astronomers until the development of higher-powered telescopes in the 1800's. Even then, the surface features appeared very faint—and sometimes fooled the eye. In the 1870's, the Italian astronomer Giovanni V. Schiaparelli believed he saw a network of fine lines running along the surface of Mars. He called these lines *canali*, the Italian word for channels, and hypothesized that they were natural streambeds. He also observed darker regions, called *maria*, which he thought might be seas.

Many people in English-speaking countries confused Schiaparelli's canali with canals, leading to the belief that these surface features may have been created by a civilization

WATER ON MARS TIMELINE

1609
First known telescope observations of Mars, by Italian astronomer Galileo, confirm that Mars is a planet.

1870's
Italian astronomer Giovanni V. Schiaparelli describes *canali* (channels) on Mars (right).

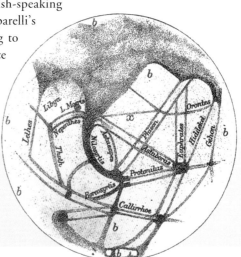

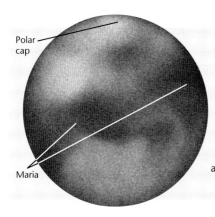

Polar cap

Maria

A telescopic view of Mars taken in 1956—before the dawn of the space age—reveals few surface details other than dark regions, called maria, that appeared to change in size and shape. Scientists later determined that maria were areas of dark rock that were covered from time to time by lighter soil dispersed by dust storms. Other details seen on Mars before space probes and space-based telescopes provided clearer views of the planet included white caps at the north and south poles, similar to the polar ice caps of Earth.

of intelligent Martians. This idea was popularized by United States astronomer Percival Lowell in the late 1800's and early 1900's based on his observations.

When astronomers used more powerful telescopes to view Mars in the 1900's, the canali were nowhere to be seen. In reality, they were optical illusions. However, the maria were there, and astronomers observed these dark regions change in size and shape throughout the year. Some scientists attributed these changes to the seasonal growth and death of plant life. Further observations, however, suggested that the maria were areas of dark rock that became covered from time to time by lighter soil dispersed by dust storms.

Astronomers also observed white caps at the north and south poles, which grew and shrank with the planet's seasons. Because of the white caps' similarity to the polar ice caps on Earth, scientists assumed that the Martian polar caps were also made of ice.

Scientific knowledge about Mars grew as telescopes became increasingly sophisticated. Astronomers also began using radar and other scientific instruments for astronomical observations, with some of these instruments incorporated into telescopes. Among the most important such instruments were *spectrometers*. These devices spread out light and the other types of electromagnetic waves into a *spectrum* (band of radiation) for study. Different chemical elements emit and absorb different wavelengths of electromagnetic energy. As a result, the wavelengths detected in a light source's spectrum reveal the chemical nature of the light source. By combining this method with telescope observations and

The author:
Michael DuRoss is the physical science editor for *The World Book Encyclopedia.*

Late 1800's–early 1900's
American astonomer Percival Lowell popularizes the idea that Mars has canals built by an intelligent civilization.

Early 1900's–mid-1900's
Telescope/spectrometry observations allow scientists to analyze the basic makeup of the Martian atmosphere and surface.

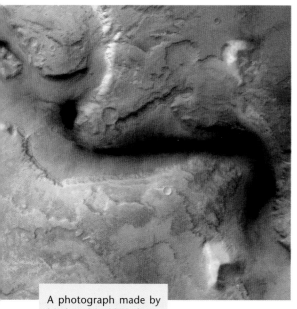

A photograph made by Mariner 9 in 1971 shows an outflow channel on Mars, similar to a riverbed on Earth, that appears to have been formed by a great flood. The photo, originally in black and white, was colorized to mimic the actual colors of the Martian surface. Mariner 9 provided scientists with the first photographic evidence that Mars was once a watery world.

radar analyses, astronomers were able to produce a detailed picture of Mars and the makeup of its surface and atmosphere.

Because of its distance from the sun and its thin atmosphere, Mars is cold. The fourth planet from the sun, Mars is about 1.5 times as distant as Earth, the third planet. Compared with Earth, Mars is smaller in size and *mass* (amount of matter), which means that it has weaker gravity—about one-third of that on Earth. Because gravity exerts only a weak pull on the planet's atmosphere, atmospheric gases more easily escape into space than they do from Earth. The Martian atmosphere, composed mainly of carbon dioxide, has only about 1/100 the density—and, therefore, the pressure—of Earth's atmosphere. For brief periods, Mars becomes warm enough to melt water-ice. However, the low atmospheric pressure on the planet means that warmed ice is likely to sublimate rather than melt.

In the mid-1900's, scientists concluded that sublimation plays a role in the changing sizes of the polar ice caps on Mars. The caps are a mix of dust, water-ice, and solid carbon dioxide. In the Martian spring and summer, carbon-dioxide ice in the caps sublimates into the atmosphere, causing the caps to shrink. In the Martian autumn and winter, carbon dioxide condenses out of the atmosphere as frost, causing the caps to increase in size—sometimes spreading almost halfway to the equator.

Space probes reveal more secrets

The first close-up look at Mars came in 1965, when the NASA spacecraft Mariner 4 made a brief fly-by of the planet. The photographs radioed back to Earth showed a surface that looked much like the moon, pockmarked with meteorite craters. Scientists soon learned that craters actually covered less than 1 percent of the Martian surface.

In 1971, the NASA probe Mariner 9 revealed a far more interesting picture of Mars in the many photos its cameras took while in orbit. Valles Marineris, an enormous canyon system that dwarfs Earth's Grand

WATER ON MARS TIMELINE

1965
Mariner 4 takes the first close-up photos of Mars.

1971
Mariner 9 photographs outflow channels (right), valley networks, canyons, and volcanoes.

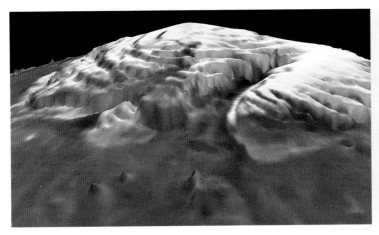

A three-dimensional image of the north pole of Mars, created in 1999, allowed NASA scientists to estimate that the ice there, if melted, would cover the planet with an ocean 9 meters (30 feet) deep. The estimates were based on laser altimeter data collected by Mars Global Surveyor.

Canyon, stunned NASA scientists. The entire canyon system is approximately 4,000 kilometers (2,500 miles) long and as much as 7 kilometers (4.3 miles) deep. Scientists believe that Valles Marineris was formed by a variety of geological processes. However, some parts of the system appear to have layered sediments, indicating that flowing water deposited soil there in the distant past.

Mariner 9 also photographed features on Mars that appear to be similar to dried riverbeds on Earth. The largest of these features, which are up to 100 kilometers (60 miles) wide and 2,000 kilometers (1,200 miles) long, look as if they were formed by great floods. Unlike Earth's river systems, which are generally made up of small streams that feed into larger rivers, many of these channels do not have networks of smaller streambeds. Instead, they appear to have been created all at once in low-lying areas. This observation led scientists to conclude that the water that formed these outflow channels burst from below ground, possibly as a result of subsurface volcanic activity billions of years ago.

Smaller valley networks on other parts of Mars look more like river networks of Earth. These networks, typically just a few kilometers wide, provide another clue pointing to liquid water flowing on the surface of Mars sometime in its past.

The twin Viking orbiters and landers arrived on Mars in 1976. Although Viking 1 and Viking 2 detected evidence of water vapor in the atmosphere, they

1976
Viking 1 (right) and Viking 2 landers take the first-ever photos of Mars from its surface.

MARS ODYSSEY MISSION

NASA's Mars Odyssey spacecraft, which began orbiting Mars in 2002, provided scientists with a vast amount of photographic evidence of past water on the Martian surface. Large channels carved by outbursts of underground water (below) billions of years ago can be traced from highlands to plains in the planet's southern hemisphere. Small gullies in a crater wall (bottom) might have been carved by ground water flowing down the side of the wall in relatively recent times, or it might have been carved by landslides of loose, rocky material.

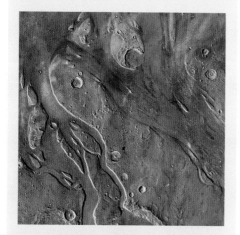

did not find water—liquid or frozen—on the surface. Nor did the instruments find any chemicals associated with life on the planet's surface. Even so, the data collected by the Vikings proved invaluable for planning future missions to search for water and life on Mars.

From 1997 to 2006, high-resolution photographs of the surface of Mars taken by NASA's Mars Global Surveyor revealed a great deal of information about the history of water on the planet, including evidence of an ancient river delta. Some of the photos showed ancient layers of sediment inside craters. Scientists theorized that these features had been created by water that had alternately deposited, and then eroded, soil. An infrared spectrometer on Global Surveyor detected high concentrations of hematite, a mineral consisting of iron and oxygen that typically forms on Earth under wet conditions, in a region called Meridiani Planum. As a result of this finding, NASA scientists selected this region as a site for additional exploration by a later mission. Global Surveyor also had a laser altimeter, capable of measuring the thickness of polar ice. Its measurements revealed that there was enough water-ice in the northern ice cap to—if melted—cover the entire planet with an ocean 9 meters (30 feet) deep.

The oldest spacecraft still operating around Mars in 2009 was the Mars Odyssey, which entered orbit in 2002. Odyssey's primary mission was mapping the surface distribution of chemical elements and minerals. A gamma ray spectrometer on the orbiter detected vast amounts of hydrogen less than 1 meter (3 feet) below the surface and as far as 35 degrees latitude from both poles. NASA scientists interpreted this finding as evidence of crystals of water-ice below the surface of

WATER ON MARS TIMELINE

1997–2006

Mars Global Surveyor photographs sediment layers in crater bottoms, gullies in crater walls, and an ancient river delta. Surveyor also detects high concentrations of hematite and measures the thickness of water-ice in the north polar cap.

1997

Mars Pathfinder includes the first rover (right) to travel across and study the Martian surface.

DISCOVERIES BY SPIRIT AND OPPORTUNITY ROVERS

The Spirit and Opportunity rovers began exploring the Martian surface in 2004. At the bottom of Gusev Crater, possibly the site of an ancient lake, Spirit photographed white, salty deposits inside a trench that it accidentally dug while making a turn (below left). Scientists interpreted the deposits as evidence of the presence of salt water in the past. Opportunity photographed round, bluish balls made of a mineral called hematite at a site known as Meridiani Planum (below right). Similar concretions form on Earth as ground water flows through porous rock and minerals from the rock collect into tiny balls.

Mars—the first firm evidence of existing Martian water in locations other than the poles or the atmosphere.

Mars Odyssey's spectrometer also gathered data in 2008 revealing that numerous places in the southern hemisphere of Mars have deposits of salt. Scientists said potassium and other elements in the salt could be evidence of an enormous ocean that existed from 3.9 billion to 3.5 billion years ago, when Mars was much warmer than it is today. This and other mineral data discovered by Odyssey indicated that at least one-third of the surface of Mars may have been covered by oceans.

NASA's Mars Exploration Rovers—Spirit and Opportunity—began their close-up explorations of the Martian surface in 2004. Their main missions were to complete a geological survey of the terrain and to determine the mineral content of soil and rocks. The rovers' landing locations were selected based on the assumption that the sites were formerly covered by liquid water.

Exploring Gusev Crater, which is possibly the site of an ancient lake, Spirit revealed geological evidence of ancient hot springs and thermal vents—though these tentative conclusions required further investigation.

2001
Mars Odyssey begins its mission; its spectrometer detects large amounts of subsurface water-ice, as well as salt deposits and other evidence of an ancient ocean.

2004
Mars Exploration Rovers Spirit (right) and Opportunity begin their missions; they detect hematite, jarosite, and other minerals associated on Earth with water.

NASA's Phoenix Mars Lander, which set down on the planet in July 2008, provided scientists with the first direct evidence of water on Mars. NASA technicians created this aerial computer-generated image of the spacecraft by combining about 300 stereoscopic photographs made by one of the lander's cameras (marked by a black spot).

Instruments on both rovers confirmed the presence of several minerals known to form on Earth in the presence of water, including the hematite previously detected from orbit by Global Surveyor. Rover photographs showed the hematite as *concretions* (solid spherical formations) resembling blueberries scattered over the ground. Such objects are known to form on Earth as ground water flows through porous rock and chemical reactions trigger minerals from the rock to collect into tiny balls.

Exploring several craters in Meridiani Planum, Opportunity found jarosite, a mineral known to form in highly acidic, wet conditions. Other minerals detected by Opportunity's instruments are found on Earth along the bottom of dried seabeds, providing further evidence of ancient Martian oceans.

The European Space Agency contributed to the exploration of the Martian environment with the Mars Express orbiter, which began studying the red planet in 2004. Spectrometer data from Mars Express revealed that the south polar cap of Mars has enough water-ice to—if melted—cover the planet's surface with an ocean 11 meters (36 feet) deep.

In July 2008, scientists finally got their first direct evidence of Martian water from NASA's Phoenix Mars Lander. Shortly after the disappearance of the bright patches uncovered by the lander's robotic arm, controllers on Earth directed the arm to scoop up some of the white material and deposit it in a sensitive analytical instrument on the lander. The

WATER ON MARS TIMELINE

2004

Mars Express estimates the amount of water-ice in the south polar cap.

2006

Mars Reconnaissance Orbiter (right) begins its mission; it detects phyllosilicates and other mineral evidence of water.

EVIDENCE OF WATER ON MARS

Since the 1970's, several spacecraft missions have collected evidence suggesting that there once was or still is water on Mars.

Spacecraft	Evidence
Mariner 9 (1971) **National Aeronautics and Space Administration (NASA)**	• Outflow channels formed by floods • Valley networks similar to those on Earth • Layered sediments in canyons
Mars Global Surveyor (1997–2006) **NASA**	• Layered sediments inside craters • Gullies in crater walls • Channels from an ancient river delta • High concentrations of hematite, a mineral that typically forms on Earth under wet conditions, in Meridiani Planum • Remote sensing data indicating that the north polar cap has enough water ice to, if melted, cover Mars with an ocean 9 meters (30 feet) deep
2001 Mars Odyssey (2002–) **NASA**	• Vast amounts of hydrogen less than 1 meter (3 feet) below the surface—evidence of crystals of subsurface water ice • Deposits of salt in the southern hemisphere—evidence of an ancient ocean that covered at least one-third of the surface
Mars Exploration Rovers, Spirit and Opportunity (2004–) **NASA**	• Possible geological evidence of ancient hot springs and thermal vents • Confirmation of the presence of hematite, photographed as round, blueberry-like spheres • Presence of jarosite, known to form on Earth in highly acidic, wet conditions
Mars Express (2004) **European Space Agency**	• Discovery of enough water-ice in south polar cap to, if melted, cover Mars with an ocean 11 meters (36 feet) deep
Mars Reconnaissance Orbiter (2006–) **NASA**	• Deposits of phyllosilicates, known to form as clays are eroded by rivers • Hydrated silica (opal), known to form on Earth in the presence of water • Underground glaciers in mid-latitude region • Gullies formed by flowing water as recently as 1.25 million years ago
Phoenix Mars Lander (2008) **NASA**	• Deposits of phyllosilicates • Direct chemical evidence of water-ice in the northern polar region • Falling snow detected by a laser altimeter

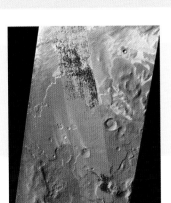

2007
Data collected by Mars Odyssey about subsurface water-ice suggest that Mars had numerous glacial epochs alternating with warmer periods. In images representing the data (right), deeper ice is indicated by red and yellow.

2008
Phoenix Mars Lander "tastes" water-ice in the northern polar region and detects falling snow.

Some scientists believe that extremophile microorganisms might live below ground on Mars, where the planet's internal heat and pressure may keep the water in a liquid state. There, microorganisms would also be protected from the harmful solar ultraviolet radiation that penetrates the thin Martian atmosphere.

An extremophile, a microbe that lives in extreme conditions, is shown in a scanning electron micrograph. The microbe was found in an ice core drilled from deep inside the sheet of ice that covers Lake Vostok in Antarctica. Biologists believe that if life can survive in such inhospitable places on Earth, similar life forms may exist on Mars. The microbe was nicknamed "Klingon" for its resemblance to the wrinkled foreheads of the space aliens by that name in the "Star Trek" television shows and films.

A somewhat comparable environment exists on Earth at Lake Vostok, a large lake that lies beneath 4 kilometers (2 ½ miles) of solid ice in East Antarctica. High pressure from the overlying ice at this depth, as well as subsurface heat, keep the waters of this hidden lake liquid. Investigators believe that the lake waters have been isolated from the atmosphere for as long as 35 million years. In the 1990's, researchers discovered living microbes in ice samples that were drilled from spots within about 150 meters (500 feet) of the lake. These findings led scientists to speculate that microbes might also live within the deep lake itself. The discovery of life at Lake Vostok would prove that life can survive without light, warmth, and air. Perhaps microorganisms that may have lived on the surface of Mars long ago, when the planet was warmer, were able to move below ground and survive after the planet cooled.

instrument heated the sample and analyzed the chemical components of the resulting vapor. The analysis revealed the signature of water.

Also in 2008, scientists working with NASA's Mars Reconnaissance Orbiter (MRO), in orbit since 2006, reported a number of water-related discoveries. The findings, NASA scientists said, proved that Mars "once hosted vast lakes, flowing rivers, and a variety of other wet environments that had a potential to support life." In October 2008, MRO's spectrometer detected minerals called phyllosilicates in the highlands of Mars. Such minerals formed on Earth as clays became eroded by river channels over millions of years—suggesting that liquid water existed on Mars for a lengthy period. MRO's spectrometer also found hydrated silica (opal), a mineral formed in the presence of water, at Gusev Crater perhaps as recently as 2 billion years ago.

In November, ground-penetrating radar on the MRO determined that a mid-latitude region of Mars contained vast amounts of water-ice covered by as much as 9 meters (30 feet) of soil and rock. Scientists said

WATER ON MARS TIMELINE

2008

Photos reveal patches of water-ice in a trench dug by the robotic arm of Phoenix Mars Lander (right).

2008

Mars Reconnaissance Orbiter detects hydrated silica (opal), as well as underground glaciers in a mid-latitude region.

that these underground glaciers, if melted, might contain enough water to fill Earth's Great Lakes.

Like the MRO, the Phoenix Mars Lander detected phyllosilicates on the Martian surface, in the Vastitas Borealis region in which it landed. Phoenix also found calcium carbonate, known to form mostly in the presence of water. In late 2008, near the end of Phoenix's mission, an onboard laser altimeter provided an important clue about the unusual water cycle on Mars when it detected snow falling from clouds 4 kilometers (2 ½ miles) above the ground.

What happened to the liquid water?

The source of the water that once filled oceans, lakes, and rivers on Mars is still a mystery. The water may have been carried to the planet by the impacts of water-rich comets and asteroids. It may have developed from chemical reactions on the planet involving atmospheric hydrogen and oxides on the ground. However, unlike on Earth, liquid water on Mars became scarce. Some water may have been lost because of impacts of asteroids and cometary fragments throughout Martian history. However, scientists believe Mars lost its surface water mainly because the plan-

METHANE ON MARS AND METHANOGENS ON EARTH

An image of Mars made with a ground-based telescope equipped with an infrared spectrometer, which reveals different chemical compounds as different colors, shows large plumes of methane gas in the atmosphere of Mars as red blotches (far right). NASA researchers said in January 2009 that this methane might have been generated by subsurface microorganisms on Mars and that the methane could have escaped through porous rock into the atmosphere. Such microbes would be similar to so-called methanogens on Earth, such as *Methanococcus jannaschii* (right), which lives near deep-sea hydrothermal vents. However, the NASA scientists added that the Martian methane may simply be the by-product of chemical reactions involving groundwater and molten rock.

2009
NASA astronomers detect methane in the atmosphere of Mars—a possible sign of microbial activity.

2009
Analyzing Mars Reconnaissance Orbiter photos, Brown University scientists identify a gully system that may have been carved by running water as recently as 1.25 million years ago.

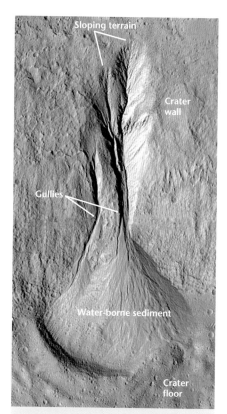

Evidence that liquid water flowed on the surface of Mars more recently than scientists had suspected appears in a gully system inside a crater in the Promethei Terra region, as photographed by the Mars Reconnaissance Orbiter. In a March 2009 analysis of the photo, scientists at Brown University in Providence, Rhode Island, said that the gullies seem to have been formed as recently as 1.25 million years ago—as sediment-laden water from melting snow and ice flowed down the sloping terrain into a wide, fan-shaped area, where the sediment was deposited.

et lost its thick atmosphere, plunging temperatures below freezing. Mars has the largest volcanoes in the solar system, though they are apparently dormant, if not extinct. Early in the planet's history, however, the volcanoes warmed the atmosphere by continually ejecting huge amounts of carbon dioxide and other heat-trapping greenhouse gases. These gases would have provided a thick "blanket" around the planet, much like the atmosphere of Earth.

When volcanic activity apparently ceased on Mars—for unknown reasons—the atmospheric gases were no longer replenished. The planet's weak gravity could not hold on to the atmosphere, and the surface became cooler. At that point, most of the liquid water would have become frozen in the ground.

Some researchers speculate that Mars may still have deep underground reservoirs of liquid water, kept in a liquid state by the planet's internal heat and pressure. However, as of 2009, there was no firm evidence to support this belief.

Little green microbes?

Did Mars have water long enough for life to have evolved? Microbial life on Earth is thought to have evolved in liquid water approximately 4 billion years ago—only hundreds of million of years after the formation of the planet. Thus, if Mars had liquid water for as long as 1 billion to 2 billion years early in its history, perhaps microorganisms also evolved on that world. The dense early atmosphere of Mars would have protected surface organisms from the sun's harmful ultraviolet radiation, further improving conditions for the evolution of life.

Although scientists have no firm evidence that life ever existed on Mars, a team of scientists claimed in 1996 to have found fossils of microscopic organisms, as well as chemical evidence of life, in a meteorite that was blasted off the surface of Mars millions of years ago. The meteorite was discovered in Antarctica. However, many other scientists dispute claims that the impressions in the meteorite are fossils and believe that the chemical evidence is better explained by geological, rather than biological, processes.

Might microbes exist on Mars today, perhaps undergound? Although Mars is a seemingly hostile world, microbes known as extremophiles are known to live in some very hostile places on Earth.

Scientists have found living microbes in deep-sea hydrothermal vents characterized by boiling temperatures and crushing pressures; in ice 4 kilometers (2 ½ miles) beneath the surface of Antarctica; in solid rock far below the ground; and in places characterized by high levels of salinity or acidity.

One possible sign of current microbial life on Mars was reported in January 2009. NASA scientists said that ground-based telescopes equipped with infrared spectrometers had detected large amounts of methane in the Martian atmosphere. They explained that methane might escape into the atmosphere through porous rock after being produced by underground microbial activity. Or, they said, the methane might simply be the by-product of chemical reactions involving underground water and molten rock.

NASA planned to launch a lander/rover mission named Mars Science Laboratory in 2011. This probe was to determine whether areas known to have had long-term surface water could have also sustained life. NASA's Mars Atmosphere and Volatile Evolution Mission, set for launch in 2013, was to study the interaction of the upper atmosphere with the sun to help scientists determine how dense the Martian atmosphere may have been in the past. NASA administrators envision eventually sending human missions to Mars. However, in 2009, the space agency had no timetable for such a mission.

Mars, early in its history, had the same ingredients for life as Earth, including carbon, hydrogen, oxygen, the sun as an energy source, and plenty of liquid water. One of the most significant and exciting scientific discoveries of all time would be finding life—either past or present—on another planet, and Mars remains among the most likely candidates for such a momentous finding.

■ FOR ADDITIONAL INFORMATION

Books

Bell, Jim. *Mars 3-D: A Rover's-Eye View of the Red Planet.* Sterling, 2008.
Chaikin, Andrew. *A Passion for Mars: Intrepid Explorers of the Red Planet.* Abrams, 2008.
Godwin, Robert, editor. *Mars: The NASA Mission Reports.* Apogee Books, 2000.

Web sites

Google Mars—http://www.google.com/mars/
Mars: NASA Explores the Red Planet—
    http://www.nasa.gov/mission_pages/mars/main/index.html
The Mars Society—http://www.marssociety.org/portal
Multimedia Tour of the Solar System: Mars—http://www.nineplanets.org/mars.html
NASA's Mars Exploration Program—http://marsprogram.jpl.nasa.gov/

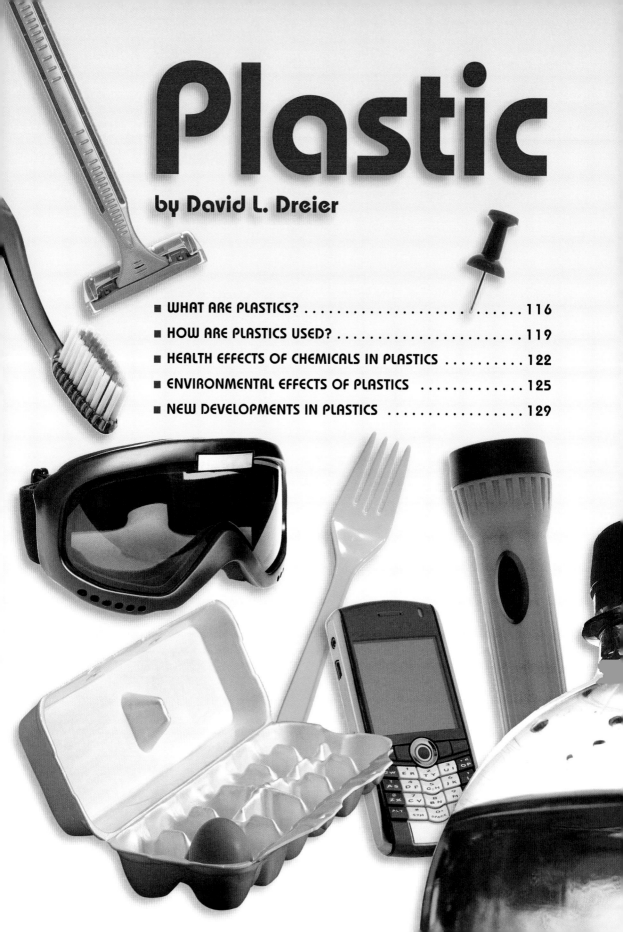

Plastic

by David L. Dreier

Planet

Imagine a world with no desktop computers, cellular telephones, DVD players, video games, or other familiar electronic items. Many kinds of clothes—anything made of nylon, polyester, or other artificial fibers—do not exist. Neither do unbreakable bottles, shatter-proof eyeglass lenses, or artificial knee joints. And what happened to the toys? There are no fashion dolls, no action figures, and no snap-together building blocks.

This is what our world would look like if plastics had never been developed. These incredibly versatile materials are among the most indispensable manufacturing supplies. In fact, plastics are so essential to modern life that it is not much of an exaggeration to say that we live on a "plastic planet."

By the early 2000's, plastics—most of which are derived from petroleum—had been around in one form or another for approximately 150 years. Although people continued to enjoy the numerous uses of plastics in their daily lives in 2009, a variety of concerns swirled around these materials. Environmental groups raised alarms about the mountains of plastic trash piling up in landfills. Plastic refuse was also polluting the oceans and other bodies of water. Public health organizations warned that some ingredients in plastics were a possible threat to human health. This controversy centered mostly on bisphenol A, a common component of plastic bottles, and phthalates, chemicals found in many toys and other products.

In response to these concerns and in the interest of producing better products, scientists sought to create new kinds of plastics. These materials would break down quickly in the environment, contain no chemicals harmful to human health, and have amazing new properties. With such research, scientists in 2009 were starting to change the face of our plastic planet.

The author:
David L. Dreier is a free-lance science writer.

What Are Plastics?

Although people commonly use the term *plastic* when talking about the material in grocery bags, ballpoint pens, and shatter-proof bottles, chemists usually refer to *plastics* because there are many kinds of these materials. Plastics may be hard or soft, transparent or opaque. Nonetheless, all plastics are made of *organic* compounds—molecules based on carbon—in the form of polymers. A polymer is a long chain-like molecule made of many repeating units called monomers, similar to a beaded necklace.

Many polymers are found in nature. The hard outer skeletons of crustaceans (shellfish), spiders, and insects consist mostly of a polymer called chitin. Cellulose, the main structural component of plants, is a polymer. The proteins and DNA (deoxyribonucleic acid, the molecule that makes up genes) in our bodies are polymers.

The manufacture of plastics

The technical process of joining monomers to form a *synthetic* (artificially created) polymer is called polymerization. In the production of plastics, chemists usually extract monomers from petroleum or natural gas—the same fossil fuels that provide the energy to power automobiles and heat homes. Chemists sometimes use monomers from coal, cotton, wood, or other substances for manufacturing plastics. After further refinement, the monomers are joined together to form plastics with a great variety of useful properties.

The characteristics of a particular plastic depend, in part, on the chemical elements it contains. The main elements in plastics are carbon and hydrogen, but many other elements may be used, including chlorine, fluorine, and nitrogen. Thousands of kinds of additives are used to modify the characteristics of plastics, including glass fibers or clay particles to improve strength, plasticizer compounds to improve flexibility, and pigments to add color.

Manufacturers use various methods to create plastic products. The most common method is molding. "Raw" plastic, in pellet or granule form, is melted and injected into molds to make products that have varying shapes, such as bottles, dolls, and telephones. In a method called extrusion, melted plastic is *extruded* (forced through) small openings in dies to create plastic films, pipes, and other products with consistent shapes. In a method called foaming, gas is added to plastic resins to create the bubbles needed to make such products as insulation and pillow foams.

The two main classes of plastics are thermoplastics and thermosetting plastics. Most plastic products are made with thermoplastics, which can be repeatedly melted and reshaped. Thermosetting plastic cannot be remelted, because heating them a second time causes them to break down. However, thermosetting plastics are stronger than typical thermoplastics, so they are usually used to make items that require resistance to high temperatures, such as vulcanized rubber in tires and medical instruments that must be heat-sterilized.

Growth of the plastics industry

Like many major industries, the plastics industry began small and advanced by fits and starts. An English inventor named Alexander Parkes introduced the first plastic in 1862, at the Great International Exposition in London. He demonstrated a hard material made from cellulose polymers that he described as "synthetic ivory," which was intended for use in the production of billiard balls. Parkes's invention, later improved and renamed Celluloid, never made good billiard balls, but it became widely used for dentures, dolls, dresser sets, men's collars, and photographic film.

In 1894, three British inventors developed a shiny cellulose-based fabric that they called viscose or art silk. An improved version of this material, called rayon, became the first widely used fiber manufactured from polymers in the early 1900's. These artificially made fabrics revolutionized the

Manufacturing plastic products

Plastic products are made of monomer molecules extracted from petroleum or other source materials. During polymerization, heat and pressure cause the monomers to form long, chain-like molecules called polymers. Various additives are incorporated to create such raw plastic forms as pellets and granules. This raw plastic is processed into plastic items through a number of methods involving additional heat and pressure, including molding, extrusion, and foaming. Finally, these items are assembled into finished products for sale.

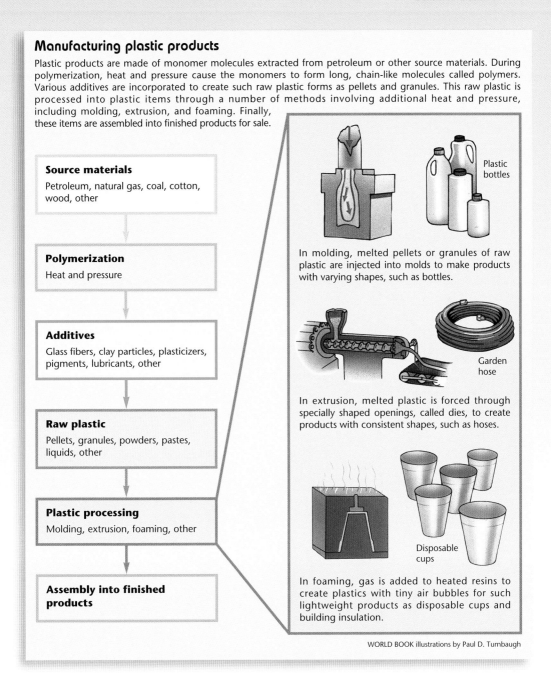

Source materials

Petroleum, natural gas, coal, cotton, wood, other

Polymerization

Heat and pressure

Additives

Glass fibers, clay particles, plasticizers, pigments, lubricants, other

Raw plastic

Pellets, granules, powders, pastes, liquids, other

Plastic processing

Molding, extrusion, foaming, other

Assembly into finished products

Plastic bottles

In molding, melted pellets or granules of raw plastic are injected into molds to make products with varying shapes, such as bottles.

Garden hose

In extrusion, melted plastic is forced through specially shaped openings, called dies, to create products with consistent shapes, such as hoses.

Disposable cups

In foaming, gas is added to heated resins to create plastics with tiny air bubbles for such lightweight products as disposable cups and building insulation.

WORLD BOOK illustrations by Paul D. Turnbaugh

textile industry because they could be mass produced cheaply. They also had certain advantages over cotton and other natural fibers for consumers, such not requiring ironing. Cellophane, which is chemically similar to rayon, became the first transparent plastic wrap during this same period.

Leo Baekeland, a chemist in the United States, patented the first completely synthetic plastic in 1909. His invention, which he named Bakelite, was made by combining two common compounds—carbolic acid (also called phenol) and formaldehyde. Baekeland applied heat and pressure to these compounds to produce a plastic that could be molded and extruded. Like rayon, Bakelite made possible the mass production of consumer items. It also allowed objects to be made in new complex

Bakelite plastic products

The invention of bakelite (BAY kuh lyt) in the early 1900's by United States chemist Leo Baekeland (right) made possible the mass production of a wide variety of new consumer items (below). Bakelite was the first completely *synthetic* (artifically created) plastic compound, made by combining carbolic acid with formaldehyde. It could be easily molded and formed into the complex shapes needed for such products as radios, televisions, telephones, record players, clocks, lamps, bottles, cups, tableware, and toys.

shapes, gaining widespread use for such products as jewelry, radios, tableware, telephones, and toys.

Many advances in plastics production were made during the 1920's. In 1926, a chemist at the Ohio-based B. F. Goodrich Company invented polyvinyl chloride (PVC), often simply called vinyl. Durable, easy-to-clean vinyl upholstery soon became common in many living rooms. PVC could also be produced in many other forms, including a transparent material suitable for bottles.

Researchers at other U.S. companies, notably Michigan-based Dow Chemical Company and Delaware-based DuPont Company, introduced a number of new plastics in the 1930's, including nylon and Teflon. After World War II (1939-1945),

plastics flooded the consumer market under a variety of trade names, such as Formica, Saran Wrap, and Styrofoam.

In the 1950's, the Corvette, a sports cars produced by General Motors Corporation of Detroit, became the first mass-produced automobile with a plastic body. The car was made with thermosetting plastics called unsaturated polyesters, combined with fiberglass. During the 1980's, researchers developed the first plastics capable of carrying electric currents. These materials became widely used in such products as batteries, wiring, and static-resistant fabrics. The plastics industry continued to introduce many new kinds of plastics in the 2000's.

How Are Plastics Used?

lastics make excellent substitutes for many traditional materials, including glass, metal, ceramics, and wood. Plastic products are usually cheaper to produce in large quantities than products made of those other materials. Plastics are sturdier than glass and keep their shape better than metals. For example, a car door made of plastic will resist impacts from shopping carts and other objects that would leave dents in a metal panel. Automobile and airplane manufacturers also value plastics because the materials' light weight improves fuel efficiency. In addition, products in plastic containers are cheaper to transport.

Plastics are also rustproof and waterproof and provide excellent insulation. Those properties make them ideal for use in such appliances as refrigerators and air conditioners. Plastics can be made as transparent as glass. A group of plastics called polycarbonates is widely used to make clear bottles, windows, car headlamps, and lenses for cameras and eyeglasses.

Plastics have become vital to the construction, electronics, and toy industries. Plastics are also widely used in surgery for such items as artificial joints and heart replacement valves. People wear plastic in the form of nylon, rayon, spandex, polyester, and other synthetic fabrics. Cosmetic cases, brushes, and applicators are made with plastic polymers, as are many cosmetics themselves.

Bottles and shopping bags

Plastic bottles and shopping bags make up a huge part of the annual production of plastics in the United States. Industry sources estimate that as many as 40 billion plastic bottles and 100 billion plastic shopping bags are manufactured each year in the United States.

Plastic bottles are used to hold a wide variety of liquids, ranging from drinking water to bleach to motor oil. Three plastic compounds commonly used to manufacture bottles are polyvinyl chloride (PVC), polyethylene terephthalate ethylene (PETE), and high-density polyethylene (HDPE). The plastic compound most often used in shopping bags is low-density polyethylene (LDPE).

Automobiles and airplanes

Numerous kinds of plastics are used in the construction of automobiles and airplanes. In addition to weighing less than most other materials, plastics are valued as important styling elements. Some sports cars owe their sleek and sexy bodies to plastics.

A car contains an average of 150 kilograms (330 pounds) of plastic materials—more than 8 percent of its weight—according to the American Chemistry Council, a professional association based in Arlington County, Virginia.

Plastics make up parts of car exteriors, such as bumpers and body panels, as well as dashboards and other interior parts. Besides making attractive design elements, plastics make car interiors quieter by dampening vibrations and road noise.

Materials called plastic composites—consisting of fiberglass and other nonmetallic fibers embedded in a hard plastic—are used extensively in the exteriors and interiors of passenger jets. They help make jet components lighter and stronger.

Building construction

Plastics are increasingly used in the construction of both houses and commercial buildings to make the buildings more durable and energy-efficient. Just about any part of a building can be made of plastics—roofing, flooring, pipes, gutters, windows, and even lumber. Engi-

neered lumber made from recycled plastic or plastic-wood composites can be more resistant to cracking and splintering than pure wood. In the outer walls of a house, an insulating material called expanded polystyrene can help homeowners save hundreds of dollars annually on heating and cooling bills.

PVC is one of the most widely used building materials. More than 70 percent of PVC produced in the United States is used in construction, for such items as pipes, siding, and window sashes.

Electronic equipment

Without plastics, we would not have most of the electronic products that we enjoy today. Modern plastics provide the durability and design flexibility needed for the components of computers, televisions, telephones, and other electronic devices. Plastics can be molded into the many complex shapes used with these products, and they have the insulating qualities required for managing electric currents. The miniaturization of computer chips and other small electronic parts relies on specialized plastics that can stand up to rugged assembly processes and long-term use. Advanced plastics have enabled electronics designers to make these components ever smaller—while also increasing a product's range of functions.

Toys

Modern plastics revolutionized the toy industry. Thermoplastics enabled toy manufacturers to produce an incredible array of toys that could not have been made otherwise, including snap-together building blocks, action figures, and flying disks.

Dolls provide an interesting example of how plastics changed the world of toys. In the 1800's, most dolls were made with fragile porcelain heads and fabric bodies, and some—so-called rag dolls—were made completely of fabric. Through much of the early 1900's, many dolls were made of Celluloid, which was highly flammable. By the 1950's, doll manufacturers were using thermoplastics to mass-produce dolls that were far more life-like and detailed, as well as safer and more affordable, than dolls of earlier times.

Health Effects of Chemicals in Plastics

Although health concerns about plastics date back more than 50 years, scientific and public scrutiny of these materials grew increasingly intense in the 2000's. Some health experts warned that certain kinds of plastics in nonstick cookware and plastic food and drink containers could release harmful chemicals into foods and drinks. Concerns about some plastics in children's toys triggered bans against those materials.

Bisphenol A and phthalates

One of the most significant plastics controversies in 2008 and 2009 centered on a chemical called bisphenol A (BPA). BPA is used mostly to make shatterproof, clear plastics called polycarbonates. Many kinds of containers, including reusable bottles for drinking water and baby formula—as well as coatings inside food cans—are made with BPA. It is one of several compounds known to be endocrine disruptors—chemicals that

mimic or block the actions of hormones. Hormones are chemicals that act as messengers in the body to help various parts of an organism function in a coordinated manner. BPA mimics the action of estrogen, a hormone that causes the growth and development of female sexual characteristics.

Researchers have demonstrated links between BPA and health problems in more than 90 government-funded studies conducted with laboratory animals. Such studies are the most common method used by scientists to determine if chemicals might be hazardous to human health, though animals sometimes react differently to chemicals than human beings do. In 2006, researchers at the University of Cincinnati in Ohio and the University of Illinois at Chicago reported that male rats exposed to BPA in their mothers' wombs showed precancerous growths in their prostate glands. In addition, some female mice exposed to BPA reached sexual maturity sooner than normal.

Plastic resin codes

In order to aid recycling efforts, plastics manufacturers often mark products with special numbered codes that indicate the types of resins, or chemical compounds, used in their production. Polyethylene terephthalate ethylene (PETE) and high-density polyethylene (HDPE) are the most commonly recycled plastics.

Code	Resin name	Common products
1 PETE	Polyethylene terephthalate ethylene (PETE)	Bottles (including those for water, soft drinks, mouthwash, and ketchup), peanut butter jars, electrical insulation, carpets
2 HDPE	High-density polyethylene (HDPE)	Bottles (including those for milk, laundry, and cosmetics), grocery bags, cereal-box liners, plastic-wood composites, electrical insulation
3 PVC	Polyvinyl chloride (PVC); includes phthalates	Imitation leather, food packaging, shrink wrap, pipe, electrical insulation, flooring, siding, cosmetics, toys
4 LDPE	Low-density polyethylene (LDPE)	Grocery bags, garbage bags, shrink wrap, milk cartons, container lids, toys
5 PP	Polypropylene (PP)	Rope, packaging, automobile parts, infant-nursing and medicine bottles, yogurt containers, appliance parts, carpeting
6 PS	Polystyrene (PS)	Clamshell food containers, cups, plates, toys, electrical insulation, building insulation, packing peanuts, radio cabinets, CD cases
7 OTHER	Other (usually polycarbonates, including bisphenol A [BPA])	Clear drinking-water and infant-nursing bottles, business machine parts, electrical connectors, windows, eyeglass safety lenses, airplane canopies, plastic lumber

Disrupting hormone activity

Some compounds in plastics, known as endocrine disruptors, mimic or block the action of hormones, chemicals produced in one part of the body that affect cell processes and activities in a different part.

Some hormones, including human sex hormones, work by binding to structures called receptors inside a cell. The resulting complex moves into the cell's nucleus, where it activates chemical changes.

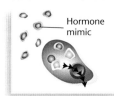

Normal hormone

Hormone receptor

Cell

Nucleus

Endocrine disruptors, such as bisphenol A and phthalates, can disrupt this process by binding to the hormone receptors as well. This action magnifies the normal effect of the hormone.

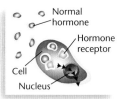

Hormone mimic

Endocrine disruptors may also bind to receptors and so block the binding of normal hormones. Because the hormones cannot bind to the receptors, they cannot carry out their normal functions.

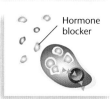

Hormone blocker

Source: National Institute of Environmental Health Sciences.

Possible health effects of plastic compounds

Medical studies suggest that exposure to certain plastic compounds may lead to adverse health effects in people. Some of these studies are based on evaluations of human patients, while others are based on research with laboratory animals. The compounds of greatest concern are polyvinyl chloride/phthalates, polystyrene, and bisphenol A.

Code	Plastic compound	Possible health effects
PVC	Polyvinyl chloride/ phthalates	Hormone disruption; birth defects, including slightly abnormal sex organs in male babies; liver damage; asthma
PS	Polystyrene	Nervous system impairment, including nervousness, fatigue, sleep disruption; menstrual cycle disruption; cancer
OTHER	Bisphenol A	Hormone disruption; reproductive and developmental abnormalities; heart disease; Type 2 diabetes mellitus; liver abnormalities; cancer

Sources: United States Centers for Disease Control and Prevention; U.S. Food and Drug Administration; U.S. National Institutes of Health; Lang et al. *JAMA.* 2008;300(11):1303-1310; Swan. *Environ Res.* 2008;108(2):177-184.

Numerous tests have revealed that small amounts of BPA leach into food and drinks when polycarbonate containers are heated or washed with strong detergents. Acidic foods or drinks may also cause leaching. In a 2004 study by the Centers for Disease Control and Prevention in Atlanta, researchers detected low levels of BPA, possibly from such leaching, in 93 percent of urine samples collected from more than 2,500 adults and children.

Two major studies on the health effects of BPA were released in September 2008. A review of scientific literature by the National Toxicology Program (NTP), a research program at the National Institutes of Health, noted "some concern" about BPA's effect on the "brain, behavior, and prostate glands of fetuses, infants, and children" at currently used levels. The NTP's expert panel reported, "There are insufficient data from studies in humans to reach a conclusion on reproductive or developmental hazards presented by current exposures in bisphenol A, but there is limited evidence of developmental changes occurring in some animal studies at doses that are experienced by humans. It is uncertain if similar changes would occur in humans, but the possibility of adverse health effects cannot be dismissed." A large study of human exposure to BPA by a team of U.S. and British scientists reported in *The Journal of the American Medical Association*, however, linked BPA to increased risks of heart disease, Type 2 diabetes mellitus, and liver abnormalities.

A number of studies, including some funded by the chemical industry, found no adverse health effects from BPA. In late 2008, the U.S. Food and Drug Administration (FDA) maintained that BPA-containing products were safe for human use. The FDA's position drew fire from many observers, including an independent panel of government and university scientists who issued their own report in October 2008. These scientists claimed that the FDA had not considered all relevant research findings about BPA. In February 2009, the FDA announced that it planned to conduct a series of studies to analyze the health effects of BPA in baby bottles and such medical devices as dental sealants. Meanwhile, Canada became the first nation to ban BPA in baby bottles. In March 2009, six U.S. companies announced they would no longer sell baby bottles made with plastic containing BPA.

Controversy also swirled around plastic additives called phthalates. These chemicals, used primarily to make polyvinyl chloride (PVC) more flexible, are found in a number of products, including toys, food packaging, cosmetics, and such medical devices as intravenous bags and catheters. Studies have indicated that most people in the United States have traces of phthalates in their bodies, perhaps as a result of ingesting the chemical from food that came in contact with plastic. Like BPA, phthalates are endocrine disruptors. Animal studies have shown that phthalates may also cause liver damage and birth defects. Furthermore, scientists at the University of Rochester in New York reported in October 2008 that pregnant women who had been exposed to high levels of phthalates had an increased risk of giving birth to boys with slightly abnormal sex organs.

Public health advocates in 2008 noted that children might be absorbing phthalates from their playthings, for example by placing plastic toys in their mouths. Although the FDA urges manufacturers to avoid using certain kinds of phthalates in medical devices made with PVC, the agency reported in June 2008 that it would take no action against phthalates in toys until more solid evidence was available about their alleged health hazards. In August, however, the U.S. Congress passed legislation banning six kinds of phthalates from children's products. The ban went into effect in February 2009, but it applied only to new products—not to products already on store shelves.

Some public health and environmental groups have called for a ban on all PVC. These groups point to research suggesting that PVC can give off an array of dangerous chemicals, including mercury and, when burned, highly toxic compounds called dioxins. Moreover, Greenpeace, the international environmental organization, has cited studies associating PVC flooring in houses with high rates of asthma in children, and PVC pipes with the release of toxins into drinking water. The American Chemistry Council, a professional association of the plastics industry, expressed dismay over efforts to ban PVC in 2008 and 2009. The council contended that the evidence against PVC was not conclusive. In apparent support of this position, the FDA, as of early 2009, had not issued any advisories or warnings against the general use of PVC.

Other plastics of concern

Another plastic that has aroused concern has been polystyrene, which is used to make such items as Styrofoam egg cartons and "clamshell" food containers. Some studies suggest that long-term exposure to polystyrene may lead to a build-up of the compound in body tissues, contributing to problems of the nervous system or other abnormalities. According to the FDA, however, normal daily exposure to food that has been in contact with polystyrene poses no threat to human health.

One of the most widely publicized disputes about a plastic intensified in the early 2000's over a chemical used to make nonstick products. The chemical, perfluorooctanoic acid (PFOA), was used in the production of the nonstick coating Teflon, in stain- and water-resistant fabrics, and in fast-food packaging, among other items.

Warnings about the possible dangers of PFOA began decades ago. In 1954, employees of the DuPont Company in Wilmington, Delaware, expressed concerns about the possible toxic effects from inhaling the chemical. The FDA, however, concluded that PFOA was safe, and the agency approved the sale of Teflon-coated cookware in 1962. Consumers loved the nonstick pans, which became a staple in American kitchens.

Concern about Teflon reappeared in the early 2000's, with experts warning that PFOA fumes emitted when Teflon is heated to high temperatures could cause respiratory problems—dubbed the "Teflon flu." In addition, neighbors of a DuPont plant in West Virginia filed a lawsuit alleging that emissions of the chemical contaminated local drinking water supplies, causing a wide range of human health problems. In 2006, a scientific advisory panel of the Environmental Protection Agency (EPA) recommended that PFOA be designated as a chemical "likely" to cause cancer in human beings. This recommendation was based on studies showing that PFOA can cause cancer in rats and organ damage in monkeys. A number of studies have found PFOA in the blood of nearly all people tested.

DuPont executives insisted that its Teflon-coated pans were safe. The company said that although it continued to use PFOA in the production of Teflon, only traces of the chemical remained in the final products. Nevertheless, DuPont and seven other companies agreed to an EPA request to reduce the use of PFOA in consumer goods by 95 percent no later than 2010 and to phase out its use thereafter. The companies also agreed to eliminate the release of PFOA into the environment by 2015. Some researchers, including those at DuPont, were seeking to develop safer polymer-based substitutes for PFOA in 2009. Experts noted that, in the meantime, consumers with concerns about PFOA could use cookware made with nonstick alternatives, including certain kinds of enamel- and ceramic-based coatings.

Environmental Effects of Plastics

Every large landfill contains uncountable tons of plastic debris, including plastic bottles and bags, broken toys, old CD players and cell phones, and discarded kitchen appliances. Enormous amounts of plastics also end up in the world's oceans and other bodies of water.

Homes, businesses, and institutions in the United States generate more than 227 million metric tons (250 million tons) of waste each year, according to the Environmental Protection Agency (EPA). Approximately 12 percent of this amount, or 27 million metric tons (30 million tons), is plastic trash. Less than 7 percent of that plastic trash gets recycled. The rest of it simply piles up in waste dumps or washes into rivers, lakes, and oceans.

The plastic bottles and bags produced today will be around for a long time. Most plastic items are not broken down by bacteria and other microorganisms in the same way as items made of wood or other natural materials—a process called biodegradation. Plastics are slowly degraded by sunlight—a mechanism known as photodegradation. However, scientists estimate that an ordinary plastic bag or bottle will last from 500 to 1,000 years before decomposing from sunlight. Even worse, much of the plastic in landfills is buried beneath mounds of other debris and so is not exposed to the sun.

Plastic in the oceans

In the oceans, vast amounts of plastic debris float on the surface or lie on the sea floor. Some of this plastic is dumped into the water from ships, but most of it washes into the seas from the land. The United Nations (UN) Environmental Program, an advocacy, education, and policy group, has

estimated that there is an average of 18,000 pieces of plastic litter in every square kilometer (0.4 square mile) of ocean. This debris ranges from plastic bottles and six-pack rings to fishing gear.

One of the worst regions of plastic pollution lies in the North Pacific Ocean between California and Japan. This region, which is twice the area of Texas,

Workers use bulldozers to level off an enormous landfill containing large amounts of plastic bags, bottles, and other plastic waste. Most disposed plastic products eventually end up in such landfills, where they accumulate year after year. Only a tiny percentage of plastic trash gets recycled.

contains an estimated 2.7 metric tons (3 million tons) of plastic. Dubbed the "Great Pacific Garbage Patch," it is created by spiraling, wind-driven ocean currents carrying trash from coastal waters and other sites throughout the North Pacific.

In the oceans, plastics are gradually broken apart by sunlight and wave action, producing smaller and smaller pieces. The resulting plastic shards pose a serious threat to marine life. Fish, sea turtles, sea birds, seals, whales, and other marine animals sometimes mistake medium-sized pieces of

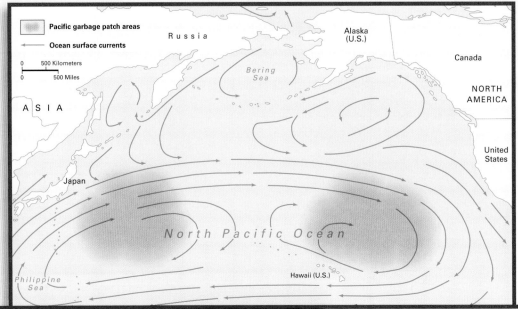

Earth's biggest trash dump

The Great Pacific Garbage Patch (above) consists of two vast, connected areas of plastic pollution in the North Pacific Ocean between California and Japan. These polluted areas, shown in orange, contain an estimated 2.7 metric tons (3 million tons) of plastic waste, which is brought together by spiraling, wind-driven ocean currents (blue arrows). The currents transport disposable water bottles, packing materials, and other plastic debris from coastal waters and other sites throughout the North Pacific.

plastic for prey and try to eat them. This plastic may get lodged in their digestive tracts, causing the animals to starve or develop lethal infections. Other animals die after becoming entangled in plastic fishing lines and nets. UN researchers have estimated that plastic debris may kill more than 1 million sea birds and at least 100,000 sea turtles and marine mammals every year.

Smaller marine animals, such as jellyfish, feed on the tiniest plastic particles, which they mistake for plankton. As the animals eat this debris, toxic chemicals from the plastic become concentrated in their body tissues. These toxins are passed up the food chain, becoming more and more concentrated, as larger animals feed on smaller ones. This toxic food chain ultimately leads to human consumers of seafood.

Searching for solutions

As environmental threats from plastics mount, concerned organizations, citizens, and scientists are searching for solutions. The EPA notes that two of the best ways to reduce plastic trash in landfills are for manufacturers to use less plastic in their packaging and for consumers to use reusable shopping bags rather than plastic ones. In 2008 and 2009, some retailers, including Whole Foods Market, Inc., a leading grocery chain, stopped using plastic bags. San Francisco in 2007 became the first large city in the United States to ban plastic bags. Many other U.S. cities were considering similar bans in 2009. Certain countries have banned or placed high taxes on plastic bags to discourage their use, including China, Ireland, and South Africa.

Numerous items made of plastic can be seen in the stomach of the decomposed body of an albatross on Kure Atoll, in a remote part of the North Pacific Ocean. This large sea bird unfortunately mistook these plastic items for food while flying over the ocean in search of fish to eat. Plastic debris can be found in the sea even in geographic regions that are virtually uninhabited by people.

Some environmentalists note that avoiding the use of bottled water would go a long way toward reducing plastic waste. They point out that the quality of much bottled drinking water may be no better than that of tap water. In October 2008, the Environmental Working Group, an environmental research organization based in Washington, D.C., reported that its tests revealed that many brands of bottled water contained just as many impurities as tap water.

Increased recycling is another obvious way to reduce the amount of plastic debris clogging landfills and polluting the environment. Unfortunately, some plastic items, such as Styrofoam containers, cannot be recycled. The same is true of plastic bottles that contained paint, motor oil, or toxic chemicals. Because many plastic items are made with or contaminated with harmful substances, recycling offers only a limited solution to the problem of plastic waste.

Governments around the world have taken a number of actions to address the problem of plastic pollution in the oceans. These steps include efforts to halt plastic dumping and to clean up plastic already in the water.

The International Convention for the Prevention of Pollution from Ships, known as MARPOL (for "marine pollution"), is a global agreement aimed at protecting the seas. MARPOL, in place since 1973, seeks to stop ships from jettisoning plastic debris and other waste into the oceans. Article V of MARPOL, which regulates plastic pollution, was encoded into U.S. law in 1987 as the Marine Plastic Pollution Research and Control Act. This law requires the U.S. Coast Guard to monitor coastal waters of the United States for the illegal disposal of plastics by boats and ships. In addition, the EPA, under its Marine Debris Program, has regulatory authority to prevent and reduce debris entering U.S. waters from vessels and wastewater.

The best solution to all problems of plastic waste may be the creation of plastics that undergo biodegradation. These plastics would break

A sea turtle, with its attached remora passenger, swims past a clump of plastic bags drifting in the ocean. By ingesting or becoming entangled in such plastic debris, some 100,000 sea turtles and marine mammals and 1 million sea birds may be killed every year, according to researchers with the United Nations. These researchers estimated that there is an average of 18,000 pieces of plastic litter in every square kilometer (0.4 square mile) of ocean.

Fascinating facts about plastics

Only about 7 percent of plastic trash in the United States is recycled.

A plastic bag or bottle may take more than 1,000 years to decompose from exposure to sunlight.

As many as 18,000 pieces of plastic may litter every square kilometer (0.4 square mile) of the oceans.

Plastic debris may kill more than 1 million sea birds every year.

The amount of plastic manufactured in the United States increased by 1,000 percent from 1960 to 2000.

People in the United States use up to 100 billion plastic bags every year.

Toothbrushes account for more than 45 million kilograms (100 million pounds) of plastic waste each year.

Enough fiberfill can be extracted from five 2-liter (2-quart) recycled plastic bottles to make a ski jacket.

The consumption of bottled water more than doubled from 1995 to 2005.

Manufacturing plastics from recycled material uses two-thirds of the energy required to make plastics from raw materials.

Five of the top six chemicals whose production generates the most hazardous waste are commonly used by the plastics industry, according to the U.S. Environmental Protection Agency.

The concentration of chemical pollutants in plastic pellets found in the ocean may be 1 million times as high as that of the surrounding seawater.

Plastics and the food chain

Toxic chemicals in plastic debris polluting the ocean can spread through the food chain. As the debris is broken down by sunlight, polychlorinated biphenyls and other potentially harmful substances are released. These chemicals are taken in by tiny, plant-like organisms called phytoplankton. Tiny animals called zooplankton feed on the contaminated phytoplankton, as well as on plastic particles they mistake for food. The toxins become increasingly concentrated in the tissues of animals that are higher up the food chain—ultimately leading to human consumers of seafood.

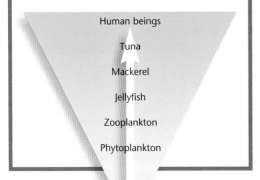

Human beings

Tuna

Mackerel

Jellyfish

Zooplankton

Phytoplankton

down quickly into harmless molecules, mostly water and carbon dioxide. Some biodegradable plastics, made mostly from cornstarch or soybean concentrate, were in use in 2009. Products that may contain such biodegradable plastics include certain shopping bags, packing "peanuts," and disposable tableware.

Various problems limited the use of biodegradable plastics in 2009. One problem was that these plastics were 2 to 10 times as expensive to produce as conventional plastics. Furthermore, they did not degrade in landfills. In order for biodegradable plastics to decompose, they had to be transported to and processed in commercial composting facilities. In these facilities, biodegradable plastics are exposed to a temperature of 140 °C (284 °F), which breaks them down within 60 to 90 days.

In 2009, scientists continued to search for ways to produce low-cost plastics that could decompose in any environment. Researchers at the Missouri University of Science and Technology in Rolla were among those playing key roles in this endeavor. That team developed a variety of experimental hybrid polymers, containing both plant-based and petroleum-based ingredients, which the researchers said could biodegrade in a landfill within four months.

New Developments in Plastics

The capabilities of advanced plastics were moving far beyond those of traditional plastics in 2009. For example, researchers were developing plastics that were tough enough to stand up to extremely high temperatures and pressures. Some research even involved the manipulation of individual molecules to create plastics with new, useful properties. Scientists were also making plastics that resembled biological materials, including skin and muscle, in both structure and function. Other types of new plastics were magnetic.

A firefighter wearing a heat-resistant suit made of polybenzimidazole climbs into a burning building.

Ultrapolymers and high-performance thermoplastics

Ultrapolymers sit at the top of a class of plastics known as high-performance thermoplastics, which are designed to function at much higher temperatures and pressures than conventional thermoplastics. The molecules that make up these plastics are bonded together strongly, creating an extremely solid, rigid structure. High-performance thermoplastics are further strengthened by the addition of such toughening materials as glass and carbon fibers.

Polybenzimidazole (PBI), developed in the 1980's by researchers at the Celanese Corporation in Charlotte, North Carolina, is one of the toughest of these plastics. Commonly used to make protective suits for firefighters, machine parts, and other items that need to withstand intense heat, PBI keeps its structural properties at temperatures as high as 427 °C (801 °F). Moreover, it can withstand pressures as great as 4,075 kilograms per square centimeter (58,000 pounds per square inch)—roughly equivalent to the pressure sustained by the type of reinforcing steel that is commonly used in concrete and masonry construction. PBI is also highly resistant to acids and other corrosive chemicals.

In 2009, ultrapolymers and other high-performance thermoplastics were becoming increasingly common alternatives to metals, ceramics, and thermosetting plastics for numerous applications, including automobile and aircraft parts and electronic components.

Many automobile experts believe that vehicles will eventually be made almost entirely of such materials, with bodies and frames—even engines and transmissions—made primarily of plastic. These cars, say the experts, would be both lighter and more durable than the mostly metal automobiles of today.

Biomimetic plastics

Synthetic substances designed to resemble materials found in nature are called biomimetic, because they mimic biological materials. Biomimetic plastics under development in 2009 were designed to mimic a number of natural substances, including skin, bone, muscle, and cartilage.

Some researchers in 2009 were perfecting plastics that could be used to create artificial muscles. These plastics, called electroactive polymers (EAP's), contract or expand in response to variations in an applied electrical current. The use of EAP's would enable engineers to build robots that are similar to the human body—without gears, bearings, or cables. EAP's might also be used to make prosthetic arms and legs for people who have lost limbs or been born without them.

Since 2005, the Jet Propulsion Laboratory in Pasadena, California, a leader in the EAP field, has hosted a "Grand Challenge" arm-wrestling competition to gauge the strength of synthetic muscles compared with real muscles. The contest pits human competitors against a few of the latest artificial arms made with EAP musculature. As of 2009, artificial arms were still no match for human arms, but many researchers were convinced that the EAP muscles would eventually triumph.

A polymer-based artificial cornea for use in eye surgery, developed in 2007 by scientists at the Fraunhofer Institute for Applied Polymer Research in Potsdam, Germany.

A young woman challenges one of the Jet Propulsion Laboratory's electroactive polymer-based robotic arms to an arm-wrestling match.

A ruptured microcapsule is seen in this scanning electron micrograph after it released its restorative compound to seal a crack in a piece of self-repairing plastic.

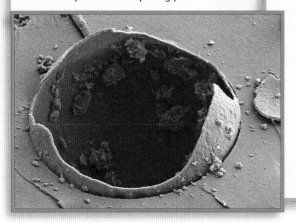

Self-repairing plastics

Taking a cue from natural body tissue, in which cuts and other wounds can heal themselves, scientists are working on self-repairing plastics. One of the first such materials was developed in the early 2000's at the University of Illinois at Urbana-Champaign. Scientists there produced a polymer-based material embedded with microscopic capsules containing a restorative compound. When a rupture occurs in this plastic, the microcapsules in that area release the compound, which seals the break. Similar materials have since been invented at other research centers, including the University of California at Los Angeles. Self-repairing plastics could be useful in objects for which repairs are difficult, such as spacecraft and bridges.

Plastic magnets

Another kind of advanced plastic consists of polymers that have magnetic properties—that is, plastic magnets. Researchers at the University of Durham in the United Kingdom introduced the first plastic magnet that worked at room temperature in 2004. The scientists combined two polymers, including one that forms special kinds of charged particles, called free radicals, over time. Inside the plastic, the free radicals line up the same way that spinning *electrons* (negatively charged particles) do inside a metal magnet, thereby generating a magnetic field. The British investigators noted that plastic magnets might be used for such applications as plastic hard disks for computers and plastic cochlear implants for people with hearing impairments.

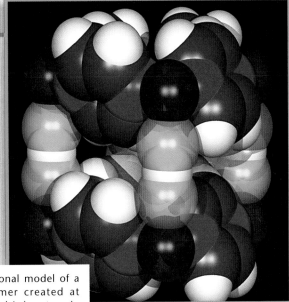

A three-dimensional model of a magnetic polymer created at Argonne National Laboratory in Illinois shows its various components coded by color, according to type of monomer.

Plastics from nanotechnology

Some advances in plastics are being achieved with the expanding science of nanotechnology, the manipulation of matter at the molecular and atomic levels to create larger structures. Plastics engineers foresee using nanotechnology to create many new products. Among these are polymer paints that are completely scratch-resistant, highly advanced plastic electronic components, and *photovoltaic cells* (devices that produce electric current when exposed to sunlight) that could be made cheaply and molded into any desired shape.

Nanotechnology is providing manufacturers with new ways to create stronger plastics. Investigators at the Massachusetts Institute of Technology (MIT) in Cambridge reported in 2007 that they had developed polymers containing clay nanoparticles that greatly increased the plastics' toughness. The researchers noted that their polymers could be used in a variety of products, including automobile parts and rugged but lightweight fabrics.

Also in 2007, engineers at the University of Michigan in Ann Arbor described the development of a transparent plastic that was as strong as steel. Like the MIT material, this plastic contained clay nanoparticles. The nanoparticles were layered between sheets of a glue-like polymer—a layer-by-layer structure similar to that of mother-of-pearl, one of the strongest materials in nature. Mother-of-pearl is the colorful lining of mussel and oyster shells. The developers said that a possible use for this "plastic steel" would be lighter, stronger body armor for soldiers and police officers.

A seemingly ordinary-looking sheet of plastic is actually as strong as steel. Developed at the University of Michigan, it is a mix of clay nanoparticles and a polymer called polyvinyl alcohol.

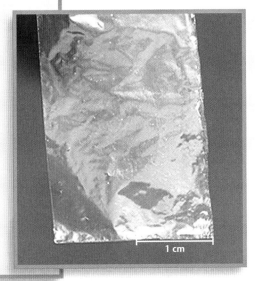

1 cm

CONSUMER SCIENCE

Topics selected for their current interest provide information that the reader as a consumer can use in understanding everyday technology or in making decisions—from buying products to caring for personal health.

Consumers are fencing their yards with long bamboo canes and laying down bamboo planks on kitchen and family-room floors. Bamboo lovers are setting their family china atop woven-bamboo place mats. They are completing their décor with bamboo-bordered flat-screen TV's and using computer mouse devices made of strips of molded, polished bamboo. Why are so many people crazy about bamboo?

Bamboo is attractive, strong, durable, and lightweight. It also has a "green" profile because it grows rapidly and is easily renewable. To many environmentally minded consumers, bamboo seems to be a better choice than the pine, oak, maple, and other slow-growing woods commonly used in construction and for home furnishings.

Environmental concerns for the world's forests are justified. About 13 million hectares (32.1 million acres) of forest disappear annually, according to the 2005 Global Forest Resources Assessment, the most recent study on forest coverage published by the Food and Agriculture Organization of the United Nations (UN). Although it is possible to manage forests wisely so as to preserve them even while selectively harvesting trees, much of the world's logging occurs without constraints or regulation. Such clear-cutting often leaves barren, stump-studded tracts of environmentally degraded land.

Bamboo seems similar to wood, but it is actually a member of the grass family—Poaceae—and is related to barley, oats, sugar cane, and wheat. Bamboo is so varied and widespread that it is difficult to determine how many *species* (kinds) of the plant exist, but there are well over 1,000 catalogued species. Most grow in tropical climates, but some temperate varieties can be found in the Himalaya, the Andes, and even in some parts of the United States.

Like the trunks of hardwood trees, the long canes of bamboo consist of lignin and cellulose. Lignin provides rigidity to cell walls and acts as a cement between cells. Cellulose forms strengthening fibers within the cell walls. The dense concentration of these two materials in bamboo stalks makes bamboo exceptionally strong. According to the Indonesia-based Environmental Bamboo Foundation (EBF),

Bamboo is a highly versatile resource to designers and manufacturers of interior fittings and furniture. The chair, side table, and coffee table base (above) are all made from fused, laminated bamboo. The flooring is manufactured from thin planks of bamboo derived from the long *culms* (stems) of the bamboo plant.

bamboo has a higher tensile strength than relatively soft low-alloy steel. (Tensile strength is the stress or weight that a material can endure before breaking.)

In most species, the woody bamboo *culm* (stem) consists of segments separated by horizontal ridges called nodes. From each node, new leafy branches or flowers may grow. Bamboo seldom blooms; in fact, some plants may go as long as 120 years before blooming. After producing flowers, the plants usu-

ally die. However, bamboo has a highly successful alternate method of self propagation: it sends out underground horizontal stems called rhizomes. From these rhizomes new buds send shoots upward, starting new canes.

After the shoots break the surface of the soil, bamboo grows very rapidly—up to 91 centimeters (3 feet) per day. Some bamboo species grow as tall as 40 meters (130 feet); others attain widths of up to 30 centimeters (1 foot).

All about bamboo

Bamboo is a member of the grass family and is distantly related to wheat, oats, and barley. The plant's stiff, sturdy stem, called a culm, is divided into segments by ridges called nodes.

There are at least 1,000 different *species* (kinds) of bamboo. Some species grow up to 40 meters (130 feet) high and 30 centimeters (1 foot) in diameter.

Dense bundles of fibrous materials called lignin and cellulose appear in a magnified cross section of a bamboo culm. The fibers give bamboo exceptional sturdiness and strength.

Bamboo culms can grow up to 91 centimeters (3 feet) a day and reach their full height in less than 60 days. Over time, the culms grow thicker and stronger.

Whatever the species, bamboo reaches its full size quickly—in an average of 60 days. Although it stops growing vertically at this point, the plant continues to mature, as the culm walls thicken and strengthen over time.

If the bamboo is to be used for such construction products as flooring planks, experts recommend waiting until the culms are adequately thick and strong before harvesting them. Responsible harvesters cut the bamboo at from four to seven years, depending upon the species. Up to 50 percent of the canes in a bamboo grove can be safely taken in one harvest. Within a year, new shoots emerge from the rhizomes to replace the harvested canes. As a result, harvesting bamboo does not kill the plant or the grove. In addition, the widespread network of roots provides continued protection against erosion, a serious problem in clear-cut areas.

Bamboo offers environmental advantages beyond rapid growth. Like most plants, bamboo carries out photosynthesis, a process that involves the intake of carbon dioxide and the release of oxygen. According to the EBF, a bamboo grove gives off 35 percent more oxygen than a timber forest of equivalent size. Certain varieties of bamboo even *sequester* (take in and store) as much as 12 tons of carbon dioxide per hectare (4.9 tons per acre). Thus, bamboo shows promise of helping to "scrub" the air of excess carbon dioxide, a greenhouse gas believed to be a major contributor to global warming.

People in tropical regions have long used bamboo as a building material, but the sturdy grass relative is now showing up in construction worldwide. In many temperate regions, carpenters have traditionally milled planks from such hardwoods as oak or maple for flooring. Similarly, planked bamboo can be used to create flooring. However, because bamboo has a rounded stem, it has to be processed into planks. To form the planks, bamboo culm is cut into thin strips, which are layered and fused together using glue and extreme pressure. Any bamboo product manufactured to offer a "hard-

Bamboo scaffolding envelops a mid-rise building under construction in Hong Kong. In many parts of Southeast Asia, construction companies use bamboo, which rivals steel in *tensile* (flexing) strength, to support workers and materials along the faces of the structure.

wood" look undergoes a similar pressure-treatment process.

Another bamboo product for flooring and other applications is strand board (also called oriented strand board). This is also a processed product, but instead of fusing planks together, the factory operator crushes the bamboo into thin strands and then fuses these into "boards." A related product, Plyboo®, is fabricated in a similar way, but the sheets are stacked with the grain at right angles (like plywood) and then fused.

The natural color of bamboo is light yellow, similar to that of ash or maple. To obtain a darker, richer color, producers use a process called caramelization. During caramelization, the bamboo is essentially cooked with

A bamboo fence provides privacy and strength as well as natural beauty. This fence was constructed by lashing together narrow bamboo culms.

steam, causing the sugars in the culm to darken to honey or coffee hues. The process slightly softens the bamboo. For this reason, bamboo that has been caramelized is not recommended for flooring in high-traffic areas.

Advantages and disadvantages of bamboo

Advantage	Disadvantage
Grows quickly and is easily renewable.	Overexploitation of natural groves and planting of single-species plantations harms biodiversity.
Can be harvested repeatedly without replanting (unlike wood).	Processing bamboo into planks or boards is energy-intensive.
Could reduce wood consumption and thereby save forests.	Product glues may contain high levels of potentially harmful volatile organic chemicals.
May help reduce emissions of heat-trapping carbon dioxide into atmosphere.	Products generally offer a more limited color palette than wood products.
Is exceptionally hard and strong.	Is more prone to bleaching in the sun than wood.
Products are less affected by humidity changes than wood.	Flooring cannot be sanded down as many times as hardwood.
Cost is falling and becoming comparable to that of wood.	Caramelized products (those with deeper color) may be too soft for high-use areas.

Sources: Environmental Bamboo Foundation; U.S. Green Building Council; Tropical Forest Foundation.

Some manufacturers apply stain to bamboo products to obtain a wider color palette. However, some bamboo experts dislike the process because staining obscures the attractive natural striations in the product.

With so many available products, market demand for bamboo is growing. According to a report issued in 2005 by Dovetail Partners, Inc., a Minnesota-based nonprofit corporation that promotes sustainable practices in forestry, the global demand for bamboo fueled a $12-billion industry annually. The report projected $20 billion in annual sales by 2015. The world's chief bamboo-producing regions are southern China, southeast Asia, India, and Indonesia, with China currently producing about 85 percent of globally marketed bamboo.

With such great market growth and demand, however, some practices for bamboo cultivation are tarnishing bamboo's "green" status. Environmentalists have charged that to maximize profits, some entrepreneurs are exploiting natural bamboo stands beyond prudent limits. Other producers are clear-cutting native stands to make way for monoculture plantations—farms that grow a single bamboo species especially suited for commercial production. These actions disturb natural biodiversity and endanger animals that depend on bamboo for food. Animals that are threatened by the commercial cultivation of bamboo include the red panda, Himalayan black bear, and giant panda in China and the mountain gorilla in Africa, according to a 2004 joint report issued by the UN Environmental Program–World Conservation Monitoring Center and the International Network for Bamboo and Rattan.

Some environmentalists also question whether processing bamboo for commercial uses is as Earth-friendly as harvesting timber in an environmentally sound way. They point out that processing wood for hardwood floors involves mainly sawing planks from logs. However, many bamboo products, such as planks for flooring, must be processed in a factory with heat, pressure, and glue to form the planks. Environmentalists also note that most bamboo marketed in Europe and the United States must be shipped great distances, whereas timber is generally harvested closer to home. The energy required to transport products long distances is a significant factor when considering sustainability.

A related environmental issue concerns the composition of processed bamboo products, specifically the glue that is used to bind pieces of culm or culm fibers into boards. Many of the most effective glues contain toxic chemicals, such as urea and formaldehyde, that are categorized as volatile organic compounds (VOC's). Over time, VOC's give off toxic gases, which can cause respiratory ailments and may be linked to some forms of cancer. Responsible manufacturers of bamboo products select glues and binders that are free of or contain low levels of VOC's.

Experts who analyze the trade in commercial bamboo note that there is, at present, no independent, nonprofit international body devoted exclusively to the evaluation of bamboo products for quality and environmental sustainability. Such an entity does exist to evaluate wood products—the Forest Stewardship Council (FSC). The FSC evaluates commercial wood products and issues the FSC label to certify conformance with environmental standards of harvesting and

Choosing bamboo products

- When possible, purchase products that bear a label from the nonprofit Forest Stewardship Council (FSC). (FSC evaluation of bamboo products began in 2008, so the absence of such a label does not necessarily mean that products do not offer quality and environmental sustainability.)
- Look for statements about the age at which the bamboo was harvested. Culms harvested before 5 years are likely to be immature.
- Look for information about moisture content. Ideal products have a moisture content of less than 8 percent.
- Look for information about the types of glues used by the manufacturer. Ideally, glues should have volatile organic chemical (VOC) ratings no higher than 0.10 parts per million (ppm).*
- Examine the manufacturer's color palette and determine how the color is achieved. Bamboo can be stained, but many experts argue that staining diminishes the natural beauty of the material.
- Do not purchase bamboo products wholesale, because quality and color may vary widely. Find a reputable supplier who will verify color and finish and will stand behind guarantees and warranties.
- Research the company's track record and look for consumer ratings.

*VOC standards vary widely, and there is no scientific consensus about what is a "safe" level. However, most state and national standards fall within the recommended range.

Sources: APA, The Engineered Wood Association; Bamboo Society of Australia; Forest Stewardship Council; U.S. Green Building Council.

production. In April 2008, the organization issued the FSC label for the Plyboo® product fabricated by the Smith and Fong Company of San Francisco, California. This certification marked the first time that the organization had conferred its label on a bamboo product. Industry analysts hope that the FSC label will offer a marketing advantage that will prompt other bamboo producers to implement more rigorous environmental standards.

Bamboo is an attractive, plentiful material to use in construction, particularly in such interior elements as flooring, walls, and cabinetry. It also has many other applications, including furniture and accessories. Bamboo's ability to grow fast and easily renew itself endows it with an especially green profile. However, appropriate methods of cultivation and harvesting are critically important to minimize environmental damage.

■ Melissa White-Fournier

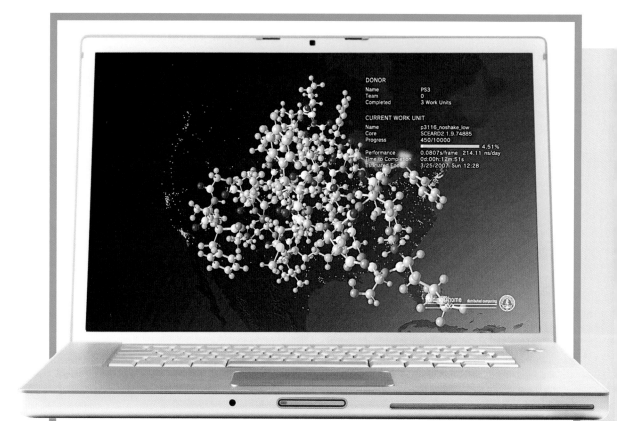

DONOR
Name   PS3
Team   0
Completed   3 Work Units

CURRENT WORK UNIT
Name   p3116_noshake_low
Core   SCEARD2 1.9.74885
Progress   450/10000
                                4.51%
Performance   0.0807s/frame 214.11 ns/day
Time to Completion 0d:00h:12m:51s
Estimated End   3/25/2007. Sun 12:28

folding@home   distributed computing

Distributed Computing: Supercomputing@home

A three-dimensional image of a protein under study serves as the screensaver for the distributed computing project Folding@home.

How would you like to help researchers find a cure for cancer, accurately predict Earth's climate 20 years from now, or seek intelligent life beyond Earth? You can do these things and more without further education or advanced degrees. In fact, while you are reading this, millions of home computers are churning away to achieve these goals. Their owners are participating in a new type of computer processing called distributed computing. In distributed computing, central computers in a laboratory or other research facility harness the untapped computing power of individual computers beyond the lab—potentially millions of them—through the medium of the Internet.

Since the 1960's, scientists and researchers who need to process massive amounts of data have often looked to supercomputers. These powerful, room-sized data processors, however, are affordable only to institutions with deep pockets. The Earth Simulator, a supercomputer owned by research institutions in Yokohama, Japan, reportedly cost $380 million. Besides being costly, supercomputers have scalability issues. That is, they can only process data volumes for which they were designed. If the volume of data exceeds the processor's ability, the supercomputer cannot be used or the project has to be scaled back.

With the rapid development of Internet services in the 1990's, computer experts began to explore the possibility of linking outside computers with the computing resources of scientific laboratories and other centers of computer-intensive activity. They were particularly interested in the potentially vast computing resource represented by home computers. Most home computer users search the Internet, create documents, send and receive e-mail, and, perhaps, download music and video and play games. Even so, according to researchers, the average home computer user employs no more than 15 percent of his or her computer's total processing power. Computer experts realized that the collective "people power" of personal computers, if successfully harnessed, could rival or surpass the computing power of supercomputers.

In the 1990's, scientists with SERENDIP (Search for Extraterrestrial Radio Emissions from Nearby Developed Intelligent Populations) were using computers to examine radio signals captured by the radio telescope at the Arecibo Observatory in Puerto Rico. SERENDIP is a joint project of the SETI Institute in Mountain View, California, and the University of California at Berkeley (UC-Berkeley). (SETI refers to the Search for Extraterrestrial Intelligence.)

The scientists programmed their computers to look for patterns that do not appear to be random and thus could indicate transmission from intelligent beings in space. However, they hit a roadblock. The sheer volume of the data swamped the project's computational resources. SERENDIP would either have to buy a supercomputer, at a cost far beyond the project's means, or recruit volunteers from the public to offer the resources of their home computers.

With the help of computer scientists at UC-Berkeley, the SERENDIP researchers figured out how to slice up their data into work modules that could be processed by individual home computers. The scientists then developed

software to interface with these computers over the Internet.

In 1999, SERENDIP made history by launching the first distributed computing project, which it named SETI@home. Dan Werthimer, one of the creators of SETI@home, later said he originally thought that SETI@home would be lucky if it attracted as many as 10,000 participants. In fewer than five years, however, the project had recruited nearly 5 million home participants worldwide, with a collective computing power that surpassed that of any existing supercomputer.

Since the debut of SETI@home, other distributed computing projects have successfully recruited their own Internet-based, home-computer communities for scientific number-crunching. Some researchers have even formulated research tasks in the form of competitive computer games that end-users play, all the while furthering specific research objectives.

Playing games for science

A computer game called "Foldit" is attracting a community of cybercompetitors. The object of the game is to "fold" a squiggly, multifaceted protein molecule, such as the one seen on this computer screen, as compactly as possible. Protein folding involves the precise way in which a protein—which is, in essence, a long chain of simpler molecules—assumes its characteristic three-dimensional shape. The game provides a tutorial to train participants in the rules of protein folding in the cyberworld simulation. Foldit is the brainchild of David Baker, a molecular biologist at the University of Washington-Seattle who has been instrumental in developing the distributed computing project Rosetta@home. Interested gamesters can find Foldit online at www.fold.it.

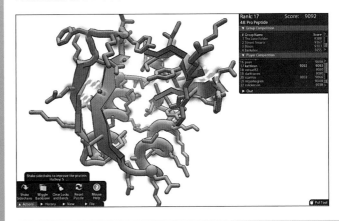

How distributed computing works

To set up a distributed computing network, laboratory personnel first install master software on an Internet-linked, in-house computer. They then instruct end-users to install a client software package on their home computers. These software programs enable the lab to send jobs over the Internet to participating computers and to receive finished work back through the Internet connection.

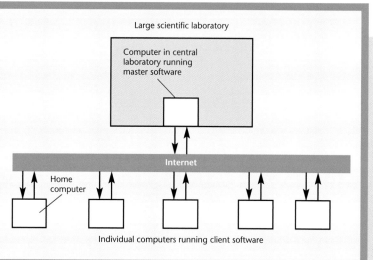

Large scientific laboratory

Computer in central laboratory running master software

Internet

Home computer

Individual computers running client software

Computing experts point out that not all computational problems lend themselves to distributed computing. Research programs with elements that need to communicate constantly with each other, for example, are better handled by an onsite computer. Such an installation features very rapid internal communication channels, as opposed to the relatively slower Internet. Nonetheless, researchers have suc-

cessfully adapted distributed computing to a number of scientific applications.

One of the hottest topics in biochemistry and medicine is the study of how proteins fold. A protein is a complex organic molecule consisting of a long chain of components called amino acids. Proteins perform most basic biological functions at the cellular level in organisms. In order to become activated, a protein must assume its characteristic three-dimensional shape in a process called folding. If a protein misfolds, it will fail to function properly, possibly leading to such illnesses as Alzheimer's disease, Parkinson disease, or others. Because the number of ways any one protein can fold is nearly infinite, folding studies require fast, powerful computing resources to simulate all of the possibilities.

Several large distributed computing projects are assisting scientists in performing protein-folding simulations. Folding@home, supervised by chemist Vijay Pande of Stanford University in Stanford, California, is one such project. Launched in October 2000, Folding@home reported more than 1 million registered participants by early 2008. In March 2007, Folding@home became the first distributed computing project to sign up users of Sony's PLAYSTATION® 3 video game consoles. These devices possess high-performance graphics processors that boost distributed computing power, according to Pande.

Distributed computing Web sites

Distributed computing projects typically provide continuously updated screensavers that display on client computers when the home users are not performing computing activities. This client screensaver, for SETI@home, displays various data about the home user community as well as frequencies of the radio telescope data currently being analyzed. The goal of the analysis is to identify extraterrestrial communications.

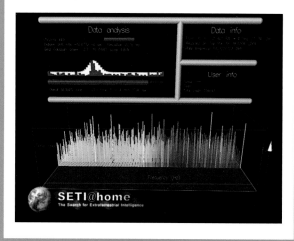

Rosetta@home, a distributed computing project based at the University of Washington at Seattle, is also working on the problem of protein folding. Other distributed computing projects are investigating causes of cancer and analyzing the molecular properties of potential AIDS drugs. Still others are developing improved climate modeling and sifting through mountains of data from the Large Hadron Collider, a European physics facility that is investigating the tiniest particles of matter.

What makes these and other distributed computing projects feasible is specialized software designed to work over the Internet. The client software, which provides a user interface, can be downloaded from the central laboratory facility. Client software enables a participating machine to receive work units from lab computers, process the work, and return it. The most widely used distributed computing software is the Berkeley Open Infrastructure for Network Computing, or BOINC.

Distributed computing projects

Project name	Purpose
The Clean Energy Project	To test the molecular structure of laboratory-fabricated materials for their possible use in solar cells or fuel cells; based at Harvard University in Cambridge, Massachusetts. http://cleanenergy.harvard.edu/
Climateprediction. net	To develop reliable computer models to predict changes in the global climate to the year 2080; based at Oxford University in Oxford, United Kingdom. http://www.climateprediction.net/
FightAIDS@home	To evaluate prospective drugs for the treatment of people with AIDS; based at Olson Laboratory of the Scripps Research Institute in La Jolla, California. http://fightaidsathome.scripps.edu/
Folding@home and Rosetta@home	To model the ways in which proteins are most likely to fold. Understanding protein folding may lead to treatments for diseases believed to be caused by misfolded proteins, including Alzheimer's disease and Parkinson disease. Folding@home is based at Stanford University in Stanford, California; Rosetta@home, at the University of Washington at Seattle. http://folding.stanford.edu/ http://boinc.bakerlab.org/rosetta/
Help Conquer Cancer	To assess data from X-ray crystallography experiments with proteins to improve researchers' ability to analyze proteins that may play a role in the development of cancer; based at the Ontario Cancer Institute, Princess Margaret Hospital, in Toronto, Canada. http://www.worldcommunitygrid.org/: under "What We Do," select "Help Defeat Cancer"
LHC@home	To run particle simulations for the Large Hadron Collider, a massive underground facility near Geneva, Switzerland, being used to investigate fundamental particles of matter; sponsored by the European Council for Nuclear Research (CERN) and based at Queen Mary, University of London. http://lhcathome.cern.ch/
Malariacontrol.net	To model various aspects of malaria research, including transmission patterns of *Plasmodium falciparum*, the parasite that causes the deadliest form of malaria; based at the Swiss Tropical Institute, Basel, Switzerland. http://www.malariacontrol.net/
Nutritious Rice for the World	To examine proteins in rice plants to improve pest and disease resistance, crop yield, and nutritional benefit; based at the University of Washington at Seattle. http://protinfo.compbio.washington.edu/rice/
SETI@home	To examine data from radio telescopes, seeking radio wave patterns that might come from intelligent life beyond Earth; based at the University of California at Berkeley. http://seti@home.berkeley.edu/

Joining a distributed computing project

A number of distributed computing projects in science and technology maintain Web sites from which they recruit volunteers. Distributed computing experts offer the following guidelines to people interested in joining a project.

- Visit the Web site of a project you would like to join: See the "Distributed computing projects" chart or visit www.worldcommunitygrid.org.
- Respond to questions about system requirements to determine if your computer can run the workloads successfully and efficiently. You may be asked to provide the following information about your computer and Internet connection:

  – computer processing unit (CPU) speed in gigahertz (GHz); alternatively, you may be asked to specify the name of the processor that forms your computer's CPU.

  – available hard-drive disk space, measured in megabytes (MB) or gigabytes (GB).

  – computer memory, or random access memory (RAM), measured in MB's.

  – Internet connection: type, such as dial-up or broadband.

- Read the license agreement and accept or reject: You must accept to participate. Most agreements insist that the user must own the computer that is being signed up. Users should not offer computing time on business or school computers without specific written permission to do so.

  Note that all projects post statements that they assume no liability for damage to your computer or loss of data. This is standard legal practice.

- Make sure that you have the option of withdrawing from the project at any time.
- Download the software that matches your operating system (such as Windows, MAC OS, or Linux).

Sources: Folding@home; Rosetta@home; SETI@home; www.worldcommunity.grid; Federal Communications Commission (FCC).

Some projects distribute client software through the World Community Grid (WCG), www.worldcommunity grid.org. WCG is a public computing grid launched by the IBM Corporation of Armonk, New York, in 2004. WCG centralizes networking management of distributed computing projects. If a project is using WCG, its Web site links users to the appropriate WCG Web page to download the client software.

Once client software is installed on a user's home computer, it automatically downloads work units. Depending upon user choice, the downloaded program runs in the background all the time or runs only when the user is not working at the computer. Most distributed computing projects display a special screen saver while processing is taking place on an otherwise idle computer. For example, the Folding@home project displays a three-dimensional view of the protein molecule under investigation. When a work unit is completed, the client software sends it back to the main lab, where data from participants are reassembled and analyzed.

Distributed computing has a few pitfalls. First, many projects cannot be neatly dissected into multiple tasks. Second, a project is compatible with the distributed computing model only if offloading work units to multiple users achieves efficiencies. The amount of time needed to process a unit needs to be greater than the download time and require little or no communication with the research laboratory. For example, an ideal task can be downloaded, run passively on a home computer for about eight hours, and then returned to the research lab automatically.

One question that users in a distributed computing project are likely to ask is "How safe is my computer?" The prospect of yielding a portion of one's home computer to unsupervised outside use makes some owners uncomfortable. They may fear hacking schemes that aim to take over computers through Internet links and turn them into "zombies" that can be controlled, often for illegal purposes, without the owner's knowledge.

Distributed computing experts give projects such as SETI@home, Folding @home, and others high marks for maintaining tight security. According to Dave Anderson, head of the BOINC development project at UC-Berkeley, SETI@home has maintained a 100-percent safe security record with its subscribers. Computer security experts note that users can protect themselves from ill-intended intruders by maintaining up-to-date antivirus or other security software, by downloading files only from sources known to be legitimate, and by refraining from following links in an e-mail from an unknown sender. ■ Melissa White-Fournier

Vitamin D: Is It a Miracle Vitamin?

Scientists have long recognized the key role that vitamin D performs in helping the body absorb calcium to build strong bones. One of the triumphs of United States public health efforts in the 1900's was the eradication of rickets, a deforming disease of the bones in children caused by vitamin D deficiency. This feat was accomplished by fortifying such foods as milk and breakfast cereals with vitamin D, a practice that the U.S. food industry began in the 1930's.

Since the early 2000's, medical researchers have reported extensive new evidence about the health effects of vitamin D. According to a growing number of studies, low blood levels of vitamin D increase the risk of acquiring many serious diseases, and high levels substantially lower those risks.

Some medical experts have adopted a cautious attitude toward the findings and have advised the public not to regard vitamin D as a new "magic pill." They recall earlier vitamin crazes, including those for vitamin C in the 1970's and vitamin E in the 1990's. These vitamins, though necessary for good health, failed to meet heightened expectations for a wide range of supposed benefits. Nevertheless, vitamin D research has

engaged the attention of medical professionals and the public alike.

The name *vitamin D* actually refers to a group of related chemical compounds. Chief among these are plant-derived vitamin D_2 and animal-derived vitamin D_3. Both forms are usable by human beings, but most research has concentrated on D_3. Like all vitamins, these compounds regulate chemical reactions by which the body converts food into energy and living tissue. Vitamin D, however, is unique among vitamins in that it functions as a hormone after undergoing changes inside the body. A hormone is a chemical messenger that helps body systems interact in a coordinated way. Hormones are capable of influencing a wider range of body processes than vitamins are.

Human bodies manufacture vitamin D_3 by a chain of chemical processes beginning in the skin. Sunlight triggers the transformation of a chemical in human skin, called 7-dehydrocholesterol, into a form of vitamin D. To be usable by the body, this basic form of the vitamin undergoes a two-part conversion process, starting in the liver and ending in the kidneys. At the end of this chemical process, vitamin D is said to be "activated," or capable

In addition to obtaining vitamin D through exposure to sunlight, people consume some of the nutrient in food. Oily fish, such as the salmon steak (above), provide the highest levels of vitamin D in food. Milk and milk products are fortified with vitamin D during processing. Lesser amounts of the vitamin can be obtained by eating nuts and vegetables.

THE SUNSHINE VITAMIN

Vitamin D begins to form in the body when the skin is exposed to sunlight. The chemical produced by the skin must be further processed in the liver and kidneys to become "activated"—that is, capable of being used by body cells.

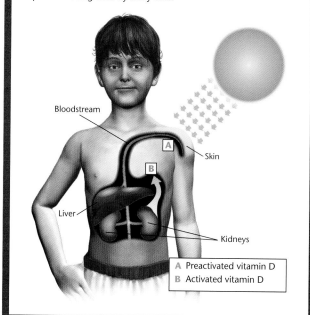

Bloodstream

Skin

A

B

Liver

Kidneys

A Preactivated vitamin D
B Activated vitamin D

from sunlight, all ingested forms have to be activated in the liver and kidneys.

A number of recent medical studies have linked vitamin D deficiency with diseases of the heart and circulatory system. In 2007, researchers with the Framingham Heart Study—a long-term, Massachusetts-based study of individuals at risk of heart disease—revealed that participants with low levels of vitamin D had twice the risk of heart attack and stroke as did people with normal levels. The researchers called for new clinical studies to determine whether boosting blood levels of vitamin D could broadly protect populations from heart and circulatory disease.

Several studies have indicated that vitamin D levels affect individuals' risk of developing cancer. A four-year study of middle-aged women sponsored by the Creighton University School of Medicine in Omaha, Nebraska, and publicized in 2007 yielded what seemed to be dramatic results. Participants receiving vitamin D supplements of 1,100 international units (IU)—nearly three times the daily dosage recommended by U.S. government agencies—experienced a 60-percent decline in cancer risk (for all types of cancer) compared with the control group, which did not receive the supplements. It should be noted that medical professionals do not agree on the potential health effects of taking large doses of vitamin D.

In 2007, a research team with the Moores Cancer Center of the University of California at San Diego publicized the results of a study investigating the impact of vitamin D on the risks of acquiring colon cancer and breast cancer. The researchers reported that subjects given daily doses of 2,000 IU's of vitamin D (5 to 10 times the level currently recommended by federal guidelines, depending upon the subject's age) were half as likely as the general population to develop these forms of cancer. Medical studies have also provided evidence of a linkage between vitamin D deficiency and increased risk for ovarian and kidney cancers.

Scientific studies also reveal a vital role for vitamin D in multiple sclerosis

of being utilized in chemical processes of the body.

Not all people manufacture or utilize vitamin D equally efficiently. People with dark skin, for example, need longer exposure to sunlight than do light-skinned people to manufacture the same amount of vitamin D. Obese people tend to have lower levels of vitamin D circulating in their blood than do thinner people, because fat layers under the skin absorb much of the vitamin D that skin synthesizes.

Vitamin D production also differs among people from different climates. Studies have shown that people who live close to the equator, where the climate receives ample sunlight, tend to produce more vitamin D than do people who live in temperate and colder latitudes. These latitudes are farther away from the equator and receive less direct sunlight each year.

In addition, people acquire vitamin D by consuming such foods as oily fish—salmon, mackerel, tuna, and sardines; foods fortified with vitamin D; or vitamin supplements containing vitamin D. As with the vitamin D produced

(MS), an often disabling autoimmune disorder. In autoimmune diseases, elements of the immune system wrongly identify normal body tissues as alien invaders and attack them. In MS, nerve-insulating tissue in the nervous system comes under attack, interfering with the brain's ability to communicate with other parts of the body.

In early 2009, a research team led by George Ebers of the University of Oxford in the United Kingdom announced the discovery of a biochemical process by which vitamin D activates a gene that issues instructions to the body's immune system. If the gene does not become activated, due to vitamin D deficiency, MS may develop. This medical breakthrough provided the first direct scientific evidence for a long-observed statistical pattern of MS—that it is much more common at high and low latitudes, such as Scotland and New Zealand, respectively, than in the tropics. The researchers concluded that vitamin D synthesis in the presence of sunlight explained these statistics. They theorized that ensuring adequate vitamin D in populations living in temperate and polar regions might, over time, reduce the incidence of multiple sclerosis.

Vitamin D may protect proper brain functioning as well. In 2008, scientists at the Children's Hospital and Research Center in Oakland, California, found that sufficient levels of vitamin D are necessary for healthy brain development in children. The researchers noted that vitamin D affects proteins known to be involved in such brain functions as learning, memory, and control of body movements. Later in life, vitamin D may play a role in the onset of Alzheimer's disease. According to a 2009 study cosponsored by the Peninsula Medical School in Exeter in the United Kingdom and the University of Michigan in Ann Arbor, people over age 65 with low levels of vitamin D were more than twice as likely to suffer impaired reasoning as those with high levels. Impaired reasoning is a major symptom of Alzheimer's disease.

Pregnant women receive substantial benefits from sufficient vitamin D levels, studies show. A 2007 study from the University of Pittsburgh Schools of the Health Sciences found that women with low vitamin D levels were about five times as likely to develop preeclampsia, a disorder characterized by high blood pressure during pregnancy and, often, premature birth. According to the nonprofit Preeclampsia Foundation, this serious condition leads to the death of 76,000 mothers and 500,000 babies around the world each year.

A growing body of research suggests links between vitamin D and the two major forms of diabetes, Type 1 and Type 2. Type 1 diabetes occurs when the body does not produce insulin, a hormone that enables people to absorb and use sugar. This more serious form of the disease usually begins in childhood and always requires treatment by insulin injection. Type 2 diabetes develops when people, particularly in middle age, lose the ability to produce enough insulin or to use their insulin efficiently.

Researchers at the Moores Cancer Center published a study in June 2008 documenting a lower rate of Type 1

Bone density

Vitamin D helps maintain strong bones. The body processes calcium, the principal mineral in bones, only in the presence of vitamin D. In older people, deficiencies of vitamin D and calcium can lead to osteoporosis, a condition in which bones lose tissue and become fragile.

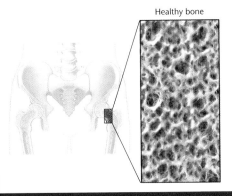

Healthy bone

Fragile bone

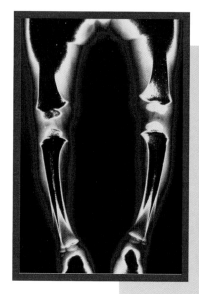
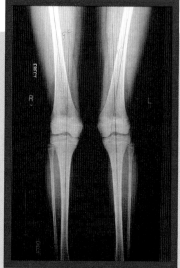

Normal bones in a child (above right) contrast markedly wth the deformed bones of a child suffering from rickets (above left). A lack of vitamin D may cause bones in children to soften and develop abnormal shapes. The practice of fortifying milk and certain other foods with vitamin D has largely eliminated the disease in the United States.

diabetes among people living near the equator than those living in temperate or polar regions. As with other studies, the finding suggested sunlight-induced vitamin D may be a critical factor.

Two recent studies have suggested that people with higher blood levels of vitamin D have a lower risk of acquiring Type 2 diabetes than the general population. Both research teams—one at the National Public Health Institute in Helsinki, Finland, and another at Tufts University in Medford, Massachusetts—recommended large-scale follow-up clinical studies.

With new research linking vitamin D to such a wide range of medical conditions, medical professionals are reevaluating recommendations for the daily intake of vitamin D. The U.S. government's current recommendations were issued in 1997 by the Food and Nutrition Board (FNB) at the Institute of Medicine of the National Academies. These guidelines recommend 200 IU's of vitamin D daily for people under 51 years of age; 400 IU's for people ages 51 through 70; and 600 IU's for people 71 and older.

The 1997 FNB guidelines, however, have come under increasing criticism from a variety of medical organizations. In June 2008, the Chicago-based American Medical Association passed a resolution calling for federal agencies to increase their vitamin D recommendations. As of mid-2009, the federal guidelines were still under review.

Other medical groups have recently released updated guidelines for vitamin D intake. The Canadian Cancer Society recommends that adults in Canada should supplement their diet with 1,000 IU's of vitamin D each day during the fall and winter, when sunlight hours become scarce. This group also recommends that older adults take a supplement with 1,000 IU's of vitamin D throughout the year.

Not all experts, however, agree that recommending higher levels of vitamin D is good health policy. Overdosing poses a danger because excess vitamin D can boost blood calcium to an unsafe level, possibly resulting in mental confusion, abnormal heart rhythms, or the formation of kidney stones. Some medical professionals question whether the available data are sufficient to warrant updating recommendations; they note that many of the studies showing vitamin D benefits are based on analyses of previous medical studies rather than new clinical studies.

Some medical experts worry that press reports about vitamin D will prompt people to seek sunlight, increasing their risk of skin cancer. Studies show that exposure to ultraviolet rays in sunlight can cause skin cancer. According to the American Cancer Society, more than 1 million people are diagnosed with skin cancer each year in the United States.

As medical researchers continue to investigate vitamin D's effect on human health, most health experts recommend following the government's 1997 vitamin D guidelines and pursuing healthy lifestyles through diet and regular exercise. Consumers can also stay informed about any revisions to existing guidelines by visiting the Web site of the National Institutes of Health-Office of Dietary Supplements (http://ods.od.nih.gov) or by visiting Web sites of major national medical associations or societies.

■ Melissa White-Fournier

How to "Green" Your Lawn

The dream of many an American homeowner has long included the "perfect" lawn. Lovingly tended and intensively cultivated, such lawns "green up" our towns and suburbs. In the United States, these traditional lawns cover an area equivalent to the entire state of Kentucky.

The lawns that so many Americans love come with a price tag, however. The National Gardening Association's annual National Gardening Survey revealed that U.S. consumers in 2007 spent about $35.1 billion on lawn and garden products. Homeowners' lawn and garden costs were further boosted by high water bills.

The price of maintaining a traditional lawn is counted in more than dollars and cents. In recent years, people have begun to recognize a host of environmental problems related to maintaining such lawns in all places and under all conditions.

Intensively cultivated grass lawns require extensive irrigation, except in ideal weather conditions—which are rarely common and persistent. Lawn watering is now overtaxing many local water resources. According to the Environmental Protection Agency (EPA), lawn irrigation uses up to 30 percent of the municipal water supply in the eastern United States and up to 60 percent of these water resources in the drier western states.

Traditional lawn maintenance, in pursuit of that elusive ideal of perfection, has become highly dependent on the application of chemicals, many of them toxic. These chemicals include *insecticides* (insect killers), *fungicides* (fungus killers), and *herbicides* (weed killers)—all of which are collectively referred to as *pesticides*. Pesticides can mix with rainwater and drain into streams and rivers. This extends their impact far beyond suburban lawns. In fact, the effects of pesticide overuse are now showing

An attractive, environmentally friendly lawn coordinates a variety of elements, including flower beds, shrubs, trees, ground cover, and patches of grass. Many homeowners now prefer this approach to landscaping, as opposed to sweeping spans of uninterrupted *turf* (varieties of spreading lawn grass).

up in many parts of the environment.

Fish, birds, and amphibians, such as frogs, are highly susceptible to many of the chemicals that are part of the intensive-cultivation regime for traditional lawns. The University of Florida Institute of Food and Agricultural Sciences Extension has identified more than 60 commercially available pesticides that are "highly toxic" to fish—that is, they kill on contact. A number of these pesticides are available to home gardeners. Other studies have shown that a widely available class of insecticides called organophosphates is especially deadly to frogs. Birds are not exempt from poisoning, either. According to the U.S. Fish and Wildlife Service, 67 million birds die annually in the United States from direct contact with agricultural or lawn pesticides.

In addition, many beneficial insect populations are imperiled by insecticides, most of which target insects indiscriminately. Beneficial insects include mantids and ladybugs, which devour voracious plant-eating insects; and bees, which serve the critical function of pollinating flowering plants.

Finally, the accumulation of pesticides in the environment may pose dangers to human health. According to the EPA, the degree of danger depends on the type of pesticide, how it is used, and the degree of exposure.

The good news is that a variety of techniques are available to environmentally conscious gardeners. Among

Turfgrass varieties

Name	Description	Where best used in the United States	Drought tolerant
Bentgrass	Deep green color; forms dense mat; winter-hardy	Northeast and Pacific Northwest	
Bermuda	Coarse, hairy, low-growing	Southeast, South-Central states, California	✓
Blue grama	Narrow-bladed, leafy at base; winter-hardy	Northern Great Plains	✓
Buffalo grass	Gray-green, hairy leaves; winter-hardy	Great Plains and semiarid West	✓
Centipede	Coarse, light green, low-growing	Southeast	
Fescue, fine	Blue-green, needle-like leaves; winter-hardy	Upper South, Northeast, Midwest, Pacific coastal areas	
Fescue, tall	Coarse leaves; winter-hardy	Upper South, Mid-Atlantic region, Pacific coastal areas	✓
Kentucky bluegrass	Fine, soft texture; dark green; winter-hardy	Upper South, Northeast, Midwest	
Kikuyu	Medium green, hairy leaves	Southwest and California	✓
Perennial ryegrass	Looks similar to bluegrass; winter-hardy	Upper South, Northeast, Midwest, Pacific Northwest	
St. Augustine	Coarse texture	Coastal Southeast, Gulf coast, California	
Zoyzia	Light green, hairy leaves; low-growing	Southeast, South-Central states, California	✓

Source: Various state university extension services.

these techniques are water conservation; use of such non-turf garden features as ground covers and shrubs; and integrated pest management (IPM), an environmentally friendly way to reduce harmful pest populations.

The first step toward creating a more environmentally sustainable lawn is to rethink the overall lawn design, many lawn experts suggest. Consider including trees, shrubs and smaller garden plants to limit the expanse of green grass. Where possible, plant native species, which are uniquely adapted to a region's soil and climate and are, therefore, more likely to resist drought and pests. Trees shelter wildlife and protect the soil from erosion. In addition, buildings with ample shade cover from trees require one-fourth as much energy to cool in summer as do unshaded buildings, according to energy conservation experts.

Water conservation is at the heart of ecofriendly garden design. Technically, lawn grass varieties are called turfgrass, to distinguish them from varieties of grasses that do not spread to form a dense, carpet-like ground cover. Most turfgrass species are water-greedy and thrive best where rainfall is ample and frequent.

However, grasses possess a strategy for withstanding periods of drought: they become dormant. During dormancy, the visible part of the grass plant, the aboveground grass blades, withers and dries up, turning brown or straw-colored. At the same time, any remaining moisture is concentrated in the belowground *rhizomes* (underground stems) and roots. After a good rainfall wets the soil, these parts of the plant send up tender new shoots, "greening" the whole lawn.

A lawn's ability to tolerate drought depends on many factors, including the variety of turfgrass, the health of the plants, and the condition of the soil. However, an extended period of

A home gardener fills his watering can from a rain barrel placed to capture rainwater runoff from the roof of his house. Using rain water helps conserve water from municipal systems.

drought can kill even the underground parts of grass, which is why no turfgrass grows naturally in arid desert climates. Because almost all turfgrasses require at least 51 centimeters (20 inches) of rainfall per year to survive—and many require at least 76 centimeters (30 inches)—residents of semiarid and arid regions should consider alternatives to grass lawns.

Homeowners wishing to cultivate a grass lawn should consider their turfgrass variety's water requirements and determine how long the lawn can stay dormant. In regions with water restrictions, homeowners may be able to justify a level of irrigation that will keep the grass roots alive but will still allow the lawn to turn brown during hot, dry weather. On average, experts recommend watering at least 2.5 centimeters (1 inch) per week in the absence of rainfall to maintain a green lawn. To merely keep the lawn alive during dormancy, they recommend, on average, 1.3 centimeters (½ inch) every three weeks.

Each turfgrass variety has particular characteristics and requirements. Some marketed varieties are actually mixtures. The labels of such products usually specify the varieties in the mix.

Water conservation involves wise use of water resources as well as

Drought-tolerant plants and such nonliving elements as rocks and gravel fill a xeriscape garden (above left). Thriving on very little water, xeriscape gardens are ideal for desert and semiarid climates. A native prairie garden (above right) combines grasses and flowers native to Midwestern regions of the United States that once were covered by treeless prairies.

appropriate plantings. Garden experts suggest installing rain barrels at the bottom of roof gutters to capture and hold rainwater. Using efficient watering techniques can conserve precious water. During rainless periods, water plants deeply at soil level once a week. Consider using drip hoses, which apply water directly on the ground and minimize evaporation. Except in humid weather, avoid using whirling sprinklers, which lose much water through evaporation.

An increasingly popular alternative to the traditional lawn in semiarid and arid regions is the xeriscape garden. Xeriscaping is a technique that strongly emphasizes water conservation. (The word *xeriscape* comes from the Greek root *xeros,* meaning *dry.*) Xeriscapes feature such drought-tolerant plants as cactuses and succulents (sedums and hens-and-chicks, for example) as well as such nonliving features as rocks, pebbles, and sand.

An effective, environmentally responsible alternative to high-powered synthetic chemicals is integrated pest management. Among other techniques, IPM incorporates the use of such low-impact insecticides as insecticidal soap, a soaplike compound, and diatoma-

ceous earth, a powder ground from a porous rock. Both of these substances kill insects by degrading or removing their protective *exoskeletons* (hard outer shells) without poisoning other living things. IPM also uses certain botanical insecticides, chemicals that occur naturally in plants and break down easily in the environment. Pyrethrins, derived from a type of daisy, are a useful family of botanical insecticides.

IPM also emphasizes some common-sense approaches to insect pests. For instance, when only a few plants are badly infested, gardeners can pick off the insects and douse them in alcohol or bleach. IPM recommends pulling weeds by hand or applying natural herbicides. One such herbicide is acetic acid, also called horticultural vinegar, which can be purchased at gardening stores. This substance, effective against dandelions and other stubborn weeds, must be used carefully as it will damage grass and other garden plants as well. However, it breaks down quickly into harmless natural substances.

Proper mowing techniques promote lawn health and reduce turf stress during drought. Mower blades should be positioned high rather than low, so that no more than one-third of the grass blade is cut off. Keep blades sharp, as dull blades will tear the grass raggedly, providing entry points for disease-causing fungal spores.

Many green gardeners dispense with gasoline-engine mowers altogether, opting for mechanical or battery-powered models. Burning gasoline emits carbon dioxide, a recognized greenhouse gas.

Some homeowners and businesses are thinking entirely "out of the box" for their lawn designs. When Sears, Roebuck and Company developed Prairie Stone, a business park in the company's home base of Hoffman Estates, Illinois, landscape professionals incorporated tallgrass prairie plantings into the design. These plots attempt to duplicate natural Illinois tallgrass stands—mixes of native grasses and such native flowers as black-eyed Susans and purple coneflowers. Natural tallgrass prairies once dominated much of Illinois, Iowa, and nearby states.

Going back to nature is a reliably "green" principle of lawn design. Tall-

grass prairies may not be appropriate for your locale and climate, but a native ground cover or xeriscaping might be a viable option. Whichever approach lawn keepers choose, it is clear that the intensively cultivated grass lawn is not the only attractive option.

■ Brad Finger

Grass pavers form a network of concrete interspersed with plugs of turfgrass. The structure, ideal for driveways, can support the weight of vehicles but also allows rainwater to soak into the ground, replenishing precious ground water.

Choosing a "green" lawn care service

About one-quarter of all U.S. households hire lawn care services. These services vary widely in their sensitivity to environmental issues. To select a "green" lawn care service, experts suggest the following guidelines.

■ Ask if the company is a member of a trade association or a state landscaping association. Associations provide their members with up-to-date industry information on new products and techniques.

■ Ask if the company intends to test your soil. If it does not, consider interviewing a different company. The first step in transitioning from an intensively cultivated grass lawn to an ecofriendly lawn is to test the soil to determine if organic materials such as compost should be added.

■ Ask if the company uses integrated pest management (IPM). Request an annotated list of all pesticides the service uses. Each item on the list should be accompanied by an explanation of its purpose.

■ If you wish to eliminate all synthetic chemicals from your lawn and garden, discuss this with the lawn care representative. The company may offer this option but at a different cost. Make sure any differences from the company's standard program of service are written into your contract.

■ Check the service's history of complaints with the Better Business Bureau or your state university's extension service. Be wary of using any service that has been accused of overapplying herbicides or other lawn chemicals.

Sources: Clemson University Cooperative Extension Service; Ohio State University Extension; Safelawns.org.

SCIENCE NEWS UPDATE

Contributors report on the year's most significant developments in their respective fields. The articles in this section are arranged alphabetically.

AGRICULTURE

In January 2009, POET Research Center of Scotland, South Dakota, became the first United States energy company to produce cellulosic ethanol from corncobs on a pilot scale. Pilot production is an experimental production run that allows engineers to improve the production process before beginning commercial production. Ethanol is a type of alcohol used as an automobile fuel. The POET pilot run was geared to an annual production rate of 76,000 liters (20,000 gallons).

Cellulosic ethanol is derived from cellulose—tough, fibrous tissue in plants—rather than starches (such as in corn kernels) or sugars (such as in sugar cane). Cellulosic ethanol can be fermented from such plant scraps as corncobs.

Some environmentalists consider cellulosic ethanol a "greener" fuel than gasoline. According to scientists at the Argonne National Laboratory in Argonne, Illinois, carbon dioxide (CO_2) emissions from burning cellulosic ethanol are 85 percent lower than from burning gasoline.

However, cellulose is extremely difficult to break down chemically. Its *polymers* (long chain-like molecules) strongly resist decomposition into simpler sugar molecules that can be fermented into ethanol. Thus, production of cellulosic ethanol historically has not been cost-competitive with gasoline.

POET chief executive officer Jeff Broin predicted that efficiencies learned by company engineers during the pilot run would eventually bring down production costs from $1 more than gasoline in early 2009 to only 50 cents by 2011. Broin further predicted that the price of cellulosic ethanol would equal that of gasoline "within 5 to 7 years." POET planned to begin commercial-scale production of cellulosic ethanol in 2011. The company's business model called for integrating cellulosic with conventional corn ethanol production in its facilities.

Doug Karlen, an Iowa-based soil scientist with the U.S. Department of Agriculture (USDA), noted an additional environmental benefit of using corncobs for ethanol production. After corncobs are harvested, up to 85 percent of the nongrain parts of the corn plant can still be left on the ground to protect soil against wind and water erosion and, ultimately, to be tilled in as a soil amendment. Karlen noted that some schemes for production of cellulosic ethanol required taking the entire cornstalk out of the field.

SEE ALSO CONSUMER SCIENCE, VITAMIN D: IS IT A MIRACLE VITAMIN? PAGE 143.

A prince of a blueberry. In late 2008, scientists released a new, early-ripening blueberry cultivar that, when grown with other blueberry varieties, will extend the growing and harvesting season for this fruit near the Gulf of Mexico. The new variety, named Prince, was developed at the USDA's Agricultural Research Service Southern Horticultural Laboratory in Poplarville, Mississippi, by Stephen Stringer, a research geneticist. Officials with the Poplarville facility projected that plants would become available from commercial suppliers in 2010.

Like other blueberry varieties hybridized for cultivation in the U.S. Deep South, Prince is a "rabbiteye" blueberry. Rabbiteye cultivars do not require a period of extended cold weather to produce fruit, as do highbush varieties that thrive in climates farther north.

Prince has several advantages over previously hybridized rabbiteye varieties. Its extended bloom period ensures that fruit will be produced even if early blossoms are nipped by frost. Prince blueberries ripen four to five days earlier than other rabbiteye blueberries. These characteristics ideally position Prince to compete in the lucrative, early-season, fresh-blueberry market period.

Scientists began hybridizing rabbiteye blueberries, native to the Deep South, for farmers on the Gulf Coast after Hurricane Camille in 1969 devastated agriculture along the Mississippi coastline. Since then, at least 13 new commercial varieties have been introduced. According to the USDA, slightly more than 1,000 hectares (2,500 acres) in Mississippi were devoted to commercial blueberry culture in 2008; before the 1970's, that number stood at zero.

Mushrooms get vitamin D boost. In late 2008, mushroom producers began boosting the vitamin D content of white, brown, and portobello mushrooms with carefully controlled exposure to ultraviolet B, or UVB, a form of ultraviolet light similar to that radiated by the sun. (Scientists categorize ultraviolet rays as UVA, UVB, and UBC, according to wavelength.) One of the first producers to market UVB-treated mushrooms was Monterey Mushrooms, Inc., of Watsonville,

AGRICULTURE continued

California, which launched its Sun Bella line in October 2008.

The new, vitamin D-fortified mushrooms resulted from research conducted by scientists with the Agricultural Research Service (ARS), a division of the USDA, and funded by the Mushroom Council, an industry association of mushroom producers. From 2005 to 2008, the scientists studied the effect of exposing mushroom crops, which are typically raised in dark conditions, to periods of UVB radiation.

According to scientists, as many as 40 percent of people in the United States consume less vitamin D than government and health agencies recommend. Human beings manufacture vitamin D in their skin when skin is exposed to sunlight. However, people who spend little time outdoors, people who live in areas with long, dark winters, and dark-skinned people are at particular risk for vitamin D deficiency.

Scientists have long understood that vitamin D helps the body absorb calcium for bone-

building and that a deficiency of the vitamin can lead to such bone disorders as *rickets* (deformation of bones detected chiefly in young people) or *osteoporosis* (a disorder found chiefly in older people in which bones lose tissue and become fragile). In recent years, a wide range of studies have indicated other health benefits of vitamin D. According to the studies, vitamin D may help to prevent diabetes, heart disease, multiple sclerosis, complications in pregnancy, and several forms of cancer.

The ARS research demonstrated that mushrooms exposed to UVB become fortified with vitamin D. Without UVB exposure, an 85-gram (3-ounce) serving of mushrooms typically provides between 3 and 5 percent of an adult's daily recommended vitamin D intake; with exposure, the mushrooms are capable of providing more than 100 percent of the daily vitamin D requirement, depending upon the length of the exposure.

Controlling the amount of UVB exposure that the mushrooms receive is important not only for nutrient content, but also for aesthetic reasons. Mushrooms, especially white button mushrooms, tend to darken as they are exposed to UV light. Some studies have suggested that using quick pulses of UV light is effective at fortifying the mushrooms without spoiling their appearance ■ Jeanne Bernick

See also **ENERGY.**

UP ON THE FARM

A vertical farm flourishes along the lakefront of Chicago in an artist's rendering of a project proposed by Dickson Despommier, a public and environmental health scientist at Columbia University in New York City. Despommier was one of a number of scientists exploring ways in which cities could grow their own food year-round in controlled conditions that use fewer natural resources than conventional farms do.

Peppers

Chives

Lettuce

Cherries

Apples

Cabbage

Strawberries

Thyme

Tomatoes

Peas

Mint

Spinach

Peaches

Brussels sprouts

ANTHROPOLOGY

The discovery of the nearly complete fossilized *pelvis* (hipbones) of an adult female *Homo erectus* was reported in November 2008, providing anthropologists with new insights into the evolutionary factors that led to the development of the modern human pelvis. Biological anthropologist Scott W. Simpson of Case Western Reserve University School of Medicine in Cleveland led the team of researchers that dated and analyzed the pelvis. The fossil, found at a site called Gona in the Afar region of Ethiopia, was dated to between 1.4 million and 0.9 million years ago. Contrary to previous indications that *H. erectus* was probably a tall and slender species, the newly discovered pelvis belonged to a short, stocky woman who had a roomy birth canal.

Bipedal walking (walking upright on two feet) is a defining characteristic of *hominids* (human beings and human ancestors). However, scientists were not sure when crucial anatomical changes to the pelvis related to bipedal walking developed. Prior to the new discovery, scientists had uncovered only a few other fossil hominid pelves that were in nearly complete condition. One such pelvis belonged to a young adult male *H. erectus*. That pelvis indicated that the individual was tall, with a height of more than 1.8 meters (6 feet). In addition, the narrowness of the pelvis suggested that the individual had a slender build.

Based on this finding, many anthropologists assumed that the typical *H. erectus* female likely also had a relatively narrow pelvis, compared with females of modern human beings (*H. sapiens*). That assumption led, in turn, to the belief that *H. erectus* babies must have been born with unusually small, developmentally immature heads and brains.

In examining the female *H. erectus* pelvis found at Gona, Simpson's team estimated that the woman was short, standing only from 1.2 to 1.5 meters (3.9 to 4.8 feet) high. The wide, flaring *ilia* (outer blades) of her pelvis suggested that the *H. erectus* woman did not share the narrow body build of the previously found male specimen. Instead, the width and depth of her pelvic opening fell within the range of that of modern human females. Thus, she would not have had difficulty giving birth to a large-headed infant. This finding suggested to the anthropologists that the demands of giving

SEE ALSO THE SPECIAL REPORT, **FASCINATING FACTS FROM FOSSIL FECES,** PAGE 12.

birth to babies with increasingly large brains was the major factor driving the evolution of the human pelvis. The finding also proved that the male and female pelvis were structurally distinct by about 1.2 million years ago.

Among modern human beings, the brain of a newborn is typically a little more than 25 percent the average size of an adult brain (about 1,500 cubic centimeters). Using the known relationship between pelvic size and adult brain size—and estimating the average size of an adult *H. erectus* brain at 800 cubic centimeters—Simpson and his colleagues estimated that the brain of a newborn *H. erectus* was approximately 35 percent the size of an adult brain. Because chimpanzees are born with a brain that is about 40 percent its adult size, the researchers noted that the pattern of growth and development of *H. erectus* was intermediate between that of apes and modern human beings.

Oldest human footprints. Prehistoric footprints found at Ileret, Kenya, document the earliest preserved evidence of large-bodied hominids with feet similar to those of modern human beings, according to a study published in February 2009. The footprints were described by anthropologists Matthew R. Bennett of Bournemouth University in England; John W. K. Harris of Rutgers, the State University of New Jersey, in New Brunswick; and an international team of other experts. The team reported that the footprints, which were left by more than one individual on two separate occasions, were made approximately 1.5 million years ago— about half-a-million years after fully human legs and feet are believed to have developed.

Footprints can provide as much information about foot structure and walking behavior as can fossils of foot bones. Footprints preserve details about the length of the feet and toes, the presence or absence of an arch, and the length of the stride. Footprints can also reveal how the weight of the body was transferred from heel to toes during walking.

In contrast to human feet, the feet of apes are adapted for climbing trees and grasping

ANTHROPOLOGY continued

branches rather than for supporting the full weight of an upright body on the ground. An ape's foot has a small heel and long toes, with a big toe that diverges from the others. A modern human being's foot has a stout heel and short toes, with a big toe that is in line with the rest of the foot. Modern human feet also have two arches—one lengthwise and the other across the foot. These arches act as shock absorbers to help protect the ankle and knee from the concentrated weight of the body.

Previously described hominid footprints from Laetoli, Tanzania, which scientists dated to 3.75 million years ago, were made by australopithecines, small-bodied hominids whose feet were intermediate in structure between those of apes and humans. Bennett and Harris concluded that the footprints at Ileret were clearly made by larger hominids than australopithecines. They estimated that all but one of the individuals who made the Ileret prints were nearly 1.8 meters (6 feet) tall. This size pointed to either *H. ergaster* or *H. erectus* as the hominid responsible for the prints.

Examination of the footprints revealed that the hominids who made them walked with a gait similar—but not identical—to that of modern human beings. The feet had short toes, with the big toe almost in line with the other toes. In addition, the impressions left by the heels and balls of the feet revealed that weight transfer and the act of propelling the body for-ward by pushing with the big toe were virtually the same as in modern human beings. The anthropologists noted that the footprints preserved a record of modern-type feet from close to the time that pioneering hominids gave up living in trees and moved out onto the savanna.

Hobbits had big feet. The diminutive "hobbits"—3-foot- (91-centimeter-) tall human-like creatures whose fossil remains were discovered on the Indonesian island of Flores in 2004—may have indeed been a species distinct from modern human beings. That was the conclusion of a May 2009 report by a team of investigators led by paleoanthropologist William L. Jungers of Stony Brook University Medical Center in New York. The term "hobbit" refers to the short, hairy-footed characters in the series of novels titled *The Lord of the Rings*, by English author J. R. R. Tolkien.

Since the excavation of the remains of the "hobbit" humans, which lived on Flores as recently as 13,000 years ago, scientists had debated exactly where these creatures fit into the human family. Some researchers argued that the creatures, which were not only small in stature but also had brains only about one-third the size of modern human brains, were a previously unknown distinct species, named *H. floresiensis*. Other researchers disputed this designation, arguing that the bones were those

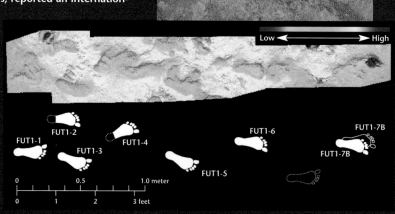

A STROLL 1.5 MILLION YEARS AGO

Footprints, 1.5 million years old, found at Ileret, Kenya, are the earliest preserved evidence of *hominids* (humans and human ancestors) who had feet and gaits similar to those of modern human beings, reported an international team of anthropologists in February 2009. The prints showed toe structure (top) like that in modern human feet. Scans of the prints made with lasers to clarify their outlines and depth (bottom) revealed that the early human who left the prints stepped and transferred weight from foot to foot much like a walking human being today.

of modern-type human beings who had certain diseases, including microcephaly, in which the brain and skull fail to develop normally.

Jungers and his colleagues conducted a detailed analysis of the fossilized foot bones of *H. floresiensis*. They determined that *H. floresiensis* had feet with a unique combination of ape-like and human-like characteristics. The big toe, for example, was in line with the other toes, as in human beings—but it was short and stubby, as in chimpanzees. The researchers also said that *H. floresiensis* had "flat" feet with no strong arch, similar to an ape. Furthermore, the feet of these creatures were more than 19 centimeters (7.5 inches) long—unusually long considering their short legs. The scientists said that the fossil feet suggested that *H. floresiensis* could walk upright, though it probably could not run.

Although many scientists had believed that *H. floresiensis* was a descendant of *H. erectus*, Jungers and his team concluded that *H. floresiensis* was likely descended from a more primitive hominid than *H. erectus*. That conclusion was also supported by an analyses of the shoulder and wrist bones of *H. floresiensis*. These creatures were, thus, a different species than any other known hominid, according to the researchers.

Despite the conclusions of Jungers's team, some other anthropologists continued to maintain that *H. floresiensis* was most likely a diseased modern-type human being. These scientists said that the brain of these creatures was far too small to be considered "normal." However, in additional research published in 2009, anthropologists Eleanor Weston and Adrian Lister of the National Museum of Natural History in London argued that the small brain and body size of *H. floresiensis* was the evolutionary result of living on a small island with limited resources. These scientists noted that fossils of extinct dwarf hippopotamuses that lived on the island of Madagascar showed that these animals also had small brains in relation to their body size—much like the "hobbits."

Cave life in a cold climate. The cave site at Zhoukoudian in northeastern China is famous for the fossils of *H. erectus* that have been discovered there. The age of the site, however, had been in dispute since its discovery in the late 1920's. In March 2009, anthropologist Guanjun Shen of Nanjing Normal University in China, geochemist Darryl E. Granger of Purdue University in West Lafayette, Indiana, and colleagues published revised dates for the earliest sedimentary layers of the cave in which *H. erectus* specimens have been found. Using a recently developed dating technique, they concluded that *H. erectus* began occupying the cave as early as 780,000 years ago—roughly 200,000 years earlier than previously believed.

The dating technique used by the researchers, called cosmogenic dating, is based on the fact that *cosmic rays* (radiation from space) cause chemical reactions in grains of quartz that are exposed on Earth's surface. In these reactions, chemicals in the quartz are altered to form radioactive *isotopes* of aluminum and beryllium. Isotopes are atoms of

ANTHROPOLOGY continued

the same element that differ in the number of *neutrons* (electrically neutral particles) they contain. The isotopes analyzed in the cosmogenic dating technique are known as aluminum 26 and beryllium 10.

These isotopes are created in a known ratio over time as long as surface grains of quartz are exposed to cosmic rays. If the quartz becomes buried—such as in sediment inside a cave—the formation of new isotopes stops, but any existing isotopes continue to decay. In cosmogenic dating, scientists determine the amounts of aluminum 26 and beryllium 10 in a sample of quartz, along with the ratio between them—thereby allowing them to calculate the length of time that has elapsed since the sample became buried. This calculation, in turn, reveals the age of human remains buried with the quartz in the sediment.

Many anthropologists believe that early human beings—that is, members of the genus *Homo*—began migrating out of Africa beginning about 1.75 million years ago. Fossils show that by 1.5 million years ago, groups of *H. erectus* were living in the relatively warm climate of Southeast Asia. Occupying northern China around this time, by contrast, would have presented greater challenges for *H. erectus* because this region was in the grip of a cold and dry climate period. Many anthropologists believe that *H. erectus* could not have survived in such conditions.

The new cosmogenic dates, however, indicated that *H. erectus* did survive in northern China when this region was still in the cold period almost 800,000 years ago. Shen and his team proposed that the spread of dry, open grassland during this period may have presented opportunities for bands of *H. erectus* to hone their skills as hunters of large mammals that roamed the grasslands. ■ Richard G. Milo
See also: **ARCHAEOLOGY**.

ARCHAEOLOGY

The boyhood home of George Washington, the first president of the United States, was discovered in northern Virginia by a team of archaeologists who reported their findings in July 2008. The leaders of the excavation project, Philip Levy of the University of South Florida in Tampa and David Muraca of the George Washington Foundation (the institution that owns the property), described the ruins of an eight-room house and numerous household artifacts dating to the early 1700's.

George's father, Augustine, built the house in 1738 just across the Rappahannock River from Fredericksburg, Virginia. The house, adjoining farm, and nearby area are sites where some of the best-known—and mythical—stories about young George are said to have taken place. Among them are the tales of his throwing a silver dollar across the river and chopping down a cherry tree (to which he supposedly admitted because he "could not tell a lie").

The archaeologists explained that the

SEE ALSO THE SPECIAL REPORT, FASCINATING FACTS FROM FOSSIL FECES, PAGE 12.

Washington farm was one of five farmsteads that occupied the property at various times. Historical records indicate that a house occupied the site earlier than the Washingtons' home. Later owners built a house in the 1850's that was torn down by Union soldiers during the American Civil War (1861-1865). The ruins of these structures complicated the archaeological record at the site, as did the ruins of other structures built at various times, including smokehouses, detached kitchens, slave quarters, other outbuildings, and several drainage ditches. Because of this complex underground archaeological record, two previous digs seeking to find the Washington home had been unsuccessful.

The archaeologists uncovered the remains

of two large chimney bases and the foundation of the Washington home. The ruins revealed that the home was 16 meters (53 feet) long and 11 meters (37 feet) wide—a rather large size for a house of that time and place. The house had five rooms on the ground floor and three rooms, thought to have been bedrooms, upstairs. The excavations also exposed the remains of slave quarters and a kitchen detached from the house.

The thousands of recovered artifacts revealed details of life inside the home. These artifacts included hundreds of fragments of dishes and glass stemware, as well as an ornate Wedgwood tea set. Among other findings were small figurines, wig curlers, bone toothbrush handles, nails, broken eggshells, and a pottery pipe with a Masonic insignia. The Masons, which Washington joined in 1753, are one of the largest fraternal organizations in the world.

The excavators also uncovered evidence of a fire that burned the home on Christmas Eve in 1740, which Washington later wrote about. Evidence of the fire included burned pottery and burned wall plaster in only one part of the house, indicating that the fire did not cause substantial damage.

When the Sahara was green. A scientific expedition involved in excavating dinosaur fossils in the southern Sahara led to the unexpected discovery of a cemetery and settlement occupied by prehistoric peoples, as described in an August 2008 report. The discovery of the site, announced by paleontologist Paul Sereno of the University of Chicago, also shed light on a period from about 12,000 to 4,500 years ago known as the "Green Sahara." During this period, the climate of the Sahara was unusually rainy, compared with its previous and present desert conditions.

Sereno had been conducting dinosaur fossil research in the Tenere Desert on the southern flank of the Sahara, in the northern African country of Niger. During field work in 2000, project photographer Mike Hettwer noticed three sand dunes where wind erosion had exposed the bones of hundreds of human burials. In addition, Sereno identified a number of animal remains at the site as those of crocodiles, hippopotamuses, turtles, fish, and clams. The bones and shells of these aquatic creatures reflected the wet Saharan climate that began 12,000 years ago.

At Sereno's invitation, archaeologist Elenea Garcea of the University of Cassino in Italy

OLDEST HUMAN REMAINS IN THE AMERICAS

An archaeologist in diving gear records observations of the oldest human remains ever discovered in the Americas, off the Caribbean coast of Mexico's Yucatán Peninsula. The woman's skeleton, reported in September 2008 by an archaeological team led by Arturo González of The Desert Museum in Saltillo, Mexico, was estimated to be 13,600 years old. The researchers said that the shape of this skeleton's skull and those of other skeletons found in nearby underwater caves suggested that these early Americans may have been related to people of South Asia. This observation came as a surprise to scientists, because most archaeologists believe that the earliest Americans migrated from North Asia.

ARCHAEOLOGY continued

began overseeing the archaeological field work at the site, known as Gobero, in 2005. Excavations yielded *potsherds* (pottery fragments) that the researchers linked to the Tenerian culture, people who engaged in hunting, fishing, and cattle herding during the late Green Sahara period, from 6,500 to 4,500 years ago. On other potsherds, Garcea recognized the wavy lines and zigzags distinctive of the Kiffian culture, a fishing-based society that lived earlier in the Green Sahara period, from 10,000 to 8,000 years ago.

The team excavated eight burials and recovered hundreds of artifacts related to both the Tenerian and Kiffian cultures. An ancient lake bed near the dunes yielded fishhooks and harpoons carved from animal bone and linked to the Kiffian people, who used the objects not only for fishing, but also for hunting crocodiles and hippos.

The cemetery consisted of two types of burials. In one type, called "bundle burials," the human remains were bound and placed into bags. In the other burial type, called "semi-flexed burials," the bodies were placed on their sides, with the knees slightly drawn up. Dating of teeth from the bodies, using radiocarbon dating, showed that the "bundle burials" were at least 9,000 years old, suggesting that they were from the Kiffian culture. The "semi-flexed burials" were about 6,000 years old, pointing to the Tenerian culture.

Evidence in some of the burials at Gobero indicated that elaborate rituals were performed when the dead were buried. This evidence included bodies wearing jewelry and bodies positioned in special poses (such as embraces), as well as bodies that had been burnt. The archaeologists noted that dozens of additional burials remained to be excavated at Gobero. However, as a result of political hostilities, the government of Niger in 2007 banned foreigners from the Tenere Desert. The team feared that the site might be looted or destroyed by desert winds before it could be studied again.

Chocolate in ancient Southwest. Trade between ancient cultures of the U.S. Southwest and Mesoamerica (Central America and southern Mexico) was more extensive than previously thought, according to a report published in February 2009. Archaeologist Patricia Crown of the University of New Mexico in Albuquerque and chemist W. Jeffrey Hurst of the Hershey Center for Health and Nutrition in Pennsylvania reached this conclusion after discovering the chemical residue of chocolate inside pottery vessels at the ancient site of Pueblo Bonito in New Mexico. Chocolate is made from the cacao beans of tropical and semitropical trees.

Cacao bean residue had previously been identified in ceramic jars at sites in Guatemala and Belize associated with the Maya culture, which reached its peak in Mesoamerica from about *A.D.* 250 to 900. The discovery at Pueblo Bonito marked the first time that cacao bean products were found in ancient sites north of Mexico.

Pueblo Bonito, where excavations have been conducted since 1896, is the largest *pueblo* in Chaco Canyon, an American Indian site in northwestern New Mexico. A pueblo is a Southwestern American Indian dwelling made of adobe and stone that resembles an apartment building. Pueblo Bonito consists of a multistoried arrangement of 800 rooms, which were occupied from *A.D.* 860 to 1128.

Beginning with the earliest digs at Pueblo Bonito, researchers noted tall, cylindrical,

EARLIEST WHALING EVIDENCE

In the earliest evidence of whaling ever found, an intricately carved walrus tusk shows scenes of people hunting whales from a boat, as well as pictures of a seal and bear. A team led by archaeologist Daniel Odess of the University of Alaska Museum of the North in Fairbanks reported the find, from Russia's Chukchi Peninsula and dated to about 3,000 years ago, in January 2009. In addition to this carved walrus tusk, the team also unearthed the remains of whale bones at the site.

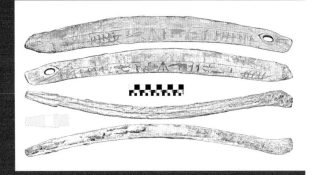

CHOCOLATE JARS IN CHACO CANYON

Clay jars, which are more than 800 years old, were used by Southwestern American Indian people for drinking a cocoa-like beverage, according to research reported in February 2009 by archaeologist Patricia Crown of the University of New Mexico in Albuquerque and chemist W. Jeffrey Hurst of the Hershey Center for Health and Nutrition in Pennsylvania. The discovery of chocolate residue in the jars—found at Chaco Canyon in northwestern New Mexico—provided the first proof of ancient chocolate use north of today's Mexican border and evidence that trade between native peoples of the Southwest and Mesoamerica was more extensive than previously believed.

ceramic jars, each about 22 centimeters (8.7 inches) high. The jars are painted with black geometric designs on a white background. A total of 166 of these jars were found at Pueblo Bonito, 111 of which were found in a single *cache* (hidden storage place) in one room. The distinctive form of these vessels led to much speculation among archaeologists regarding their function. Among proposed functions were holding important items for rituals, holding corn beer, and even serving as bodies of drums.

Crown wondered if the Pueblo Bonito jars might have had a function similar to that of cylindrical jars found at Maya sites in Mesoamerica. Archaeologists knew that the Maya used those jars for drinking a bitter chocolate drink made from cacao beans. Crown submitted potsherds from the Pueblo Bonito jars and a pitcher found with the jars to Hurst for chemical analysis. Using mass spectrometry and high-performance liquid chromatography, two methods for separating and analyzing atoms and molecules in chemical samples, Hurst identified a compound called theobromine in residue scraped from the potsherds. Theobromine is known to occur only in cacao.

Archaeologists had believed that ancient cultures of the U.S. Southwest engaged in only limited trade with the Mesoamerican cul-

tures. For example, the remains of macaws, mirrors made of iron pyrite ("fool's gold"), and bells made of copper—all originating in Mesoamerica—have been found at numerous sites in the Southwest. The discovery of cacao at Pueblo Bonito proved that trade in perishable items also took place between the cultures. Crown said that further research was needed to clarify if the chocolate drink was consumed only by an elite class at Pueblo Bonito—believed to have been the case in the Maya culture.

Shakespeare's theater uncovered. The destruction of a vacant garage to make room for a new theater led to the discovery of foundations believed to be from one of English playwright William Shakespeare's earliest theaters, reported a team of archaeologists in the United Kingdom in August 2008. The discovery, in the Shoreditch area of east London, was at a spot that historical records indicated was the site of "The Theatre," where Shakespeare's company of actors, known as "The Lord Chamberlain's Men," debuted the plays *The Merchant of Venice* and *Romeo and Juliet* in the early 1590's. The Theatre closed in about 1598, after which the more famous Globe Theatre, also linked to Shakespeare, was built on the south bank of the River Thames.

Archaeologists Jo Lyon and Taryn Nixon of the Museum of London reported that the foun-

ARCHAEOLOGY continued

dations of the building were found I.5 meters (5 feet) below the current street level. The foundations indicated that the theater was shaped like an *octagon* (a figure with eight sides and eight angles)—typical of theater architecture in the 1500's. The theater was built of bricks and timbers.

The archaeologists discovered numerous artifacts in the theater ruins. They said that one of the more interesting artifacts was a ceramic sherd painted in tan and red with the image of a human face with a beard, long hair, and ruff collar. These features were typical of many men when The Theatre was built in 1576.

Witch of the Middle East? In November 2008, archaeologist Leore Grosman of Hebrew University of Jerusalem reported the discovery of an unusual prehistoric burial of a woman inside a cave in northern Israel. The variety of items found with the skeletal remains suggested that the woman was a "witch" or *shaman* (a person considered to have healing abilities and other powers that come from direct contact with the supernatural). The burial and grave offerings were dated to 12,000 years ago, when the Natufian culture, one of the Middle East's earliest agricultural peoples, occupied the area.

The cliffside cave excavated by Grosman and her team, at a site called Hilazon Tachtit, yielded a series of burials of Natufian age. At least 29 individuals were identified in the burials. The "witch" burial—which was unique—contained the remains of an adult woman, about 45 years old, which had been placed in an oval pit. The walls of the pit had been plas-

ANCIENT NAZCA TROPHY HEADS

In the Nazca civilization, so-called "trophy heads" (below, right, and depicted on pottery below, left) may have been collected from fellow Nazca peoples rather than enemy warriors, as researchers had previously thought. Archaeologist Kelly Knudson of Arizona State University in Tempe presented this conclusion in a December 2008 report. Knudson determined that various chemical compounds related to food intake and residence location were identical in the previously unearthed trophy heads and in skeletal remains known to come from Nazca individuals. The Nazca were an ancient culture that flourished in the coastal lowlands of southern Peru from about 2,000 to 1,250 years ago.

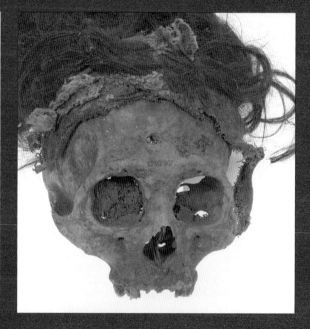

tered after the pit was chipped out of bedrock. A large stone slab covered the grave—possibly, according to the researchers, to contain the powerful spirit of the woman.

Found with the skeleton were dozens of animal remains, including bones of wild boars, leopards, and gazelles, as well as the shells of 50 Mediterranean tortoises laid around the woman's body. The archaeologists said that these items may have been representative of the woman's perceived ability to communicate with animal spirits—a power associated with shamans in many cultures. Other items found in the grave were a severed human foot, the tip of a golden eagle's wing, parts of an ox, and a pestle and mortar (possibly for grinding ingredients for potions).

The bones of the woman revealed that her *pelvis* (hipbones) and lower spine were deformed. These abnormal physical conditions may have caused her to limp and to have a bent-over posture. In many traditional cultures, people considered to be shamans have physical deformities marking them as "special." The researchers explained that the special status of the woman, who was the first person buried in the cave, made the cave a sacred place, where other villagers were later buried.

King Tut's father identified? A prominent archaeologist in Egypt announced in December 2008 that an inscription on a limestone block answered a question that historians had long asked—who was the father of King Tut, the famous *pharaoh* (king) of ancient Egypt? According to Zahi Hawass, the chief of Egypt's Supreme Council of Antiquities, the answer to that question is Akhenaten, a historically important figure who was one of Tut's predecessors as pharaoh.

King Tut, whose full name was Tutankhamun, was the young pharaoh of Egypt from about 1332 *B.C.* until his death at age 18 or 19 in about 1322 *B.C.* Although historians consider Tut's brief reign to be relatively unimportant, he became perhaps the most well-known pharaoh of Egypt after his tomb was discovered in 1922. The discovery revealed the well-preserved mummy of Tut, along with a vast collection of riches, including many gold-covered and beautifully crafted items.

Tut became pharaoh when he was only about 9 years old. He succeeded a minor king named Smenkhkare, who himself had succeeded Akhenaten. Many Egyptians considered Akhenaten to be a *heretic* (having religious beliefs different than the most accepted beliefs),

because he tried to make Egyptians stop worshipping their traditional gods and goddesses in favor of a single god, named Aten. King Tut, under the guidance of Ay, his minister of state, restored the Egyptians' traditional *polytheistic* (many gods) religion.

Scholars had long debated the identity of Tut's father. Some scholars believed that Akhenaten was his father, but others argued that Akhenaten was more likely his father-in-law or his brother. These other scholars said that a more probable candidate for Tut's father was Smenkhkare or Amenhotep III (the father of Akhenaten).

Hawass reported that he discovered the missing part of a limestone block in the storeroom of an archaeological site in the village of El Ashmunein. This village is 240 kilometers (150 miles) south of Cairo, Egypt's present capital city. The block was originally part of a temple at Akhetaten, the ancient capital city established by Akhenaten. The reassembled piece allowed Hawass to read the complete inscription on the block, which indicated that Tut lived with Akhenaten at Akhetaten.

The inscription also stated that Tut married Akhenaten's daughter—and his own sister or half sister—Ankhesenamun, a woman who was previously known to be his wife. (Marriage of brother and sister was common among Egyptian royalty.) According to Hawass, the text next to an engraved picture of Tut and Ankhesenamun identified Tut as "the king's [Akhenaten's] son of his body" and Ankhesenamun as "the king's daughter of his body." Hawass concluded that this inscription proved that Tut was the son of Akhenaten.

Despite Hawass's conclusion, some archaeologists and historians expressed doubts that the identity of Tut's father had been settled. Furthermore, the mystery of Tut's mother remained. The inscription did not indicate if Tut's mother was the famous Nefertiti, who was the primary wife of Akhenaten and the mother of Ankhesenamun, or Kiya, who was a minor wife of Akhenaten.

Archaeologists hoped that additional clues regarding the lineage of Tut and his family would be derived from an analysis of genetic material from two mummified fetuses that had been found in Tut's tomb. Researchers at the University of Zurich in Switzerland were conducting this analysis in 2009.

■ Thomas R. Hester

See also **ANTHROPOLOGY; FOSSIL STUDIES.**

ASTRONOMY

The first firm evidence that lakes on Titan, Saturn's largest moon, are filled with liquid was reported in July 2008 by a team of planetary scientists led by Robert Brown of the University of Arizona in Tucson. The liquid is made of the hydrocarbon ethane rather than water. (A hydrocarbon is a compound consisting of hydrogen and carbon.) Brown and his colleagues analyzed the lake's composition using instruments on NASA's Cassini spacecraft, in orbit around Saturn.

Titan is the second largest moon in our solar system—after Jupiter's Ganymede—and the only one with a dense atmosphere. Titan's atmosphere, like that of Earth, consists mostly of nitrogen. The great distance of Titan from the sun—about 9.5 times as great as the Earth-sun distance—means that conditions on Titan are too cold for water vapor or carbon dioxide to be substantial gases in the atmosphere. Methane, the simplest hydrocarbon, is the second most abundant atmospheric gas on Titan.

High in Titan's atmosphere, ultraviolet light from the sun breaks most of the methane into its components, carbon and hydrogen. Some of the hydrogen escapes into space, but scientists have long had evidence that much of the rest recombines with carbon to make other kinds of hydrocarbons, including ethane. Scientists also have data showing that, because of the great atmospheric pressure near Titan's surface, methane and ethane form into clouds and, occasionally, rain near the surface. Scientists speculated that sources of liquid methane, perhaps mixed with liquid ethane, might exist at or beneath Titan's surface.

Brown's team, with this information in mind, used Cassini to examine dark features in the high northern and southern latitudes of Titan that Cassini's radar and camera had previously identified as possible liquid-filled lakes. In the southern polar region, images taken by Cassini in 2005 had revealed a kidney-shaped dark feature, about 230 kilometers (143 miles) in length. Project researchers named the feature Ontario Lacus because of its resemblance to Lake Ontario on Earth. Because of Titan's thick, hazy atmosphere, however, scientists were unable to produce clear images of Ontario Lacus.

Brown's group peered through the haze

SEE ALSO

THE SPECIAL REPORT, **TELESCOPES: 400 YEARS OF STARGAZING,** PAGE 24.

THE SPECIAL REPORT, **THE SEARCH FOR WATER ON MARS,** PAGE 100.

by examining Ontario Lacus with Cassini's Visible and Infrared Mapping Spectrometer (VIMS). Like all spectrometers, the VIMS could analyze the chemical composition of a substance remotely by breaking the light reflected from the substance into its component wavelengths, seen as different colors along a band called the electromagnetic spectrum. In particular, the VIMS analyzed light wavelengths reflected from the surface of Ontario Lacus in the *infrared* (heat) portion of the spectrum. Because different chemical compounds reflect and absorb different wavelengths of infrared light, the wavelengths of light detected by the VIMS contained information about the makeup of the compounds in Ontario Lacus.

In a series of observations of Ontario Lacus using the VIMS instrument, Brown's team identified dips in light at wavelengths corresponding to ethane. The sharpness of the dips indicated that the ethane could be either liquid or solid. However, on the basis of temperatures that Cassini measured remotely in the south polar region, the team concluded that the ethane is in liquid form. The scientists noted that other hydrocarbons, including methane and nitrogen, were likely mixed with the ethane in Ontario Lacus. However, the wavelengths of these substances were more difficult to detect through Titan's atmosphere.

Methane on Mars. Three geographical regions on Mars are likely sources of large plumes of methane gas detected in the Martian atmosphere, according to a February 2009 report by a team led by astronomer Michael J. Mumma of NASA's Goddard Spaceflight Center in Greenbelt, Maryland. The team used Earth-based telescopes and infrared spectrometers to observe the spectral signature of methane in various parts of the atmosphere of Mars. It remained unclear, however, if the methane had a biological or a geochemical source.

The bulk of the thin Martian atmosphere is composed of carbon dioxide, with some nitrogen and trace amounts of oxygen and water vapor. Scientists expect that the ultraviolet rays of the sun would chemically break down any methane within hundreds of years. Even shorter destruction times are likely if methane comes into contact with the surface soils of Mars, which contain chemicals that react with mehane and other *organic molecules* (molecules containing carbon bonded to hydrogen).

Beginning in 2003, however, Earth-based telescope observations, as well as an instrument on the European Space Agency's (ESA's) Mars Express orbiter, detected tentative evidence for methane in the Martian atmosphere. The observations of Mumma and his colleagues, performed in 2003 and 2006, confirmed the presence of methane and tracked both its general location and changes over time. The astronomers used two large telescopes on Mauna Kea on the island of Hawaii—the W. M. Keck Observatory's Keck II Telescope and NASA's Space Infrared Telescope Facility.

The team's observations in 2003 revealed plumes of methane gas in the Martian atmosphere that were concentrated over three distinct regions. These regions were Terra Sabae, Nili Fossae, and the southeast quadrant of Syrtis Major. Terra Sabae lies just to the east of Arabia Terra, where the team detected enhanced amounts of water vapor. Nils Fossae is a site where the ESA's Mars Express and NASA's Mars Reconnaissance orbiter previously detected evidence of water chemically bound to rocks. Scientists believe that these rocks, called hydrated silicates, might indicate the presence of liquid water beneath the surface. Syrtis Major is the site of a large inactive volcano. Although the volcano has likely been inactive for millions of years, scientists believe that the site may retain some volcanic heat beneath the surface.

The team's observations in 2006 revealed a much lower amount of gaseous methane in these regions—about half that measured in 2003. This result led the scientists to conclude that the sources of methane are *intermittent* (occurring only from time to time). The rate of methane production in these sources was difficult to determine. However, the scientists speculated that the rate might be as high as seen in some of Earth's seep fields, places where tons of methane and other hydrocarbons leak out of cracks as liquids or gases.

On Earth, most methane is generated by biological processes. For example, many types of microbes generate methane in their *metabolic* (body function) processes. However, methane can be produced by nonbiological processes as well. When heat is available to

MOST DETAILED MOON MAP EVER

The most detailed map of the moon ever created (right) was released in February 2009 by an international research team. The map, based on data gathered by an altitude-measuring device on Japan's Selenological and Engineering Explorer (SELENE) moon-orbiting satellite, revealed previously unknown features on the moon's near and far sides. In the map, the lowest features are shown in blue and purple, and the highest features are shown in yellow and red.

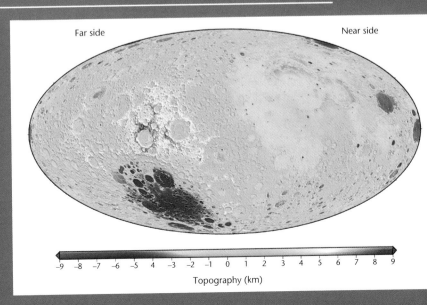

Far side   Near side

-9 -8 -7 -6 -5 4 -3 -2 -1 0 1 2 3 4 5 6 7 8 9
Topography (km)

ASTRONOMY continued

keep water in a liquid state, carbon dioxide may react chemically with the water in the presence of *basalt* (dark volcanic rock) to make methane.

Mumma's group noted that the locations of the methane sources on Mars—where a volcano exists and where water may be present in the ground—support the idea of nonbiological processes as sources of the methane. Nevertheless, the researchers noted that microorganisms might also be responsible for generating some of the methane on Mars—though there was no independent evidence for such life forms. They proposed that future spacecraft missions be designed to make the observations needed to pinpoint the methane sources.

Extrasolar planets discovered. A number of newly found extrasolar planets, planets circling stars other than our sun, were reported in 2008 and 2009. The discoveries were the latest of more than 300 extrasolar planets that astronomers had discovered. Most of these planets had been detected by observing the gravitational effects—in the form of slight wobbles—that they produced on their parent stars.

Some of the new discoveries, however, were accomplished by "direct imaging" of the infrared radiation emitted by the planets as they orbit their parent stars. This newer technique can be successful only if the planets have wide orbits around their stars.

In November 2008, a team of astronomers led by Paul Kalas of the University of California at Berkeley reported their use of direct imaging to discover a planet orbiting Fomalhaut, one of the 20 brightest stars in the sky. Infrared analysis suggested that the planet is located 119 astronomical units (AU's) from its star. (An astronomical unit is equivalent to the distance between Earth and the sun.) Also in November, a team led by astronomer Christian Marois of the Herzberg Institute of Astrophysics in Victoria, British Columbia, described their use of direct imaging to detect three planets orbiting a dim star known as HR 8799. These planets orbit their star at distances of 24, 38, and 68 AU's, respectively. The planets found by Kalas and Marois had estimated *masses* (amounts of matter) ranging from 5 to 13 times the mass of Jupiter.

GAMMA RAYS AND X RAYS FROM AN UNUSUAL STAR

Gamma rays flare into space (right, below) in an artist's drawing of an unusual star observed by NASA satellites in early 2009. Identified as a magnetar—an exploded star with one of the strongest magnetic fields in the universe—the star flares repeatedly, emitting both gamma rays and X rays. Halo-like X-ray "echoes" (right, above) were recorded around the exploding star for several days. The echoes appeared to expand because of the way X rays from the brightest flares scattered off *interstellar* (between stars) dust clouds. Astronomers at Pennsylvania State University in University Park theorized that the flares may arise when the magnetar's surface suddenly cracks, releasing energy stored in its powerful magnetic field. They classified the magnetar as a soft-gamma-ray repeater (SGR)—specifically SGR J1550-5418—only the sixth such star known.

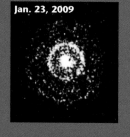
Jan. 23, 2009

Jan. 26, 2009

Jan. 28, 2009

Using the gravitational-effect method, a team led by astronomer Michel Mayor of the Geneva Observatory in Switzerland discovered the least massive extrasolar planet ever found, according to an April 2009 report. The planet, only about twice as massive as Earth, was the fourth planet detected around the faint star Gliese 581, located 20.5 light-years away. A light-year is the distance a pulse of light travels in one year, equal to about 9.46 trillion kilometers (5.88 trillion miles). The team made the discovery with the European Southern Observatory Telescope in La Silla, Chile.

In addition, the team refined the orbital location of a more massive, previously discovered planet around Gliese 581. The more accurate location placed that planet almost within the habitable zone, the region around a star in which liquid water—and, possibly, life—could exist.

Extrasolar atmosphere analyzed. An analysis of the atmospheric composition of an extrasolar planet orbiting the star HD 189733 was reported in December 2008 by a group of astronomers led by Mark Swain of the Jet Propulsion Laboratory in Pasadena, California. The team used the Near-Infrared Camera and Multi-Object Spectrometer of the Hubble Space Telescope to analyze the infrared radiation coming from the planet.

To obtain an accurate infrared spectrum for the planet, the astronomers compared the spectral emission from the star itself with the spectrum obtained when the planet was just starting to cross the edge of the star's disk. By subtracting the first spectra from the second, the chemical composition of the planet's atmosphere could be deduced. The scientists concluded that the planet's atmosphere contains water vapor, as well as carbon monoxide and carbon dioxide—the first carbon-bearing molecules ever detected in an extrasolar planet's atmosphere.

Although carbon is an essential ingredient for life, the finding did not provide any evidence of life on the extrasolar planet. The researchers planned to conduct further infrared analyses of extrasolar planetary atmospheres to seek the spectral signatures of *free* (chemically uncombined) oxygen. They noted that the presence of both carbon and free oxygen would indicate that a planet might harbor some form of life.

Milky Way mass. Scientists reported in January 2009 that the mass in the Milky Way—the galaxy in which we live—is about 1½ times as great as previously estimated. A group led by astronomer Mark Reid of the Harvard-Smithsonian Center for Astrophysics in Cambridge, Massachusetts, reached its conclusion after using a worldwide array of radio telescopes to measure the *velocity* (speed in a particular direction) of stars and gas clouds in the spiral arms of the Milky Way as they orbit the galaxy's center.

Because the orbital velocity of the material in the spiral arms depends on the mass of the material concentrated in the galaxy's center, the velocity measurements helped the scientists to estimate the total mass of the Milky Way. The calculations revealed that our galaxy is among the most massive known spiral galaxies in the universe—comparable to the great Andromeda Galaxy.

Supermassive black hole. In December 2008, two groups of astronomers reported greater measurements than previously estimated for the mass of the black hole that lies at the center of the Milky Way. A black hole is a region of space in which the gravitational force is so strong that nothing, not even light, can escape from it. Because of the high velocities of stars near the galaxy's center, researchers had previously suspected that a so-called supermassive black hole lurks there. The two groups of astronomers—one headed by Reinhard Genzel of the Max Planck Institute for Extraterrestrial Physics in Germany, and the other by Andrea Ghez of the University of California at Los Angeles—reanalyzed the velocities of 28 of these stars based on infrared telescope data gathered over a period of 16 years.

These analyses allowed Genzel and Ghez to independently deduce that the mass of the Milky Way's central black hole is equivalent to that of approximately 400 billion suns. The astronomers noted that this value is comparable to estimated masses of supermassive black holes at the centers of other spiral galaxies.

Most recent supernova. When very massive stars use up all their nuclear fuel, they explode as supernovae, which are among the most *luminous* (brightest) events observed in the galaxy. These explosions are believed to occur about once every 30 years inside the Milky Way. In June 2008, two groups of astrophysicists published their observations of a supernova that occurred approximately 140 years previously—making it the most recent supernova ever observed in the Milky Way. Before this discovery, the Milky Way's most recent supernova had been dated to 1680.

The scientists, of course, did not observe

ASTRONOMY continued

the explosion as it happened. Instead, they observed the remnants of the explosion—the expanding cosmic cloud of gas left behind by the blast. The date of the explosion itself was determined by observing the expansion rate of this gas cloud and estimating when, at the given rate, the expansion would have begun.

Supernovae emit radiation in many wavelengths of the electromagnetic spectrum. The astrophysicists measured the expansion of the gas in wavelengths of radio and X-ray energy. David A. Green and his colleagues at the University of Cambridge in England used Earth-based radio telescopes to conduct observations of the supernova remnant from 1985 through 2007. Stephen P. Reynolds of North Carolina State University in Raleigh and his colleagues used NASA's Earth-orbiting Chandra X-Ray Observatory to conduct observations of the supernova remnant. Both analyses indicated that the supernova's gas cloud, growing at a rate of 24,000 kilometers (15,000 miles) per second, began expanding in about 1868—that is, as seen from Earth.

This supernova is located approximately 26,000 light-years away. Thus, because of the time it took the supernova's light to reach Earth, the supernova blast actually occurred 26,000 years ago.

Galactic mergers. Astronomers believe that the largest galaxies grew by merging with other galaxies in the first few billion years after the big bang, the cosmic explosion that most scientists believe started the expansion of the universe 14 billion years ago. Evidence of such galactic mergers was described in 2008 and 2009 in the form of observations of distant binary black holes, two black holes (each in the center of a galaxy) that are approaching each other as their home galaxies get closer and closer. Black holes can be detected by the various forms of electromagnetic radiation emitted by material falling onto them.

In March 2009, astronomers Todd Boroson and Tod Lauer, both of the National Optical Astronomy Observatory in Tucson, Arizona, described their telescope observations of what initially appeared to be a distant galaxy, some 5 billion light-years away, with two black holes near its center. The scientists determined that the black holes were separated by a short—in galactic terms—distance of 20,000 AU's, suggesting two galaxies in the process of merging.

A new, improved method of detecting binary black holes and measuring the merger rates of their spiral galaxies was reported in June 2008 by a team of astronomers headed by Julia Comerford of the University of California at Berkeley. The team evaluated electromagnetic spectral data previously compiled in

EXTRASOLAR PLANETARY SYSTEMS

In one of the first images of planets orbiting a star other than the sun, three extrasolar planets (labeled b, c, and d) circle a relatively nearby, sun-like star known as HR 8799 (central object). The image was published in November 2008 by a team of astronomers led by Christian Marois of the Herzberg Institute of Astrophysics in British Columbia. The team created the picture using the W. M. Keck Observatory in Hawaii to detect the *infrared* (heat) radiation emitted by the planets. The astronomers estimated that each planet has several times the *mass* (amount of matter) of Jupiter, the largest planet in the solar system.

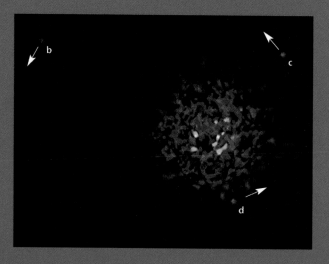

a large astronomical survey of galaxies as distant as 8 billion light-years. They identified 37 galaxies that each had two spectral emissions moving in opposite directions and at different velocities. These findings suggested the presence of binary black holes in merging galaxies. Further analyses of these data led Comerford and her colleagues to conclude that, from 7 billion to 4 billion years ago, spiral galaxies underwent approximately three mergers during every 1 billion years.

Ancient interstellar chemistry. Polycyclic aromatic hydrocarbons (PAH's)—molecules thought to have been vital to the formation of life—were present in galaxies when the universe was only about 1.8 billion years old. That conclusion, based on infrared analyses of very distant galaxies, was reported in April 2009 by a team of astronomers led by Harry I. Teplitz of the Spitzer Science Center at the California Institute of Technology in Pasadena, California.

Soon after the big bang, only light elements—primarily hydrogen and helium—were present in the cosmos, and the only molecule that could form was molecular hydrogen (two attached atoms of hydrogen). Heavier elements, such as carbon, could not form until nuclear reactions began in stars—when the universe was somewhat less than 1 billion years old. After the first stars died, the heavy elements and complex molecules they produced were released into *interstellar* (between stars) space, where they were available for new star formation.

Polycyclic aromatic hydrocarbons are complex organic molecules consisting of *hexagonal* (six-sided) rings of carbon atoms, with hydrogen atoms attached around the edges. These molecules are present on Earth today—for example, in petroleum. Biologists believe that PAH's played an important role in the formation of the first living cells. Astronomers using infrared spectrometers had previously detected PAH's in relatively nearby space. However, scientists did not know if PAH's also existed in the very distant—and, thus, very early—universe.

Teplitz's team used the infrared spectrometer on NASA's Spitzer Space Telescope to search for the spectral signatures of PAH's in very distant galaxies. Because of the time it takes light to travel through space, the scientists were looking back in time. By detecting PAH's in these galaxies, approximately 12 billion light-years away, the investigators found that organic molecules existed less than 2 billion years after the beginning of the universe. Moreover, they noted that additional observations of even more distant galaxies might be able to push the presence of these important hydrocarbons further back in time.

■ Jonathan I. Lunine and Theodore P. Snow

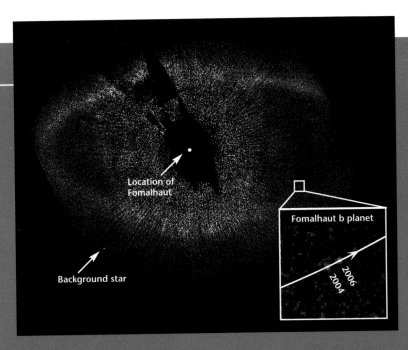

A newly discovered planet circling the bright star Fomalhaut appears in two positions along its orbit—one in 2004 and the other in 2006 (inset)—in a composite image created from photographs taken by a camera on the Hubble Space Telescope. The discovery of the planet, named Fomalhaut b, was reported in November 2008 by a team of astronomers led by Paul Kalas of the University of California at Berkeley. Also seen in the larger image is a ring of dusty debris encircling Fomalhaut and a dim star in the background.

The Milky Way: Bigger, Faster, and More Bizarre

The first detailed map of the density of stars and gas in the Milky Way's spiral arms (above) shows denser regions in darker shades of red. The map, reported in January 2009 by an international team led by astrophysicist Martin Puhl of Iowa State University in Ames, was based on an infrared survey of the sky by the Cosmic Background Explorer satellite. The map revealed that two prominent arms extend from the galaxy's core (bluish region) to its outer reaches, where they branch into four arms. The map also helped clarify how the shape and movement of the spiral arms are influenced by the gravity of the galaxy's central bulge.

The central region of the Milky Way—the spiral galaxy in which we live—was the focus of much astronomical research in late 2008 and early 2009. Most of the research was conducted with *infrared-* (heat-) sensing instruments on ground- or space-based telescopes. Some of the research was conducted with radio telescopes. Astronomers concluded that the Milky Way has more *mass* (amount of matter), and its stars move faster around the galactic center, than previously thought. Astronomers also learned more about the supermassive black hole believed to exist at the galaxy's core.

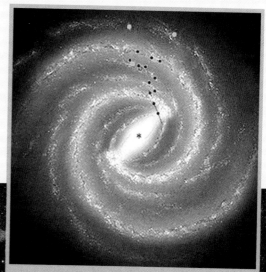

The material in the spiral arms of the Milky Way is moving much faster around the galactic center (red star, center) than previously believed, according to radio telescope measurements reported in January 2009 by Mark Reid of the Harvard-Smithsonian Center for Astrophysics in Cambridge, Massachusetts. Colored dots in an artist's rendering of the Milky Way, shown as it would appear from above, mark positions used by astronomers to track and measure the movement of stars and gas clouds in the arms. Because the *velocity* (rate of motion in a certain direction) of the material in the arms depends on the mass at the center, the finding suggested that the galaxy is much more massive than some astronomers had presumed.

An arrow points to Sgr A* (Sagittarius A*) (right), which is probably a supermassive black hole at the galaxy's core, in an image of radio waves emitted by sources in the central section of the Milky Way. Red represents the strongest sources. Astronomers believe that a black hole is a region of space in which the gravitational force is so strong that nothing, not even light, can escape from it.

Sgr A*

A near-infrared image of the central region of the Milky Way shows numerous stars, as imaged by the European Southern Observatory's Very Large Telescope array in Chile. In December 2008, a team of astronomers led by Reinhard Genzel of the Max Planck Institute in Germany reported that an analysis of the velocity of stars in this region indicated that the mass of the central black hole—Sagittarius A*—is equivalent to that of about 400 billion suns. This mass, similar to that of supermassive black holes in other galaxies, exerts strong gravitational effects on star movement.

The sharpest-ever image of the center of the Milky Way reveals large numbers of massive stars and details of complex structures within glowing clouds of hot, *ionized* (electrically charged) gas. The image, released in January 2009, was created by NASA scientists by combining infrared images taken by cameras on the Hubble and Spitzer space telescopes. The newly seen details of these stars and gas clouds provided astronomers with information regarding how massive stars form from condensing clouds of gas at the galactic center. The image also clarified how stars' gravity, radiation, and *stellar winds* (streams of charged particles ejected by stars) shape the structures of gas clouds at the Milky Way's core.

ATMOSPHERIC SCIENCE

In late January and early February 2009, the southeastern Australian state of Victoria suffered its worst-ever outbreak of wildfires. The fires, which included a combination of accidental and intentional ignitings, quickly spread through countryside parched by years of drought and several summer months of record-high temperatures.

During the weekend of February 6–8, brisk northerly winds fanned several small fires into four-story-high walls of flame that swept through the countryside 80 to 100 kilometers (50 to 62 miles) north of Melbourne, the capital of Victoria and Australia's second-largest city. State and local fire protection services estimated that more than 3,100 square kilometers (1,200 square miles) burned, destroying whole towns and killing more than 170 people. Officials described the fires as "hell on earth" and Australia's deadliest natural disaster.

Severe drought conditions had been present in southeastern Australia since 2000, reducing vegetation to bone-dry tinder. Much of the region's vegetation contains volatile resins and other flammable materials. In the wet-dry cycles of southeastern Australia's climate, periodic wildfires do occur. Older Australians recall the infamous Black Friday fires of January 1939 in Victoria, which burned 15,000 square kilometers (5,800 square miles) and took 71 lives.

Meteorologists attributed the ferocity of the February 2009 wildfires to a convergence of drought, extremely low humidity, strong winds, and record heat. On January 27, a record-setting heat wave began throughout southeast Australia.

The first sign that an exceptional heat wave was building appeared in late January on the island state of Tasmania, situated just off the southeastern tip of the Australian continent. Searing heat on January 29 and 30 toppled that state's previous record high temperature, driving the thermometer to 42.2 °C (108 °F) at Scamander, on the island's east coast, on the 30th. Meteorologists reported that the January heat wave was responsible for seven of the eight highest temperatures ever recorded in Tasmania.

Then on February 6 and 7, the heat wave intensified in Victoria. The state shat-

SEE ALSO THE SPECIAL REPORT, **METHANE: ANOTHER GREENHOUSE TROUBLEMAKER,** PAGE 42.

tered its previous record—which had stood for 70 years—on February 7, when a high temperature of 48.8 °C (120 °F) was recorded at Hopetoun. That same day, 14 other weather stations in Victoria exceeded the previous state record of 47.2 °C (117 °F). The temperature in Melbourne, a city of 3.9 million, soared to a new record high of 46.4 °C (115.5 °F).

Some news media pundits attributed the record-shattering heat and intense wildfires to global warming. Scientists, however, cautioned against jumping to such conclusions. Penny Whetton, leader of the climate

NORTH ATLANTIC TROPICAL STORMS AND HURRICANES OF 2008

The 2008 Atlantic hurricane season was unusually active. According to the National Hurricane Center, it was the tenth season since the mid-1990's to produce above-normal activity. The 2008 season ranked near the top in terms of numbers of named storms (16), hurricanes (8), and major hurricanes (5). (A hurricane is a tropical storm that attains wind speeds of greater than 119 kilometers per hour [74 miles per hour]). Meteorologists with the National Hurricane Center identified several causes for the above-average tropical storm and hurricane activity. Lingering effects of a La Niña—a distinctive recurring pattern of ocean currents and winds in the Pacific—reduced wind shear. In wind shear, strong winds aloft interfere with vertical hurricane-building activity, keeping storms from strengthening or even tearing them apart. The meteorologists also said that warmer-than-average temperatures in Atlantic waters favored the development of tropical storms and hurricanes.

change research group at Australia's Commonwealth Scientific and Industrial Research Organization (CSIRO), noted that it is "difficult to relate climate change to an individual weather event." However, Whetton and other climate scientists acknowledged that a decade-long trend toward warmer and drier conditions in Australia was increasing the probability of destructive wildfires.

A study conducted in 2008 by CSIRO scientists indicated that southern Australia has warmed by 0.9 Celsius degrees (1.6 Fahrenheit degrees) since 1950 and that the region receives 15 percent less rainfall today than it did then. Many scientists believe that significant shifts in Indian Ocean currents, possibly triggered by global warming, are responsible for Australia's hotter, drier weather.

Arctic meltdown. Several studies released in early 2009 indicated rapid continual shrinkage of the Arctic icecap, suggesting that the sea ice may disappear entirely during summers much sooner than expected. Ice forms on broad sections of the Arctic Ocean during the sunless polar winter. Historically, some of the ice formed each year survives one or more Arctic summers, growing thicker each winter. Thus, the Arctic icecap consists of both thinner first-year ice and thicker perennial ice. (*Perennial* means lasting longer than a single year.)

In terms of global climate, the Arctic has been described as Earth's refrigerating system. The ice naturally cools overlying atmosphere and underlying seawater. It also plays a role in ocean circulation. Most importantly, the Arctic icecap functions like a giant mirror, reflecting sunlight back into space during the long Arctic summer when the sun does not set. Open seawater, by contrast, absorbs energy in sunlight. Thus, the melting of Arctic ice sets up a positive feedback loop, in which melting causes heat absorption that then triggers more melting.

In early 2009, a team of three British explorers armed with scientific and communications equipment set out from the Canadian Arctic to walk 1,000 kilometers (620 miles)

Letter	Type	Name	Date
A	T	Arthur	May 31–June 1
B	MH	Bertha	July 3–20
C	T	Cristobal	July 19–23
D	H	Dolly	Jul 20–25
E	T	Edouard	August 3–6
F	T	Fay	August 15–26
G	MH	Gustav	August 25–September 4
H	H	Hanna	August 28–September 7
I	MH	Ike	September 1–14
J	T	Josephine	September 2–6
K	H	Kyle	September 25–29
L	T	Laura	September 29–October 1
M	T	Marco	October 6–7
N	T	Nana	October 13–14
O	MH	Omar	October 13–18
P	MH	Paloma	November 5–9

Abbreviation	Storm type
T	tropical storm
H	hurricane
MH	major hurricane

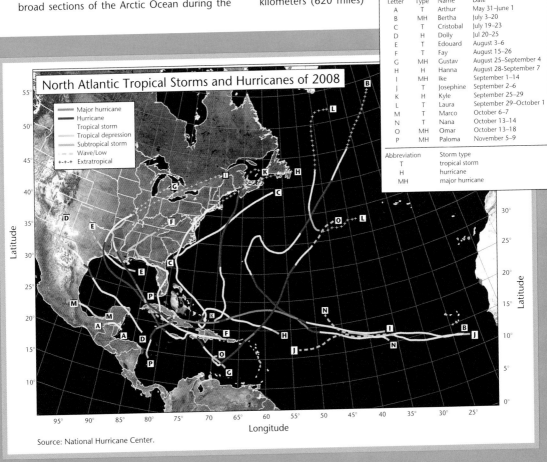

North Atlantic Tropical Storms and Hurricanes of 2008

Major hurricane
Hurricane
Tropical storm
Tropical depression
Subtropical storm
Wave/Low
Extratropical

Source: National Hurricane Center.

ATMOSPHERIC SCIENCE continued

to the North Pole. The exploration, called the Catlin Arctic Survey, was part of an international collaboration to determine the condition of the Arctic icecap and predict its future. Polar explorer Pen Hadow led the expedition.

As they proceeded, the Hadow team used drills and other instruments to take measurements of the Arctic ice. Most drillings detected ice no thicker than about 1.8 meters (6 feet), indicating that it was annual ice. Such ice is likely to melt in the subsequent summer months.

The Hadow team members had expected far more perennial ice of a thickness of 3.5 meters (11.5 feet) or greater. "To discover that there's virtually no multiyear ice in this part of the [Arctic] is a real surprise to me," said Hadow in a satellite uplink.

The data collected by the Hadow team confirmed observations from satellites that the Arctic icecap is thinner than ever and thus more vulnerable to summer melting. Data from the Ice, Cloud, and Land Elevation Satellite (ICESat), launched by the National Aeronautics and Space Administration (NASA) in 2003, indicated that during the 2008–2009 winter season, the Arctic Basin had the fifth lowest maximum ice extent on record. Since satellite monitoring of the icecap began in 1979, the six lowest maximum winter ice measurements across the Arctic Basin have all occurred in the years 2004 to 2009. Satellite data in 2009 also indicated that thicker, perennial ice comprised just 10 percent of wintertime ice cover in the Arctic Basin, down from 30 to 40 percent in the 1980's and 1990's.

CHEMICAL EQUATOR

A "chemical equator" over the western Pacific Ocean that divides the polluted air of the Northern Hemisphere from the much cleaner air of the Southern Hemisphere was discovered in 2008 by scientists led by chemist Jacqueline Hamilton of York University in the United Kingdom. The atmosphere north of a 50-kilometer- (30-mile-) wide belt contains four times as much carbon monoxide as the atmosphere south of it. Extensive forest fires north of the boundary contributed to the difference in pollution levels, the scientists said.

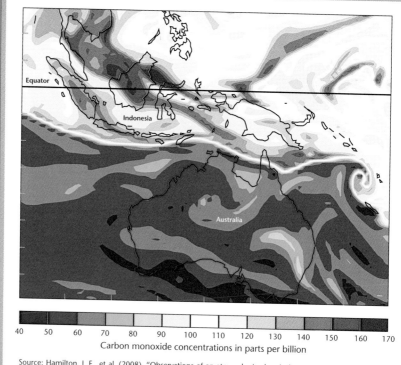

Carbon monoxide concentrations in parts per billion

Source: Hamilton, J. F., et al. (2008), "Observations of an atmospheric chemical equator and its implications for the tropical warm pool region," *J. Geophys. Res.*, 113, D20313, doi:10.1029/2008JD009940.

The maximum sea ice extent for the 2008–2009 winter, observed on Feb. 28, 2009, was 15.2 million square kilometers (5.9 million square miles). The area of coverage fell short of the average extent for the years 1979 to 2000—by an area about the size of Texas.

In April 2009, Walter Meier, an atmosphere scientist with the National Snow and Ice Data Center at the University of Colorado, Boulder, stated that an ice-free summer as early as 2013 to 2014 is "not totally out of the realm of possibility," adding that almost no one would have foreseen such a possibility five years earlier. Referring to the observed decreases in sea ice extent and thickness, Meier declared that "there is no other mechanism than climate warming that could cause the sea ice changes we're seeing." As recently as 2007, the Intergovernmental Panel on Climate Change (IPCC), a United Nations group that monitors Earth's climate, had predicted ice-free summers in the Arctic around the year 2100.

Other scientists agree with the outcome—an ice-free summer Arctic—but allow a few more years for it to happen. Climate scientist Muyin Wang of the Joint Institute for the Study of the Atmosphere and Ocean and oceanographer James Overland of the Pacific Marine Environmental Laboratory, both in Seattle, projected an Arctic free of summer ice within 30 years. The researchers published their findings in the April 3, 2009, issue of *Geophysical Research Letters*.

Wang and Overland analyzed sea-ice projections from six computer models and combined these data with satellite observations of loss of summer sea ice in 2007 and 2008. The researchers concluded that once summer ice drops below a critical tipping point of 4.6 million square kilometers (just under 1.8 million square miles), the melting of the Arctic sea ice will accelerate. They noted that ice coverage in the summer of 2007 was 4.3 million square kilometers (about 1.7 million square miles) and 4.7 million square kilometers (just over 1.8 million square miles) in the summer of 2008.

"Quiet" sun. In the first quarter of 2009, astronomers recorded the lowest frequency of sunspots detected for nearly a century. These observations followed an unusually low level of sunspot activity in 2008, convincing many astronomers that Earth was in the midst of a deep solar minimum (period of relatively little solar activity), perhaps comparable to some notable solar minimums in history.

A sunspot is a dark area on the surface of the sun. Sunspots appear dark because they are relatively cooler than the rest of the sun's visible surface. Sunspots are associated with intense solar activity, including flares and ejections of charged, energetic particles.

These flows of charged particles cause disturbances in Earth's magnetic field that are capable of disrupting radio communications and power grids. Because of these earthly disruptions, a sun with many sunspots is referred to as a "noisy" sun; a sun with few sunspots is a "quiet" sun.

The number of sunspots and the solar latitudes at which they appear vary over a period of about 11 years. This period is called the sunspot cycle. The last strong period occurred from January 1998 to February 2004. At the height of this active period, hundreds of sunspots were visible.

Solar activity entered into an unusually quiet period in 2006. It picked up briefly in 2008 but then eased off again late that year. By the spring of 2009, the sun had fewer sunspots and weaker magnetic fields than at any time since 1913. During the first three months of 2009, astronomers detected sunspots on only 13 percent of the days.

The solar minimum has produced many effects on Earth, most of which we would consider beneficial. For example, global positioning system are able to specify locations more accurately. Also, the orbits of satellites are more stable because Earth's atmospheric envelope has contracted by about 200 kilometers (125 miles). This effect results from a reduction of short-wave radiation from the sun. Such radiation heats and, therefore, expands Earth's atmosphere. The reduced atmospheric heating is also reflected in a decrease of 0.11 to 0.16 Celsius degrees (0.2 to 0.3 Fahrenheit degrees) in the annual average global temperature, slightly offsetting the general planetary trend of global warming.

Thomas Bogdan, director of the National Oceanic and Atmospheric Administration's Space Weather Prediction Center in Boulder, Colorado, said solar activity could start "anytime now." Other scientists, however, have begun to think that current solar conditions may be a replay of the 1913 minimum or even the deeper solar quiet of the Dalton Minimum, which ran from 1790 to 1830. Scientists note that the longest solar quiet period of all—the Maunder Minimum—ran for 70 years, from 1645 to 1715. ■ John T. Snow

BIOLOGY

Chimpanzees are an estimated four to eight times as strong as human beings, even though chimps and people are of similar size and genetic makeup. In April 2009, evolutionary biologist Alan Walker of Pennsylvania State University in University Park proposed that the difference in strength stems not only from the ape's more powerful muscles, but also from the role of the nervous system in controlling muscle movement. Walker described how the nervous system of a human being is capable of exerting much finer control over the body's muscles, compared with that of chimps. This fine control allows people to perform such delicate tasks as threading the eye of a needle—something that a chimp cannot do.

Besides conducting his own observations of chimp behavior, Walker said he also based his ideas on studies by primatologist Ann MacLarnon of Roehampton University in London. She found that, relative to body mass, the human spinal cord has much more gray matter than does the chimp spinal cord. Gray matter contains large numbers of *motor neurons* (nerve cells that connect to muscle fibers and regulate muscle movement). According to MacLarnon, human beings have so many motor neurons that each neuron can be devoted to controlling only a few muscle fibers, allowing for precise movements.

By contrast, the relatively few motor neurons in a chimp's gray matter mean that each neuron must trigger a large number of muscle fibers. Thus, muscle movement tends to be all

SEE ALSO

THE SPECIAL REPORT, **MUTUALISM: THE PLEASURE OF YOUR COMPANY,** PAGE 58.

THE SPECIAL REPORT, **INVASION OF THE JELLYFISH,** PAGE 72.

CONSUMER SCIENCE, **BAMBOO— THE NEW "WOOD"?** PAGE 133.

or nothing for the chimpanzee, typically resulting in sudden, massive explosions of power. Nevertheless, some biologists noted that these apes are capable of performing movements that are suited to living in their natural environment. For example, chimps can use twigs to extract termites out of nest holes for food.

Chimp brain power. Observations of a clever chimpanzee in a zoo, reported in March 2009, provided compelling evidence that chimps have the brain power and foresight to plan ahead for future needs. Mathias Osvath, a postdoctoral student in *cognitive science* (the study of perception and awareness) at Lund University in Sweden, described how a male chimpanzee at the Furuvik Zoo near Stockholm planned ahead for rock-throwing attacks on zoo visitors.

Before tossing rocks at human visitors, the aggressive chimp, named Santino, first attract-

MAGNETIC COWS

Cows line up while grazing in a field in Scotland. A team of biologists concluded in August 2008 that cattle, sheep, and other grazing mammals often face in the same direction while feeding because they can probably sense and orient themselves to Earth's magnetic field. The scientists, led by Sabine Begall of the University of Duisburg-Essen in Germany, examined thousands of satellite photographs of herds of grazing mammals. They contended that wind direction, sun location, and other factors could not account for their observations.

ed their attention by engaging in such rowdy antics as yelling and running around dragging branches. When the visitors—who were safely behind a fence—approached, the ape started throwing rocks at them. His rock supply was plentiful and within easy reach, because he gathered the rocks together every morning before the zoo opened to the public. His rock-gathering methods included prying concrete chunks off of exhibit walls and scooping rocks out of the exhibit's moat.

Osvath described how Santino's activities became more sophisticated each year. The ape even discovered how to use his hands to sculpt plate-sized disks out of the concrete chunks he tore from the exhibit. Osvath said that Santino's activities—like many activities of people—were based on perceived future needs, rather than on any immediate needs.

Mammal magnetism. Scientists have long known that many birds and fish use Earth's magnetic field to help them navigate during migration and other travels. Scientists believe that these animals have highly special-ized organs to sense magnetism. Although some mammals, such as bats and mole rats, are known to have such natural magnetic compass-es, this ability had been thought to be rare in mammals. However, researchers reported in August 2008 that sheep, cattle, and other graz-ing mammals can also apparently sense and ori-ent themselves to Earth's magnetic field.

A team of biologists led by Sabine Begall of the University of Duisburg-Essen in Germany investigated why livestock and other grazing animals tend to face in the same direction while feeding. Many observers had assumed that the animals aligned themselves to the wind or sun. After examining more than 8,000 satellite pho-tographs of herds of domestic cattle and wild deer in many parts of the world, the scientists discovered that the animals generally faced either the north or south magnetic pole—regardless of the direction of the wind or the location of the sun in the sky.

The scientists said these findings suggested that a magnetic sense might be more common among animals than pre-viously thought. However, the exact biological pro-cesses responsible for this sense remained a mystery.

INSECT RESEARCH ASSISTANT

A bee equipped with a tiny radio tracking tag alights on a flower. Zoologist Martin Wikelski at the Max Planck Institute of Ornithology in Seewiesen, Germany, used such tags in 2008 to study bee flight. Information from such studies was expected to help scientists understand the origin and nature of colony collapse disorder, a mysterious disease that has caused the deaths of millions of honey bees. The tag weighed a mere 170 milligrams (0.006 ounce)—one-third of the bee's body weight—and was attached with eyelash glue and superglue.

Killer toads and toad killers. More than half the freshwater crocodiles in some rivers in Australia's Northern Territory have died from eating poisonous cane toads (Bufo marinus), according to a study released in November 2008 by biologist Keith Christian of Charles Darwin University in Australia. The crocodiles were the latest native Australian ani-mal to suffer from eating the cane toad, which has potent poison-filled glands in its skin. Other Australian animals that had previously experienced population declines caused by consuming this toxic toad included several snakes, lizards, and mammals.

People had introduced about 100 cane toads, which are native to the American trop-ics, to northeastern Australia in the 1930's to help control beetles that were ravaging sugar cane fields. The toad became a pest as it repro-duced in vast numbers, spread westward into wetlands, outcompeted native amphibians for food, and caused the deaths of many preda-tors. By 2008, the cane toad population in Australia had increased to some 200 million.

None of the control measures tried by the Australian government were successful in stop-ping the toads. However, according to a study reported in March 2009, natural biological controls may be developing against the toad.

BIOLOGY continued

Ecologist Rick Shine and his colleagues at the University of Sydney in Australia disclosed that a species of ant called the meat ant was preying on the cane toads. Shine explained that although lighter, more nimble native frogs and toads can easily escape meat ant attacks, the larger cane toad, which can weigh more than 2.3 kilograms (5 pounds), cannot.

Shine also found that cane toads in Australia appeared to be rapidly evolving to have longer legs, thereby increasing the length of their hops and increasing their chances of escape. Shine said that this evolutionary change might be driven by ecological pressures from the meat ants.

More evolution in action. A similar example of evolution in action was reported in January 2009 by biologist Tracy Langkilde of Pennsylvania State University in University Park. Langkilde described how recent generations of fence lizards that have been increasingly exposed to attacks by biting and stinging fire ants seem to be evolving longer legs and more skittish behavior. These adaptations are suited to quickly escaping from the fire ants.

Fire ants, which are native to South America, were accidentally introduced into the southeastern United States around 1940. The ants bite fiercely, and their painful stings contain venom that can quickly paralyze and kill fence lizards and other small animals. When Langkilde studied lizards in four distinct populations at four different sites, he found that extended limbs and skittish behaviors were more common at those sites where the lizards and ants had lived together longer.

Langkilde concluded that lizards that were better at escaping fire ants—because they had longer legs and were more excitable—had a better chance of surviving and passing on their genes for these traits to succeeding generations. In this way, the characteristics of the lizard population gradually changed over the generations.

Key to life's origins. New clues to the mystery of the origin of life on Earth were reported in May 2009 by a team of chemists led by John D. Sutherland of the University of Manchester in England. The team proposed a plausible way that the building blocks of ribonucleic acid (RNA) could have assembled themselves almost 4 billion years ago.

RNA is a complex molecule that helps produce proteins in organisms. It is made of building blocks called nucleotides, each consisting of a phosphate compound, a ribose sugar, and a nitrogen-containing base. Many biologists believe that the earliest organisms carried their inheritable biological information in RNA—unlike organisms today, which carry genetic information in the somewhat more complex deoxyribonucleic acid (DNA). However, scientists have long debated how the first RNA nucleotides could have self-assembled.

Sutherland's team created RNA nucleotides in the laboratory in a series of steps involving the heating and evaporation of water mixed with relatively simple molecules thought to be present on the early Earth, including phosphates and half-sugar/half-base molecules. The scientists also exposed the mixture to ultraviolet light, as in sunlight. These experiments resulted in the self-assembly of two of the four types of nucleotides that make up RNA.

PENGUIN BIOMETRICS

A computer-processed video image of African penguins is labeled with *biometric data*, measurements of biological features that can be used to identify individuals. Scientists at the University of Bristol in England described this new video surveillance system in June 2008 as a method for identifying and monitoring animals in endangered populations without having to capture and mark them. In this example, mathematical data represent the pattern of chest spots that is characteristic of an individual penguin.

No actual RNA molecules—and no living cells—were produced in these experiments. Nevertheless, biologists noted that the results were an important advance in explaining the origin of life. They said the results also provided evidence that life began in warm surface waters, rather than in the deep sea, as some scientists believe.

First 24 hours of life. In October 2008, scientists at the European Molecular Biology Laboratory and Heidelberg University, both in Heidelberg, Germany, described a powerful new microscope technique that they used to observe cellular development in the first 24 hours of life of a *vertebrate* (animal with a backbone) embryo. These observations marked the first time that such early vertebrate development had been observed in detail. The scientists watched as a fertilized cell of a zebra fish developed into an embryo composed of tens of thousands of cells and a beating heart.

The researchers used their "digital scanned laser light sheet fluorescence microscope" to scan a living zebra fish embryo inside a laboratory dish with a "sheet" of light along many different directions. The many resulting two-dimensional images of the embryo were then assembled by a computer into a series of three-dimensional (3-D) images of the developing embryo. The 3-D images could be viewed on a computer screen from any angle, allowing the researchers to carefully examine all cellular development that happened in the first 24 hours after fertilization.

The scientists said that their microscope imaging technology could be used for studying the embryonic development of other lab animals, including frogs, mice, and chickens. Another area that could benefit from this technology, noted the scientists, was imaging of the cellular processes in some diseases.

Single-species ecosystem. A simple *ecosystem* (all the living organisms and the physical environment in an area) was discovered 2.8 kilometers (1.7 miles) below the surface in a gold mine near Johannesburg, South Africa, according to an October 2008 report. The find was the first known ecosystem composed of only a single species—a rod-shaped bacterium named *Candidatus Desulforudis*

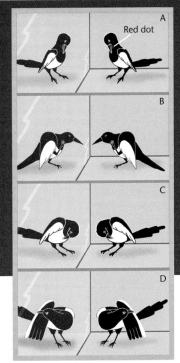

SELF-AWARENESS IN MAGPIES

Magpies are capable of self-awareness—an ability that scientists previously thought existed only in such advanced mammals as apes, dolphins, and elephants. Psychologist Helmet Prior of Goethe University in Frankfurt, Germany, reported that conclusion in August 2008, based on his observations. An artist's rendering depicts the experiment. A magpie touches a colored mark placed by a scientist beneath its beak, with its beak (A) and its foot (B) while looking at an image of itself in a mirror. The bird also searches other parts of its body (C, D).

Red dot

A

B

C

D

audaxviator. This hardy microbe lives in complete isolation and total darkness, with no oxygen, at a temperature of about 60 °C (140 °F).

The discovery was reported by scientists at the United States Department of Energy's Lawrence Berkeley National Laboratory in California, along with researchers at several other institutions. The investigators explained that the bacterium survives in its inhospitable habitat by deriving energy from hydrogen and sulfate produced by the radioactive decay of uranium in rocks. The bacterium uses the energy to make *organic* (compounds with carbon-hydrogen bonds) nutrients out of water, and inorganic carbon and nitrogen from ammonia in surrounding rocks and liquids. The bacterium has a *flagellum* (whip-like tail) that enables it to swim. It can also produce a hard covering that allows it to protect itself from dangerous chemicals, excessive dryness, and high temperatures.

The bacterium was the only living thing that the scientists found in water they collected from fractures in rock inside the gold mine. The researchers said they suspected that this bacterial species may have originally journeyed from the surface with water trickling through rock fractures millions of years ago.

According to the investigators, the discovery of living bacteria in such an extreme setting suggests that other so-called extremophile microbes might exist on other planets, including below the surface of Mars. ■ Edward Ricciuti

■ BOOKS ABOUT SCIENCE

Here are 12 important new science books suitable for the general reader. They have been selected from books published in 2008 and 2009.

Anthropology. *Margaret Mead: The Making of an American Icon* by Nancy C. Lutkehaus chronicles the life of Margaret Mead, the best known American anthropologist. Mead

belonged to a rare breed of public intellectual in the 1900's—the celebrity scientist familiar as a figure on talk shows, a writer in popular magazines, and a host of television specials. Lutkehaus, who worked for Mead as a student and became a professor at the University of Southern California, analyzes Mead's career both as a scientist and a personality. Mead's success, she concludes, was a product not only of her talent as a writer and scholar, but also of her ability to tap into some of the major cultural and economic themes of the time, such as the empowerment of women. (Princeton University Press, 2008, 392 pp. $29.95)

Astronomy. *The Crowded Universe: The Search for Living Planets* by Alan Boss explains how astronomers have refined their understanding of the origins and the distribution of planets. Since 1995, astronomers have discovered over 300 planets orbiting around stars outside our solar system. Boss, of the Carnegie Institution in Washington, D.C., has been one of the principal researchers into the origin of planetary systems and a central figure in many of these discoveries. He begins his account as a chronological series of journal entries and ends with a look into the future, when the Kepler spacecraft, successfully launched on March 6, 2009, is expected to begin

discovering Earth-size planets. (Basic Books, 2009, 256 pp. $26)

The Pluto Files: The Rise and Fall of America's Favorite Planet by Neil DeGrasse Tyson reviews the history of Pluto, describing how the distant world was first discovered in the 1930's and how the recent discovery of many Pluto-like objects in the outer solar system led astronomers to revise their definition of a planet. Tyson is the director of the Hayden Planetarium at the American Museum of Natural History in New York City. In 2000, when a new exhibit center opened at the planetarium, Pluto was grouped with similar icy bodies in the Kuiper belt rather than the four inner rocky planets or the four outer gas giants of the solar system. In 2006, the International Astronomical Union officially reclassified Pluto as a "dwarf planet." (W.W. Norton, 2009, 194 pp. $23.95)

Biology. *Made for Each Other: The Biology of the Human-Animal Bond* by naturalist and documentary producer Meg Daley Olmert traces the bond between human beings and pets back to prehistoric times. Our primate ancestors studied other species to learn how they chased and captured prey. Gradually, human beings began to incorporate animals into their families, adopting dogs, for instance, as companions in the hunt. Ultimately, however, the key to the human-animal bond is chemical: our bodies release a hormone called oxytocin when we stare into the eyes of a milk cow, pet a horse, or rub the

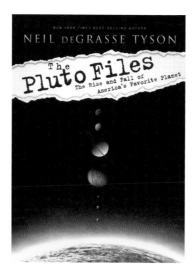

belly of a collie. This hormone brings about feelings of comfort, peacefulness, and cooperation. Our pets, Olmert concludes, not only bring us pleasure, but also make us better human beings. (Da Capo Press, 2009, 312 pp. $26)

Alex & Me: How a Scientist and a Parrot Uncovered a Hidden World of Animal Intelligence—and Formed a Deep Bond in the Process by Brandeis University biologist Irene M. Pepperberg offers fascinating insights into the workings of a mind that, in many ways,

Alex & Me

How a Scientist and a Parrot
Uncovered a Hidden World of
Animal Intelligence—and Formed
a Deep Bond in the Process

IRENE M. PEPPERBERG

is not that different from our own. Scientists have long recognized that being called a "birdbrain" is not really an insult; such birds as ravens, parrots, and other species show high degrees of intelligence. But few scientists have studied a single bird as closely as Pepperberg, who lived with Alex, an African Gray parrot, for 30 years. Alex was able to count up to at least six and had a remarkably large vocabulary. Beyond the working relationship of scientist and subject, Alex and Pepperberg developed a deep personal understanding and affection. (HarperCollins, 2008, 240 pp. $23.95)

Chemistry. *The Invention of Air* by Steven Johnson presents an absorbing tale of Joseph Priestley (1733–1804), a pivotal figure in the birth of modern chemistry and biology and a notable freethinker during a turbulent period when modern science and modern democracy were in their formative years. Priestley was the first person to recognize that plants produce a substance—which we now know as oxygen— that is essential to the respiration of animals. He was also a political radical, passionately attached to the principles of political and religious freedom when such ideas were risky. (Riverhead, 2008, 272 pp. $25.95)

Ecology. *Ivory's Ghosts: The White Gold of History and the Fate of Elephants* by nature writer John Frederick Walker surveys the flourishing black market in ivory and describes how the elephant population continues to suffer. Since the dawn of history, ivory has been treasured for its creamy texture and for the ease with which it can be carved into items of utility and beauty. Before being replaced by plastics, ivory was used widely for such household items as buttons, combs, and even piano keys. In response to this demand, by the end of the 1800's, thousands of tons of elephant tusks were being shipped annually from East Africa to factories around the world. As elephant populations dwindled and a conservation ethic took hold, ivory fell out of favor. Since 1990, there has been an international ban on the ivory trade. Walker suggests that the best way to support sustainable economies in the developing world and, at the same time, to safeguard the elephant is to wisely manage the harvesting and sale of ivory, rather than banning it outright. (Atlantic Monthly Press, 2009, 304 pp. $25)

History of science. *Decoding the Heavens: A 2000-Year-Old Computer and the Century-Long Search to Discover Its Secrets* by science journalist Jo Marchant traces the attempts of archaeologists to make sense of a 2,000-year-old mechanism salvaged from a shipwreck near the Greek island of Antikythera in 1900. It was as strange, writes Marchant, as "finding a steam engine on the ancient, pitted surface of the Moon." Before the 1900 discovery, the earliest known geared clockworks were from late medieval Europe—more than a thousand years later than the Antikythera mechanism.

Archaeologists puzzled over the device for over half a century, until a British scientist, Derek de Solla Price, obtained X-ray images of the mechanism. From these data, Price in the early 1970's developed a plausible explanation of how the device could have been used to predict the positions of the sun, moon, and planets. In recent decades, additional high-tech imaging by other scholars has fleshed out Price's original concept. As a result of this work, our appreciation of the technological achievements of our ancient Greek ancestors has undergone a major revision. (Da Capo Press, 2009, 336 pp. $25)

Flat Earth: The History of an Infamous Idea by Christine Garwood focuses on the weird claims of flat-Earthers in Victorian England in this entertaining social and scientific history. The spherical shape of Earth was known to the ancient Greeks, who made fairly accurate measurements of its diameter. However, in the United Kingdom of the

IVORY'S GHOSTS

The White Gold of History and the Fate of Elephants

JOHN FREDERICK WALKER
Author of *A Certain Curve of Horn*

BOOKS ABOUT SCIENCE continued

mid-to-late 1800's, both true believers and downright charlatans kept the theory alive. Although few people today believe the Earth is flat, some Web sites advance flat-Earth ideas. (Thomas Dunne Books, 2008, 448 pp. $27.95)

Mathematics. *Is God a Mathematician?* by Mario Livio, an astrophysicist at the Hubble Space Telescope Science Institute, presents the history and philosophy of mathematics, starting with the ancient Greek philosopher and mathematician Pythagoras and continuing into the 1900's. One of the most mysterious things about the universe is that it can be described so effectively using numbers. Livio poses the question, "Are the laws of nature somehow 'out there,' as if nature itself spoke in the language of mathematics?" If this is the case, scientists are like explorers, and equations such as $E = mc^2$, formulated by German-born physicist Albert Einstein, are like unknown continents, already in existence and waiting to be discovered. Many scientists agree with this theory. Others, however, believe that the mathematical laws of nature are pure inventions, resulting from our brain's obsession with imposing order on chaotic sensory perceptions. Which is the correct view? Livio's provocative book invites readers to decide for themselves. (Simon and Schuster, 2009, 320 pp. $26)

Natural history. *Owls of North America* by Canadian nature writer Frances Backhouse makes the case that owls are among the most talented, resourceful, and (by human standards)

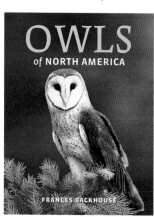

admirable birds of all. Most owls, for example, are family-oriented. Males mate with the same female for at least several years and actively help in feeding and raising their young.

In addition to descriptions of the bodies and behavior of the approximnately 20 species of North American owls, the book also features dozens of remarkable candid photographs of the birds in flight and at rest. In one, a diving saw-whet owl, talons outstretched, is inches away from striking an unsuspecting deer mouse. In another, an entire clutch of young burrowing owls gazes at the camera with the sanguine grace of wealthy siblings in a portrait by the American painter John Singer Sargent. (Firefly Books, 2008, 216 pp. $34.95)

Paleontology. *Feathered Dinosaurs: The Origin of Birds* by Australian paleontologist John Long and nature artist Peter Schouten serves as a kind of prehistoric field guide to the *protobirds* (early forms of birds) of the Cretaceous Period (about 145 million to 65 million years ago). Over the past several decades, a number of paleontologists have become convinced that dinosaurs are the direct ancestors of birds. Long and Schouten's collaboration will convince readers as well. Schouten's colorful portrait of the dinosaur *Avivimus portentosus*, for instance, shows a creature whose feathered forelimbs are displayed with the fanfare of a pheasant or a turkey.

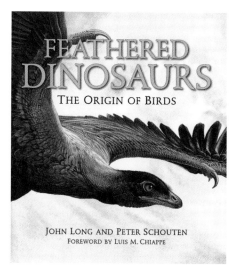

The finely rendered illustrations of 70 other species in this book, based on the hard data of paleontological research as well as on analogies with present-day bird species, make it possible to imagine what these pioneering avians looked like in real life, even down to feather configuration and coloration. Introductory remarks and detailed captions by John Long make clear the state of the fossil evidence and the chain of inference behind each picture. (Oxford University Press, 2008, 208 pp. $39.95)   ■ Laurence A. Marschall

BOOKS ABOUT SCIENCE FOR YOUNGER READERS

The following books about science are suitable for younger readers. They have been chosen from among books published in 2008 and 2009.

Anthropology. *Written in Bone: Buried Lives of Jamestown and Colonial Maryland* by Sally M. Walker follows a team of scientists led by anthropologist Douglas Owsley as they study human remains discovered at burial sites in Jamestown, Virginia, and other early colonial settlements in the Chesapeake Bay region. Walker explains how observations and scientific tests can help answer questions about each person's identity, age, diet, birthplace, and length of time in the New World. With color photos on nearly every page, this unusual book reveals the enthusiasm and expertise of scientists working together to unravel mysteries from 400-year-old clues. (Lerner/Carolrhoda, 2009, 144 pp. illus., grades 7–11, $22.95)

Biology. *Living Sunlight: How Plants Bring the Earth to Life* by Molly Bang and Penny Chisholm explains why photosynthesis is essential to plants and, by extension, to all the animals that survive by eating plants. Beginning with the sun's radiant energy striking our planet, this beautifully illustrated picture book shows how sunlight makes plant and animal life possible on Earth. The illustrations, which incorporate scientific as well as decorative details, teem with color. Well-written notes provide valuable additional scientific details. (Scholastic/Blue Sky, 2009, 40 pp. illus., preschool–grade 3, $16.99)

Redwoods by Jason Chin pairs a clearly written text that provides a science-based overview of redwood trees with illustrations that develop the story line. A young boy riding on the subway conjures up an imaginary adventure as he reads a book called *Redwoods*. Mentally transported from the bustling city to a redwood forest, he explores the giant trees from the ground and then climbs into the canopy to observe the many plants and animals living there. Although the story soars into fantasy, the book never flies too far from reality, providing young readers with a basic scientific understanding of redwood forests. (Roaring Brook Press, 2009, 40 pp. illus., preschool–grade 3, $16.95)

General science. *Extreme Scientists: Exploring Nature's Mysteries from Perilous Places* by Donna M. Jackson challenges the stereotype of scientists in lab coats gazing at their test tubes. Jackson introduces three courageous explorers working in scientific fields: Paul Flaherty, a *meteorologist* (weather forecaster) who flies into hurricanes; Hazel Barton, a biologist who explores out-of-the-way places aboveground and below to find exotic microbes; and Stephen Sillett, a *botanist* (scientist who studies plants) who climbs into the canopies of redwoods. The scientists themselves explain what they do and why they do it while color photos bring them and their unusual workplaces into focus. (Houghton Mifflin Harcourt, 2009, 80 pp. illus., grades 4–8, $18.00)

Space technology. *Mission Control, This Is Apollo: The Story of the First Voyages to the Moon* by Andrew Chaikin with Victoria Kohl takes readers along on a dozen missions of the Apollo space program, which included the first human landing on the moon, in 1969. Relying on extensive research, including interviews with most of the 24 lunar astronauts, Chaikin relates stories of the various Apollo missions, illuminating the technological as well as the human dimensions. Among the many colorful illustrations are NASA photos and reproductions of paintings by artist and Apollo 12 astronaut Alan Bean, who offers commentary and shares memories in captions. (Viking, 2009, 128 pp. illus., grades 5–9, $23.99)

Moonshot: The Flight of Apollo 11 by Brian Floca celebrates the 40th anniversary of Apollo 11's flight to the moon in 1969 with beautifully composed ink-and-watercolor drawings that illustrate the space journey from inside and outside the spacecraft. Accompanying these images is the author's narration in succinct prose that occasionally borders on the poetic. *Moonshot* is a memorable account of humankind's first direct contact with the moon and an appropriate introduction to one of the greatest events in history. (Atheneum/Richard Jackson Books, 2009, 48 pp. illus, kindergarten–grade 4, $17.99)

■ Carolyn Phelan

CHEMISTRY

The creation of a previously unknown solid form of the element boron was reported in January 2009 by a team of researchers in the United States, France, and Italy. The new chemically stable, ultrahard, crystalline form of boron was unusual in that it had an ionic structure. Such a structure is composed of *ions* (positively or negatively charged atoms or molecules) that cling together because their opposite charges attract each other. A typical ionic solid is composed of more than one element, such as the positively charged sodium ions and negatively charged chlorine ions in sodium chloride (common table salt). The new boron solid was the first known ionic solid composed of a single element. The group that reported the new *phase* (physical form) of boron was led by crystallographer Artem R. Oganov of Stony Brook University in New York.

Oganov's team discovered their new phase of boron with the aid of a computer *model* (simulation), which enabled them to predict the arrangement of atoms in the solid, ionic phase. To make the material, the scientists heated a highly purified form of boron to temperatures above 1,400 °C (2,550 °F), while squeezing it under pressures of about 120,000 atmospheres (120,000 times atmospheric pressure at sea level). They isolated the new phase of boron in the form of gray crystals, which were nearly as hard as diamonds.

The ionic structure of the boron was possible, explained the researchers, because the new material consisted of two types of boron atom clusters. One cluster, made of a 12-membered ring of boron atoms, was slightly negatively charged. The other cluster, a dumbbell-shaped pair of two boron atoms, was slightly positively charged. These charges caused the atom clusters to attract each other in an orderly crystal arrangement. According to Oganov, it may be possible to create other ionic solids that consist of single elements. Some scientists believe that these phases might have certain industrial applications, including in the electronics industry.

Less expensive fuel cells. In April 2009, scientists in Canada reported a major advance in the technology of *fuel cells* (batteries that convert the chemical energy of fuels into electric energy). The scientists used inexpensive iron rather than expensive platinum to make fuel cell *electrodes* (electrical conductors). This development had the potential to reduce the high cost of fuel cells, allowing them to be more practical options for supplying energy to hydrogen-powered cars, trucks, and buses. The research was reported by chemist Jean-Pol Dodelet and colleagues at the Institut National de la Recherche Scientifique (INRS) in Varennes, Quebec.

Fuel cells that use hydrogen for fuel offer a promising way of generating nonpolluting electric power for motors that propel vehicles. A hydrogen-based fuel cell has a metal electrode, called an anode, that removes *electrons* (negatively charged subatomic particles) from hydrogen gas and transfers them to an external circuit. The removal of the electrons causes the hydrogen atoms in the gas to become positively charged hydrogen ions. The ions are carried by an electrically conductive membrane called an electrolyte to an electrode on the fuel cell's opposite side. At this opposite electrode, known as a cathode, the hydrogen ions combine with oxygen from the air and electrons from the external circuit to form ordinary water molecules as a by-product. As this process repeats itself, the electric current in the external circuit can be used to drive an electric motor.

In most existing fuel cells, both the anode and cathode are made of particles of platinum, a rare and expensive metal, sprinkled on rods of solid carbon. Attempts to make fuel cell electrodes from much cheaper iron particles had previously been unsuccessful, because the iron electrodes had limited electrical output. More than 60 times as many chemical reactions occur per second at each electricity-producing site on a platinum electrode as on an ordinary iron electrode. As a result, fuel cells made with platinum electrodes deliver far more electric current than fuel cells made with typical iron electrodes.

SEE ALSO

THE SPECIAL REPORT, **THE SEARCH FOR WATER ON MARS,** PAGE 100.

SCIENCE STUDIES, **PLASTIC PLANET,** PAGE 114.

The iron electrodes made by the INRS team had more electricity-producing sites than were previously possible. To accomplish this task, the researchers mixed together carbon black—a black, powdery form of carbon—with compounds containing iron and nitrogen atoms. The scientists heated this mixture to temperatures of about 800 °C (1,472 °F) in the presence of ammonia gas, which consists of nitrogen and hydrogen. At those high temperatures, chemical reactions created millions of microscopic pores in the carbon particles. Nitrogen atoms chemically bound along the walls of these pores latched onto iron atoms and held them firmly in place inside the pores.

The millions of pores with iron atoms inside resulted in far more sites for electricity-producing chemical reactions than were present in previous iron-carbon electrodes. The INRS investigators found that the *current density* (electric current output per unit volume) of their new iron-based electrodes was the same as that of typical platinum electrodes. Despite these encouraging results, Dodelet said that additional research was needed before the new type of iron-carbon electrodes would be ready for widespread use in hydrogen-based fuel cells.

Flexible computer displays. A technological advance that could potentially lead to practical applications for an unusual form of carbon called graphene was reported in January 2009 by scientists in South Korea. Graphene is an ultrathin, honeycomb-shaped structure made of carbon atoms that was discovered in 2004. Because of its transparency and ability to carry an electric current, graphene has been seen as a possible component in computer displays that could be stretched, bent, or folded, as well as in other electronic products. Until the new development, however, scientists had not been able to make graphene in the inexpensive but high-quality forms needed for such applications. The Korean researchers, led by chemist Byung Hee Hong of Sungkyunkwan University in Suwon, described an efficient technique for preparing pure films of graphene.

Graphene consists of a single flat layer of interconnected six-membered rings of carbon atoms, a structure that resembles the honeycomb of a beehive. Graphite, the black form of carbon used to make the "lead" of pencils, also consists of interconnected six-membered carbon rings, though in many layers instead of one. Because graphene is so thin—no thicker than the carbon atoms that compose it—it is completely transparent. In addition, electrons

can zip through sheets of graphene at up to four times the speed at which they travel through silicon, the material used to make the semiconductor chips of computers. Both of these properties suggest that graphene might be useful for advanced electronic devices.

Previous methods for making graphene were inefficient. One method involved using a type of sticky tape to peel off layers of carbon rings from samples of graphite. Another route to graphene production was to expose silicon carbide, a tough and costly substance, to very high temperatures. The method reported by Hong's team for making graphene was faster and cheaper and yielded more product than such previous methods.

In the first step of the new procedure, the researchers produced a mixture of two gases—methane (the carbon-containing compound in natural gas) and hydrogen. They allowed this mixture to flow over a thin, flat layer of the metal nickel at a temperature of 1,000 °C (1,832 °F). Nickel, which is a *catalyst* (a sub-

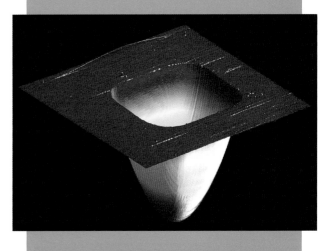

WORLD'S THINNEST BALLOON

A membrane made of graphene, a form of carbon consisting of a single layer of atoms, stretches like a balloon in this atomic force microscope image of an experiment reported in September 2008. Scientists at Cornell University in Ithaca, New York, demonstrated the strength of this membrane by subjecting it to changing pressures that caused it to bulge in and out without breaking. They noted that graphene's strength and leak-proof traits make it useful in various areas of research.

CHEMISTRY continued

stance that promotes a chemical reaction without being changed itself), caused the methane and hydrogen to form a layer of graphene on top of the nickel. The scientists dissolved the underlying nickel with a chemical solution, leaving a layer of pure graphene.

The researchers found that the graphene layer they produced could easily stick to plastic films. They also found that stretching and bending the graphene-coated films did not diminish their ability to carry an electric current.

According to Hong, the new technology could permit the use of graphene in future flexible computer image displays, as well as in special chemical sensors and low-cost *photovoltaic* (solar) cells, which convert sunlight into electric current. Hong noted, however, that before such products become a reality, researchers needed to determine if the procedure could be economically scaled up to commercial production levels.

Self-repairing paint coatings. In March 2009, researchers at the University of Southern Mississippi in Hattiesburg unveiled a new family of plastic coatings that were capable of repairing their own scratches—much like skin can

heal small cuts. According to the developers of the coatings, chemists Marek W. Urban and Biswajit Ghosh, such materials may find applications in self-repairing paint finishes on automobiles and other painted commercial products.

Although previous investigators had reported self-repairing plastic coatings, those materials were made with expensive chemical additives, and some required exposure to high temperatures to function appropriately. By contrast, the active ingredient in the new coating was derived from crab and lobster shells, waste products from the seafood industry that are cheap and readily available. Moreover, the new repair process was initiated by the ultraviolet rays in sunlight and could take place at ordinary temperatures.

Some previous kinds of self-repairing plastic coatings have been made with microscopic glass capsules filled with a monomer, a single molecule that can combine with other molecules to form long chains called polymers. A crack in the coating causes these capsules to break and release the monomers, which then combine to form polymers. The polymers plug up the crack in the coating.

MICROSCOPIC ROBOTIC HANDS

The development of microscopic metallic robotic "hands" that, with the aid of magnets, could be used to pick up and move cells and other microscopic objects in medical treatments and scientific research was reported by scientists at Johns Hopkins University in Baltimore, Maryland, in January 2009. These so-called "microgrippers" were made of a gold (Au) and nickel (Ni) "palm" with six attached copper (Cu) and chromium (Cr) "fingers." Exposure to either heat or acetic acid dissolved a *polymer* (chain-like molecule) within the hand's hinge, causing the fingers to close. Then, exposure to hydrogen peroxide dissolved the copper layer, causing the fingers to open again.

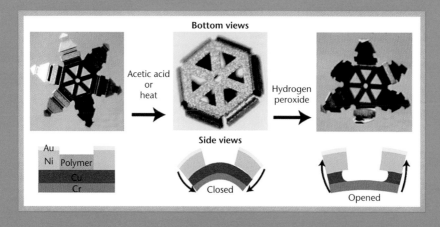

The coating system developed by Urban and Ghosh required no microcapsules or other complex additives. Its main component was a form of polyurethane, a tough and durable polymer that is widely used in automobile paint finishes. Chemically, polyurethane consists of a carbon backbone with attached hydrogen, oxygen, and nitrogen atoms. To make polyurethane self-repairing, the researchers linked the long polymer chains on their sides with a connector molecule, a process called cross-linking. The connector molecule was another polymer, called chitosan, a clear, water-soluble form of plastic obtained by chemically treating crab and lobster shells. The researchers also attached to the chitosan polymer a chemically reactive molecule called oxetane, a four-membered ring made of three carbon atoms and one oxygen atom.

When Urban and Ghosh put scratches in films made from their polymer mixture, they found that exposure to ultraviolet rays, such as in sunlight, caused the two sides of the cuts to knit back together in less than an hour. The scientists explained that a scratch caused the oxetane rings at the site of the damage to pop open, leaving behind attached oxygen atoms that were free to form new chemical bonds. The ultraviolet light caused some of the chitosan links to separate from the polyurethane chains, leaving behind dangling fragments of molecules that were free to reconnect elsewhere. The highly reactive oxygen atoms that were linked to one polyurethane chain formed new bonds with the free, dangling ends of the chitosan linked to another polyurethane chain. This cross-linking pulled the polyurethane chains together, mending the scratches.

The researchers demonstrated the repair process with scratches that were approximately 10 micrometers wide (about one-fifth as wide as a human hair). They planned to test whether the process also worked with larger scratches. ■ Gordon Graff

CLIMATE CHANGE

Increases in global average temperatures caused by human-induced climate change will persist for at least 1,000 years, even if emissions of greenhouse gases are substantially reduced in the near future, according to a study by an international team of researchers published in January 2009. The study, funded by the National Oceanic and Atmospheric Administration (NOAA) and led by NOAA senior scientist Susan Solomon, was published in the *Proceedings of the National Academy of Sciences.*

The researchers noted that global average temperatures have risen 0.75 Celsius degrees (1.4 Fahrenheit degrees) since the mid-1800's. Climate scientists project that the Earth will warm at least an additional 0.6 Celsius degrees (1.1 Fahrenheit degrees) during the remainder of this century and, potentially, as much as 2.4 to 6.4 Celsius degrees (4.3 to 11.5 Fahrenheit degrees) if current trends in emissions continue.

Scientists attribute most of the observed increase in global temperatures to rising lev-

SEE ALSO THE SPECIAL REPORT, METHANE: ANOTHER GREENHOUSE TROUBLEMAKER, PAGE 42.

els of carbon dioxide (CO_2) and other greenhouse gases in the atmosphere. (Greenhouse gases such as CO_2 and methane cause the atmosphere to trap heat that otherwise would be radiated back into space.) Such human-influenced activities as burning fuels spew massive amounts of greenhouse gases into the atmosphere.

Atmospheric CO_2 has increased steadily in recent years. During the period 2000–2008, the Mauna Loa Observatory in Hawaii detected an average annual increase in atmospheric CO_2 of 1.98 parts per million (ppm) compared with an average yearly increase of 1.50 ppm for the period of from 1990 to 1999.

The Solomon team performed statistical analyses on weather records and used *computer modeling programs* (complex programs that

CLIMATE CHANGE continued

make predictions of future conditions) to carry out their study. They concluded that interactions between the atmosphere and the oceans would perpetuate the effects of global warming almost indefinitely. The oceans serve as a vast reservoir for CO_2 and excess heat. The researchers predicted that long after levels of greenhouse gases have stabilized in the atmosphere, the oceans will continue to return CO_2 and radiate heat back into the atmosphere.

The NOAA study suggests that warming that already is occurring will persist for hundreds of years. The study's authors caution that the world's people and communities must either work to reduce greenhouse gas emissions and halt additional warming or adapt to significant, long-term warming in the future.

China edges out the United States. In June 2008, researchers from the Netherlands Environmental Assessment Agency (PBL) released a report documenting national emissions of CO_2. As of 2007, China had surpassed the United States in total yearly CO_2 emissions, with each country accounting for from 20 to 25 percent of global emissions annually. One stark difference between the two nations'

economies remained, however: the wealthier United States still produces about four times the amount of emissions per person as China.

The report noted that in 2007, China accounted for about two-thirds of the global increase in CO_2 emissions. Officials with the United Nations (UN) Framework Convention on Climate Change (FCCC), the agency that monitors adherence to treaties on global climate change, said that the PBL report underscored the importance of obtaining China's agreement to any future world climate treaty.

The United States rejected the Kyoto Protocol, the global treaty on climate change adopted by most of the world's nations in 1997. China ratified the treaty, but, along with other developing nations, is not bound by emissions reduction requirements. The Kyoto Protocol is set to expire in 2012; an FCCC conference scheduled for Copenhagen, Denmark, in December 2009 is charged with drafting a new global climate treaty.

Ocean acidification. In November 2008, researchers from the University of Chicago (UC) published a study indicating that the oceans may be acidifying 10 times as rapidly as

ACID LEVELS IN THE CARIBBEAN

Ocean waters in the northwest Caribbean Sea, the Gulf of Mexico, and adjacent Atlantic waters have become more acidic in the last 20 years, according to a study conducted by scientists from the National Oceanic and Atmospheric Administration (NOAA) and the Rosenstiel School of Marine and Atmospheric Science in Miami, Florida. One way to gauge acidification is by measuring levels of aragonite in the water. Aragonite is a form of calcium carbonate ($CaCO_3$) that such sea animals as clams and reef-forming corals use to make their shells. As atmospheric carbon dioxide (CO_2) levels increase, ocean water becomes more acidic and aragonite levels decline. The researchers warn that as aragonite becomes less available in ocean waters, shellforming animals will likely suffer population declines.

Ocean acidification in the northwest Caribbean, February 1988

Source: National Oceanic and Atmospheric Administration.

previously thought. Such a change could imperil marine organisms and *ecosystems* (systems of organisms in their physical environment), oceanographers warn. The study, led by UC ecologist Timothy Wootten, was published in the Dec. 2, 2008, issue of *Proceedings of the National Academy of Sciences.*

Acidification, or a change toward a more acid condition, is measured by the pH scale. The scale ranges from 0 to 14. Falling numbers on the scale indicate a move toward stronger acid concentration; rising numbers indicate weaker acid concentration. The number 7 on the scale is considered neutral. The pH values of most natural substances cluster around the middle of the scale, so small number changes can indicate significant environmental changes for living things.

The UC researchers studied the shoreline of Tatoosh Island in the Pacific Ocean off the northwestern coast of Washington state from 2000 to 2008. During that period, the pH of the ocean water declined by approximately 0.05 per year, a much faster change than climate models had predicted.

The cause of the trend toward ocean acidification, climate scientists believe, is rising levels of carbon dioxide (CO_2) in the atmosphere. When CO_2 comes in contact with the ocean surfaces, some of the gas dissolves in seawater. This gas then enters into chemical reactions that produce carbonic acid, lowering the ocean's pH value.

The UC researchers also kept counts of several species of marine life that inhabit the intertidal zone, a section of seashore extending from the high-water to the low-water mark of daily tides. One species in particular, the Californian mussel, which dwells in a calcium carbonate shell that it excretes, showed a steady decline in numbers over the eight-year study period. The research team theorized that because acid dissolves calcium carbonate, the increasing acidity of the seawater interfered with the mussels' ability to maintain their protective shells.

The researchers warned that other species with calcium carbonate protective shells or skeletons—such as corals, clams, oysters, and some forms of algae and *plankton* (masses of tiny floating organisms)—could suffer because of ocean acidification as well. Disruption of these species would likely cause severe

Sea animals that depend on aragonite to build hard shells include diatoms, microscopic single-celled organisms that are part of the mass of drifting organisms called plankton. Diatoms are an important food source for fish and other marine animals.

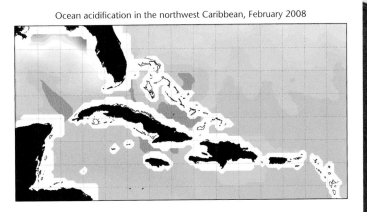

Ocean acidification in the northwest Caribbean, February 2008

Aragonite saturation, parts per billion

4.50
4.40
4.30
4.20
4.10
4.00
3.90
3.80
3.70
3.60
3.50
3.40
3.30
3.20
3.10
3.00

CLIMATE CHANGE continued

problems for coral reefs, fisheries, and other important marine ecosystems.

Melting ice sheets and sea level. In December 2008, climate researchers reported that sea levels are likely to rise faster during this century than previously thought. The study, commissioned by the U.S. Climate Change Science Program (CCSP), updated an estimate for sea level rise that had been issued by the Intergovernmental Panel on Climate Change (IPCC), a UN committee, in a 2007 report. (The Climate Change Science Program is a U.S. program sponsored by 13 federal agencies and overseen by 4 government groups.)

In its 2007 report, the IPCC had projected a rise in sea level of up to 0.5 meters (about 1 ½ feet) by the year 2100. The CCSP researchers, however, estimated that global sea levels could rise as much as 1.2 meters (4 feet) by that year.

A small rise in sea level has already been observed, measured currently at about 3 millimeters (0.1 inch) per year, according to climate scientists. Many scientists believe that the increase in sea level will accelerate as global warming leads to greater melting of sea ice and ice sheets. Ice sheets are thick masses of ice sitting on land. They are surrounded by ice shelves that protrude from the ice sheet into the surrounding ocean. Because ice shelves are already floating in water, their melting does not contribute to sea level rise. But scientists worry that the collapse or diminishment of ice shelves due to the warming atmosphere and ocean waters may accelerate the flow of land-based glaciers behind the shelves. In addition, meltwater collecting on the surface of ice sheets creates rivers that may be finding their way to the bottom of the ice sheets, lubricating the base of the sheets and causing them to flow faster.

The CCSP researchers based their revisions on a better understanding of the mechanics of ice sheet melting derived from recent research and also on satellite data showing accelerated melting of Arctic sea ice in the period 2007 to 2008. The disappearance of sea ice accelerates warming because ocean water absorbs heat from sunlight; ice reflects most sunlight.

Earth's major ice sheets are in Greenland and Antarctica. The consequences of rapid melting of these enormous ice masses would be profound. Complete melting of the Greenland ice sheet would cause a worldwide increase in sea level of about 7 meters (23 feet), while complete melting of the West Antarctic ice sheet would cause 6 meters (20 feet) of sea level rise. (The ice sheet on the continent of Antarctica is divided by a mountain range into western and eastern segments. The western segment is more vulnerable to rapid melting, according to geologists, because it rests on rock that is 2,000 meters [nearly 6,600 feet] below sea level.) Scientists estimate that if all the ice in Greenland and Antarctica were to melt, the seas would rise 70 meters (230 feet).

The rate at which melting of the ice sheets occurs will depend on the rate at which the Earth heats up. The models that scientists use to estimate melting rates incorporate a certain amount of uncertainty.

No single research team could lay claim to the definitive prediction of rise in sea level, however. In another 2008 study, researchers attempted to define an upper limit for possible rises in sea level by 2100. The research team, funded by the National Science Foundation

DYING MUSSELS

A bed of dead and dying mussels off the northwest coast of Washington state illustrates the threat posed to shelled animals by ocean *acidification* (increasing acid concentrations). Rising levels of atmospheric carbon dioxide trigger chemical changes in water that interfere with the ability of mussels, clams, corals, and other marine animals to make and maintain their hard shells.

(NSF) and led by glaciologist Joel Harper of the University of Montana, Missoula, studied data which indicated the speeds at which chunks of ice flow from glaciers in ice sheets to the point at which they break off and float into seawater. This process is called calving. The researchers theorized that most of the melting ice that could add significant water volume to the oceans would come from such glacial calving.

Based on currently available data on ice-flows in Greenland and Antarctica, the Harper team predicted that sea levels should rise no more than 0.8 meters (2.6 feet) by 2100. However, if the ice-flows speed up substantially over time, levels could rise as much as 2 meters (6.6 feet) by then. The Harper team concluded that a sea level increase of greater than 2 meters by 2100 is extremely unlikely, because glacial flow will probably not attain speeds fast enough to support that extent of calving and melting. This research was summarized in an article in the Sept. 5, 2008, issue of *Science*.

Antarctica. Much of the focus on ice sheet destabilization has been on the Greenland ice sheet, in part because scanty temperature data from Antarctica have previously not provided a convincing case for a warming trend there. Researchers have observed long-term temperature increases on the Antarctic Peninsula, which extends northward from western Antarctica, but some areas of eastern Antarctica have exhibited a cooling trend.

New research published in *Nature* in January 2009, however, concluded that temperatures for the whole of West Antarctica have increased by 0.17 Celsius degrees (0.31 Fahrenheit degrees) per decade since 1957, or more than 0.8 Celsius degrees (1.5 Fahrenheit degrees) in the 50-year period following 1957. The researchers, led by climatologist Eric Steig of the University of Washington at Seattle and funded by the NSF's Office of Polar Programs, applied a complex statistical formula to data from ground-based observations from 1957 through 2006 and to satellite data obtained since the 1970's. The formula enabled them to fill in numerous gaps in the Antarctic continent's temperature record for the past 50 years.

The Steig team's analysis shows that average Antarctic temperatures increased by 0.12 Celsius degrees (0.22 Fahrenheit degrees) per decade between 1957 and 2006, or about 0.5 Celsius degrees (1 Fahrenheit degree) for the whole 50-year period. Thus, despite the apparent cooling of parts of eastern Antarctica, the continent as a whole has experienced a warming trend.   ■ Michael D. Mastrandrea

See also **ATMOSPHERIC SCIENCE**.

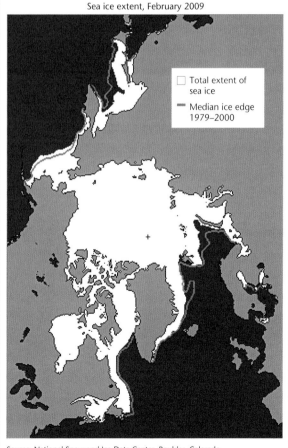

SHRINKING ARCTIC SEA ICE

Satellite data from February 2009 show the extent of sea ice in the Arctic Ocean, compared with the *median* (average) extent of the ice from 1979 to 2000. Since 2000, scientists have observed a thinning of the sea ice as well as shrinking coverage.

Sea ice extent, February 2009

☐ Total extent of sea ice

━ Median ice edge 1979–2000

Source: National Snow and Ice Data Center, Boulder, Colorado.

■ COMPUTERS AND ELECTRONICS

The first-ever high-definition three-dimensional (3-D) television commercial was presented on Feb. 1, 2009, during the broadcast of the Super Bowl, the National Football League championship, by PepsiCo, Inc., and DreamWorks Animation SKG, Inc., in collaboration with Intel Corporation. (DreamWorks is based in Glendale, California; PepsiCo, in Purchase, New York; and Intel, in Santa Clara, California.) The commercial featured a trailer from the DreamWorks animated 3-D movie *Monsters vs. Aliens* (2009) and an advertisement for PepsiCo's SoBe LifeWater energy drink. Home viewers could enjoy the 3-D special effects only by wearing special glasses that PepsiCo had previously distributed through retail outlets such as grocery stores, drugstores, and box discount retailers.

The television event marked the public debut of a partnership formed in July 2008 between DreamWorks and Intel for the purpose of transforming the studio's cinematic output entirely into digital 3-D format. In a January 2009 interview, Jeffrey Katzenberg, chief executive officer of DreamWorks, said that all future DreamWorks feature films would be shot and processed in Intel's InTru3D technology or subsequent generations of the company's 3D film-authoring process.

Digital 3-D had made its debut in a live-action feature film in *Journey to the Center of the Earth* released by Warner Brothers in July 2008. By early 2009, movie studios had announced the release of at least 20 3-D feature films planned for 2009 and 2010.

The use of 3-D effects in movies is not new. The first movie to feature such effects was the 1922 film *The Power of Love*. In the 1950's, 3-D movies briefly became the rage, enlivening cheesy science fiction movies as well as more "up-market" releases, such as Alfred Hitchcock's *Dial M for Murder* (1954).

The stereoscopic, or 3-D, effect is an optical illusion achieved by presenting slightly offset images of the same view. The offset simulates the difference in view perceived by our two eyes, placed as they are, on either side of our face.

In the 1950's, the 3-D effect was achieved by simultaneously filming scenes with cameras positioned at slightly different angles. To create

SEE ALSO

THE SPECIAL REPORT, **TELESCOPES: 400 YEARS OF STARGAZING,** PAGE 24.

CONSUMER SCIENCE, **DISTRIBUTED COMPUTING: SUPERCOMPUTING@HOME,** PAGE 138.

the illusion in the theater, two precisely positioned projectors were operated simultaneously. The illusion was completed by the cardboard-and-cellophane glasses that patrons wore; the glasses' polarized filters caused the slight overlapping of images that rendered the image in 3-D. The 1950's technology yielded less than perfect synchronization, however, which often resulted in headaches for viewers.

Today's 3-D is an outgrowth of the digital revolution in video and movies. One digital camera with multiple lenses captures the action. Likewise, a single digital projector is used at the other end of the moviemaking process. The 3-D moviemaking technology employs sophisticated computer hardware and software to precisely align the offset shots in every frame of the movie.

IS ONE PICTURE WORTH A THOUSAND WORDS?

Words from the inaugural address given by President Barack Obama on Jan. 20, 2009, appear in a word cloud, a graphic created with an online program called Wordle (www.wordle.net). The size of the words in the cloud depends on how often they are used in the text. Wordle allows users to easily create word clouds from any available text. It also allows users to vary the color or font of the words. Word clouds are a form of data visualization—graphic representations of information. People create word clouds to reveal patterns in speeches and other texts that might otherwise be easy to miss. Links to word clouds may be shared on e-mail and blogs.

After the movie is made, viewers are still required to wear 3-D viewing glasses. That is because the glasses apply a filter that renders the 3-D effect, leaving viewers without glasses still able to view the movie in standard 2-D. Today's viewing glasses, in contrast to the 1950's versions, use precise polarizing plastic lenses to achieve the filtering. Another change made to upgrade the image quality is the use of highly reflective viewing screens in theaters, rather than the traditional screens. The new screens reflect more light, enriching the image.

Many moviemakers and industry experts predict that 3-D will be the wave of the future, but others think the effects, which are very expensive to produce, may be reserved for the "big" movies that studios hope will prove to be blockbusters.

Quick-charge batteries. In surveys, users of cell phones and other battery-powered gadgets identify hours-long recharging sessions as the major downside of using such devices. Slow recharging may soon become yesterday's annoyance, according to a March 2009 announcement from scientists with the Massachusetts Institute of Technology (MIT) in Cambridge. Researcher Gerbrand Ceder reported in the March 12 issue of *Nature* that he and his colleagues at MIT had developed a new lithium ion battery technology that allows charging in mere seconds. Ceder and his col-

leagues predicted that new, fast lithium batteries could be commercially available in as few as two years.

The technology involves coating the lithium iron phosphate particles inside the batteries with a glass-like material called lithium pyrophosphate. In laboratory tests, a lithium battery incorporating the new technology charged and discharged 100 times as fast as conventional lithium batteries.

The standard lithium batteries currently in use contain high levels of energy. However, the charge-bearing lithium ions can cross barriers from particle to particle only at certain "gateways," a limitation that greatly slows the migration of the electric charge. The MIT scientists' lithium pyrophosphate coating provides a conductive surface all around each particle; as a result, the lithium ions speed across the battery.

The MIT scientists note that the fast lithium batteries could be useful for a number of applications. They would enable cell-phone users to recharge their batteries in a couple of minutes. The batteries could also make battery-powered cars more attractive to consumers, because fast battery discharge would make it possible for the cars to accelerate rapidly. Moreover, rapid charging might make it possible for drivers to stop at electric service stations where they could recharge their cars' lithium batteries quickly—instead of relying on slow, all-night recharging.

COMPUTERS AND ELECTRONICS continued

Green computing. In January 2009, Hewlett Packard (HP) Company of Palo Alto, California, and Intel jointly released a report that estimated the total annual costs to the United States federal government of electric power to run the government's many data centers and computer laboratories. According to the report, titled "Go Green Power Play," the government incurs $479 million in such costs each year. The authors calculated these costs by multiplying the total number of federal computer installations by an estimate of energy cost per average installation and then adding estimates for such overhead costs as cooling, data storage, and power loss due to inefficiencies.

According to the HP-Intel report, the federal government could save nearly $1 billion over a 5-year period and nearly $2 billion over a 10-year period by modernizing data centers and incorporating "green" computing practices.

The report's focus on energy costs in computer data centers highlighted the information technology (IT) industry's new focus on "green computing"—that is, providing computing resources that meet processing needs using as little energy as possible. According to statistics compiled by the U.S. Environmental Protection Agency (EPA), data-processing facilities consumed 1.5 percent of all electric power used in the United States in 2006 (the latest year for which statistics were available). The EPA reported that, nationwide, energy costs associated with computing had doubled from 2000 to 2006, and the costs were likely to double again by 2011.

According to computing experts, about 60 percent of energy costs for data centers and large supercomputers is for the cooling required to dissipate the heat generated by computer circuitry. Many computing experts believe that achieving more efficient cooling may be the best way to "green up" data centers. In August 2007, Hewlett Packard IT Vice President Paul Perez noted that "the way data centers are cooled today is like cutting butter with a chain saw."

Large companies and governments are investigating ways to lower these costs using several strategies. One is to install more energy-efficient climate control equipment. Another may be to use water cooling in some large installations, particularly in supercomputers.

The search for greener computing practices involves many disciplines related to computers and computing. Engineers seek to design computer architectures for supercomputers and other large computers that maximize use of all processors so that none stay idle for very long. Software programmers revise programs to better use this enhanced computer hardware. Electrical engineers work to streamline conversion of alternating current (AC), which comes from the mainline electric grid, to the direct current (DC) required by certain components in computers. AC-to-DC conversion (and vice versa) is one of the most inefficient activities within a computer installation, according to computing experts.

There has always been a trade-off in large-scale data processing between prudent energy use and fulfilling the information technology mission. In the late 2000's, that delicate balance seems to be tipping toward energy conservation, experts agree.

Wireless mesh networks come of age. In August 2008, Bill Vogel, chief executive officer (CEO) of Trilliant Networks, Inc., of Redwood City, California, announced that the maker of utility meters had received $40 million in venture capital funds to invest in developing state-of-the-art smart grid systems. (Venture capital funds are large financial investment firms that provide money for start-up companies and new technologies.)

The so-called "smart grid" is the electric grid equipped with high-tech, battery-operated, wireless devices capable of minutely monitoring and controlling distribution and use of electric power as well as locating damage in the grid. Utilities, motivated by energy scarcity and cost as well as pressure from government energy policies, are investing in "smart-grid" upgrades to their electric grids.

Trilliant's smart grid is based on a wireless mesh network architecture. A mesh network is a wireless local area network (LAN) in which each *node* (device in the network) is connected to some or all of the other nodes. Thus, a mesh network is considered "self-healing." That is, if one node goes down, the others can still communicate with each other.

State-of-the-art wireless mesh networks combine mesh architecture with low-energy, highly miniaturized, wireless sensing devices. One of the chief advantages of wireless mesh networks is their low cost and ease of installation. The high cost and time that would be required to wire in monitoring systems is eliminated. Also, the wireless mesh devices are low energy and low maintenance; the frequency of battery recharges or swap-outs is extremely low.

The wireless mesh technology enables continuous monitoring of a network—such as all electrical devices in a home or commercial building. Interconnected webs of wireless mesh networks can monitor larger networks, such as a regional electric grid. In the United States, wireless mesh technology is widely based on the ZigBee standard, an industry standard for developing wireless mesh commercial products.

Wireless mesh networks can be adapted to many useful applications. In an electric grid, this technology can optimize distribution of electric power by helping utility companies reconfigure in response to use patterns, such as unusually heavy loads. The technology also revolutionizes metering, providing consumers with detailed usage information that can enable them to change usage patterns and cut costs.

Wireless mesh network technology has many other possible applications, including lighting control systems to regulate the use of energy for lighting in commercial buildings; monitoring and control of municipal water supplies; and home security systems. In the

COMPUTING IN THE CLOUDS

A form of computer processing called cloud computing continued to grow in popularity in 2009. Computer users of all types—individual as well as commercial—are now "going to the clouds" for their computing resources. A computing architecture called *cloud computing* may transform computer usage patterns in the near future.

Cloud computing designates a computer architecture that concentrates massed processing hardware and software in a central location. Outside users, from individuals with PC's to large corporations, access that supercomputing power through Internet connections. The diagram illustrates a cloud computing architecture. Within a data center are located massed computers capable of providing supercomputer processing power, massed storage facilities, and application servers on which are stored a wide range of computer programs—from common Word processing programs to specialized database programs used by large corporations.

In a sense, cloud computing democratizes computing resources. In the recent past, only government agencies, universities, and large research labs could afford supercomputing resources. Soon, through cloud computing, most users will be able to do so.

Experts predict that revenues generated by cloud computing services will expand rapidly. According to analysts at Gartner Inc., an information technology market research company based in Stamford, Connecticut, such revenues were expected to grow by nearly 300 percent from 2008 to 2013.

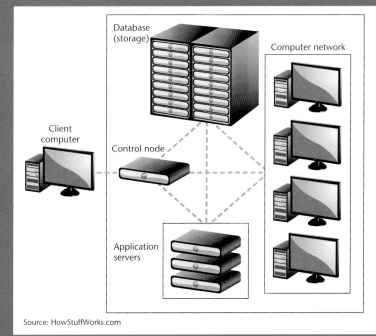

Source: HowStuffWorks.com

COMPUTERS AND ELECTRONICS continued

Netherlands, the world-class Thialf skating arena in Heerenveen uses wireless mesh technology to control the condition of the ice for the professional skaters who practice and perform on the rink. The mesh network comprises numerous wireless sensors embedded in and above the ice.

In the United States, applications of wireless mesh technology geared for home use began to

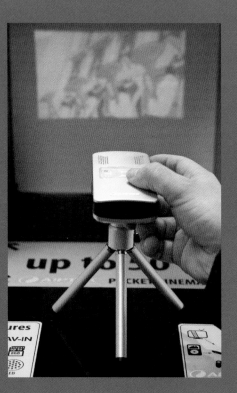

PROJECTOR OUT
OF THE POCKET

The pocket-sized AIPTEK Pocket Cinema T10 projector projects a widescreen movie in a demonstration at the CeBit fair, a major international technology fair, in Hanover, Germany, in March 2009. AIPTEK International Inc. is based in Taiwan. The device is one of a growing number of so-called "pico projectors"—devices typically weighing from 100 to 200 grams (3.5 to 7.0 ounces)— that were entering the electronics market in 2008 and 2009.

appear in 2009. In March, Avaak Inc. of San Diego launched its Vue Personal Video Network. The product consists of wireless, golfball-sized video cameras that can be mounted by their peel-and-stick backs where monitoring is desired. The minicams are tied together in a wireless mesh network that users monitor through a Web browser on their home computers. Industry experts predicted that other similar home monitoring systems, ideal for checking up on small children or maintaining security, would reach the market in the near future.

Augmented reality leaves the lab. Cell phones took a step toward putting augmented reality onto the streets in January 2009 when United Kingdom-based T-Mobile UK Ltd. launched a new cell phone-based feature called nru (for *near you*). Augmented reality (AR) involves superimposing a real-time cyberlayer of useful information on a real-life layer, such as a camera view of a physical place.

The nru feature turns a cell phone into a compass-enhanced, real-time information bank. Users can access information about nearby service venues, such as theaters and restaurants. The display window of the nru-equipped G1 phone (a T-Mobile product) provides a simple map with the user at the center; arrayed around the user in every direction are such venues as restaurants (if that category has been selected). As the user moves or turns, the display adjusts the map to keep the user at the center and the service venues at the proper relative positions.

The user can access additional information about the venue. If restaurants are displayed, for example, the user can access a menu, hours of operation, or customer reviews. He or she can contact the restaurant to make a reservation.

In addition to a compass, the nru-enhanced phone contains accelerometers— tiny sensors that determine whether the device has been tilted or turned—so that the AR overlay of data will be accurate. The device also accesses GPS satellite data to position the service venues on the map overlay accurately.

As of mid-2009, nru was available only in the United Kingdom through T-Mobile UK. Telecommunications experts, however, predicted that similar nru functionality would quickly be picked up by other wireless phone providers in Europe and the United States.

■ Peter Andrews

CONSERVATION

In October 2008, researchers led by microbiologist David Blehert of the United States Geological Survey (USGS) reported that they had identified the fungal species that has been infecting bat populations in the U.S. Northeast since 2007. The white, powdery mold infects bats' bodies and often shows up as a white patch on the nose. The condition is called white-nose syndrome (WNS). Through DNA analysis, Blehert's team found that the fungus is a previously undescribed form of *Geomyces*, a *genus* (group) of fungi that thrives between 5 °C and 10 °C (41 °F and 50 °F). This range of temperature is typical of bats' caves.

Blehert and colleagues examined 117 dead bats of different species from 18 sites within the area affected by WNS—states in the northeastern United States. Most of the bats had fungal infections penetrating their skin. These same bats also had little or no reserve of body fat, a sign of malnutrition. Blehert and his team reported their findings in the Oct. 30, 2008, online edition of *Science*.

WNS was first observed in the winter of 2006–2007 in a few caves west of Albany, New York. Since then, naturalists and biologists have observed WNS in bats in caves in other sections of New York and in the states of Connecticut, Massachusetts, New Hampshire, New Jersey, Pennsylvania, Vermont, Virginia, and West Virginia. The syndrome has affected six species of bat, all of which hibernate in caves or abandoned mines. Among bats infected with the fungus, very high percentages are dying within or near caves.

SEE ALSO CONSUMER SCIENCE, BAMBOO— THE NEW "WOOD"?, PAGE 133.

Although the *Geomyces* fungus is associated with the bat deaths, scientists have not established that it is the cause. They theorize that the cause could be another infectious agent or an environmental factor, for example. The fungus may be an opportunistic infection that takes hold in bats already weakened by another cause or causes. For this reason, biologists continued to pursue several lines of research to discover the ultimate cause of the bat deaths.

What is known is that the infected bats rouse more frequently than normal from their lethargic states in hibernation, causing them to burn the limited body-fat reserves they need to survive the cold winter. Unable to feed during the winter to replace the body fat, the bats then die of malnutrition. Some roused bats even go out into the winter cold to search for insects—a futile task.

Bats perform a critical ecological service. They feed on such insects as mosquitoes, moths, and beetles, which can destroy crops and spread disease.

On Feb. 20, 2009, some of the top researchers working on WNS participated in a *webinar* (interactive, Web-based seminar) to share information about their ongoing research. Bat physiologist DeeAnn Reeder of Bucknell University in Lewisburg, Pennsylvania,

WILDEBEEST MIGRATION

Wildebeests cross the Masai Mara National Reserve in Kenya. Up to 25 percent of migrating species may no longer travel seasonally, according to research reported in June 2009 by Grant Harris of the Center for Biodiversity and Conservation at the American Museum of Natural History in New York City. In studies of 24 species of *ungulates* (hoofed, plant-eating animals), Harris and his colleagues found that farming, water restrictions, and other human changes to the landscapes were interfering with the animals' movements and contributing to declines in their populations.

CONSERVATION continued

reported on her research into the patterns of arousal in hibernating bats. Preliminary results from field data taken from caves in New York, Pennsylvania, and Vermont confirmed that WNS-infected bats are rousing more frequently than unaffected bats. The arousal pattern in healthy bats is to wake up every 13 to 17 days. However, in compromised bats, the arousal rate ranges from every 4 to every 8 days.

Reeder also reported significant WNS fungal damage on bats' thin wing membranes. This observation suggests that even bats that survive winter hibernation may succumb in the summer, because damaged wings would likely interfere with feeding. Insect-devouring bats feed mainly in flight.

Also participating in the February webinar were biologist Thomas Kunz and graduate student Jonathan Reichard of Boston University. These scientists wondered if the low body fat detected in many WNS-afflicted bats was acquired during disrupted hibernation—as many scientists theorized—or if the bats entered hibernation already fat-depleted. Pre-

liminary results from field data collected by Kunz and Reichard indicated that bats that subsequently developed WNS entered their hibernacula (hibernation caves) already exhibiting low body weight. This result suggests that a factor or factors in the bats' ecology may be contributing to their rapid decline and death. Such factors might include loss of habitat for roosting and feeding or stresses from pesticide contaminants consumed when bats eat contaminated insects.

In March, biologist Craig Willis of the University of Manitoba in Winnipeg, Canada, and biology graduate student Justin Boyles of Indiana State University in Terre Haute published a mathematical model that projected that equipping hibernacula with heated boxes could sharply reduce bat deaths from WNS. The purpose of the boxes was to provide a warm place where aroused bats could rest. The scientists' research appeared in the March 5 issue of the journal *Frontiers in Ecology and the Environment*.

Willis and Boyles also reported that they were preparing to test their hypothesis by

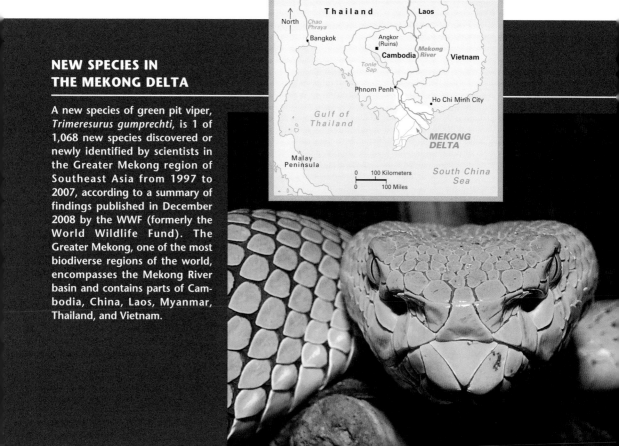

NEW SPECIES IN THE MEKONG DELTA

A new species of green pit viper, *Trimeresurus gumprechti*, is 1 of 1,068 new species discovered or newly identified by scientists in the Greater Mekong region of Southeast Asia from 1997 to 2007, according to a summary of findings published in December 2008 by the WWF (formerly the World Wildlife Fund). The Greater Mekong, one of the most biodiverse regions of the world, encompasses the Mekong River basin and contains parts of Cambodia, China, Laos, Myanmar, Thailand, and Vietnam.

equipping a bat cave near Grand Rapids, Manitoba, with heated boxes and, as an experimental control, unheated boxes. The researchers emphasized that they did not regard provisioning bat caves with heated boxes as a solution to WNS; their aim, rather, was to reduce deaths from the syndrome or—in a worst-case scenario—preserve a remnant population.

In March 2009, the U.S. Fish and Wildlife Service asked individuals other than research scientists to voluntarily stay out of caves within a 17-state geographical area. The area encompassed the Northeast and parts of the Midwest affected by WNS. Scientists and federal officials expressed concern that the presence of amateur cave explorers, who are unlikely to be fitted with sterile clothing and equipment, would spread the sickness to WNS-free caves.

Gorilla census. In August, scientists reported that they had counted about 126,000 western lowland gorillas in the northern part of Congo (Brazzaville). The census, sponsored by the New York City-based Wildlife Conservation Society (WCS) and the government of Congo (Brazzaville), revealed a surprisingly dense concentration of gorillas in a region that previously had not been well studied. The scientists announced their findings at the biennial Primatological Congress held in August in Edinburgh, Scotland.

All gorillas live in Africa. There are two species: lowland gorillas and eastern gorillas. Western lowland gorillas, a subspecies of lowland gorillas, comprise the most populous group by far. In addition to Congo (Brazzaville), western lowland gorillas live in Congo (Kinshasa), the Central African Republic, Equatorial Guinea, Nigeria, and Uganda.

The census-taking scientists focused on a remote, heavily forested, 47,444 square-kilometer (18,318 square-mile) region of Congo (Brazzaville). Because gorillas avoid contact with human beings, the scientists counted the sleeping nests the gorillas make from leaves and tree branches each night.

In 1996, scientists had estimated the population of all western lowland gorillas at about 95,000 individuals. Most scientists agreed that the population had declined since then at an unknown rate.

Discovered in the Lansak district of Thailand's Uthaithani Province, the Dragon millipede (above), *Desmoxytes purpurosea*, likely uses its "shocking pink" neon coloring to warn predators of its poison.

The *Aeschynanthus mendumiae* orchid (below) was discovered on the southeastern slopes of Laos' Phuo Yang Mountain.

CONSERVATION continued

The Gland, Switzerland-based International Union for Conservation of Nature and Natural Resources (IUCN) lists the western lowland gorilla as critically endangered. (The IUCN, a nonprofit group, publishes "the Red List," a list of all known threatened species.) The addition of 126,000 individuals to the gorilla population is a significant discovery, but conservationists note that many factors continue to threaten gorilla survival.

Conservation scientists Emma Stokes, Richard Malonga, and Hugo Rainey—all participants in the WCS-Congo census and authors of the census report—recommended that the lowland gorillas not be *downlisted* (demoted to a less urgent preservation category) by the IUCN. They further urged conservationists and regional governments to work to remove the threats that endanger gorilla populations in Africa.

Chief among these threats are the hunting of gorillas for *bush meat* (the meat of wild animals taken from forests) and for body parts used in some Asian medicines; loss of habitat, particularly through legal and illegal commercial logging; and diseases such as the deadly Ebola virus, which in 2003 killed about 800 gorillas in the Lossi Gorilla Sanctuary in Congo (Kinshasa).

Gorillas belong to the primate subgroup known as the great apes, which also includes chimpanzees, bonobos, and two species of orangutan. Next to chimpanzees and bonobos, gorillas are our closest evolutionary relatives. These species and orangutans are at risk of extinction.

Pacific preserves. In January 2009, U.S. President George W. Bush designated three areas of the Pacific Ocean as national monuments, granting them the highest level of conservation protection afforded by the federal government. The three areas, which together comprise the largest marine conservation set-aside in history, are the Mariana Trench Marine National Monument, the Pacific Remote Islands Marine National Monument, and the Rose Atoll Marine National Monument.

The combined surface area of the three national monuments is 505,757 square kilometers (195,274 square miles). These Pacific preserves join the 362,000-square-kilometer (140,000-square-mile) Papahanaumokuakea Marine National Monument, set aside by President Bush in the western Hawaiian Islands in 2006.

The Marianas Trench Marine National Monument encompasses the 14 islands of the United States Commonwealth of the Northern Mariana Islands and the United States Territory of Guam. These islands emerge from an undersea ridge known as the Mariana Volcanic Arc, which flanks the Mariana Trench, the deepest oceanic trench on Earth. The waters are biologically diverse and include numerous explored and unexplored deep hydrothermal vents that are home to unusual species of marine life and bacteria. In addition, highly diverse and pristine coral-reef ecosystems exist near the islands.

The Pacific Remote Islands Marine National Monument includes Wake, Baker, Howland, and Jarvis Islands, Johnston Atoll, Kingman Reef, and Palmyra Atoll, to the southwest of Hawaii. The national monument encloses these islands within a marine area of 225,039 square kilometers (86,888 square miles). Wake Island—the site of a famous battle in World War II (1939–1945)—supports several species of nesting birds, including two albatross species, three species of boobies, and the great frigatebird.

The coral reefs around the atolls and islands of the monument are inhabited by hundreds of fish species. Local nutrient-rich upwellings in the ocean waters account for an exceptionally high fish biomass, according to oceanographers.

Rose Atoll is the easternmost island in the Samoan island chain. Rose Atoll Marine National Monument takes in the tiny atoll and Pacific waters surrounding it and comprises 34,838 square kilometers (13,451 square miles). This protected area encompasses a unique and pristine coral-reef ecosystem hosting 100 species of stony corals and 272 species of reef fish; at least 7 species of these fish are found nowhere else. Hawksbill turtles, a species designated as endangered since the 1973 enactment of the U.S. Endangered Species Act (ESA), use Rose Atoll as a nesting site. Sea birds, some of them protected under the ESA, also nest on the atoll.

In each of the three marine monuments created in January 2009, commercial fishing is prohibited, though *subsistence* (fishing for personal consumption) and recreation fishing is permitted. Commercial and military shipping traffic are also permitted in these protected areas.　　■ David Barker

Białowieźa: The Remains of a Primeval Forest

It was once a playground for dukes, princes, czars, and kings. During World War II (1939–1945), guerrilla fighters died there and were buried in unmarked graves. Now, children come every winter to visit "Grandfather Frost," the equivalent of Santa Claus for many Eastern Europeans. The place is Białowieźa (byah woh VYE zhuh) Forest, a roughly 150,000-hectare (370,660-acre) tract that straddles the border between Poland and Belarus. (In Belarus, the name of this forest is written as "Belovezha.")

Some scientists believe that Białowieźa Forest contains one of the last pristine remnants of ancient forest that once covered most of Europe. (A pristine forest is one that is virtually unchanged from its natural, prehistoric condition.) These scientists urge that the forest be strictly protected from logging and other human activities. Other scientists argue that no place on Earth remains untouched by human influence and that sustainable development—including logging and tourism—is a wise way to manage the forest. In 2009, government leaders in Poland and Belarus were seeking to balance the interests of scientists, industries, and tourists regarding Białowieźa Forest.

Thousands of years ago, thick forests of *deciduous* trees (those that shed their leaves each year) covered the temperate lowlands of most of what is now Europe. Among these trees were oaks, maples, ashes, birches, and poplars. By about 6000 B.C., the people of southeastern Europe abandoned hunting and gathering and began growing their own food. By 3000 B.C., the practice of farming had spread to all but the northernmost areas of Europe. Farms, roads, and cities soon covered most of the land.

In north-central Europe, however, an assortment of tribes—referred to as "barbarians" by the ancient Romans—delayed the development of the land by their frequent fighting. Waterways, rather than roads, served as the primary means of transportation in this region. It was not until the A.D. 800's that organized nations began to form in north-central Europe. Roads did not become common in this area until the 1300's.

Even as the people of north-central Europe cleared forests to build roads, farms, and towns, Białowieźa Forest remained relatively untouched. In the early 1400's, Władysław II Jagiełło, grand duke of Lithuania and king of Poland, set aside the woodland as a reserve from which he could take red deer and wisent (European bison) to feed his armies. In the centuries that followed—as the area changed hands from one nation to another—Białowieźa became, in turn, a "royal forest" and a private hunting ground for Russian czars. By the late 1600's, several villages had been established in the area to process iron ore and to make tar from wood products.

During World War I (1914–1918), Białowieźa Forest, which had been owned by Russia for nearly 30 years, came under German control. German

"Old-Growth" Forest

Białowieźa Forest, on the border between Poland and Belarus (maps above), has parts in both countries that are designated as national parks. Large numbers of moss- and lichen-covered logs, characteristic of pristine, "old-growth" forests, can be found in much of Białowieźa Forest (above).

CONTINUED

and Russian soldiers, as well as local *poachers* (people who hunt illegally), hunted the forest's wisents to extinction by 1919. The Germans also laid railroad track through the forest to establish a lumber industry in the area. After the war, Poland gained control of western Belarus, including Białowieża.

During World War II, first the Soviet Union, then Nazi Germany controlled the forest. After the war, forest ownership was divided between Poland and Belarus (which was a part of the Soviet Union at the time). A fence that neither people nor large animals could cross was built through the woods to mark the border between the two nations.

As ownership of Białowieża Forest passed from country to country, parts of it came under varying degrees of protection. In 1921, a 4,747-hectare (11,730-acre) section of the Polish-owned forest became a national forest reserve, and in 1932, a national park, in which logging is banned. The Polish government enlarged the national park to 10,500 hectares (25,946 acres) in 1996 and established an additional protected area outside the park in 2003. The Polish government also set aside a 275-hectare (680-acre) section of land for the breeding of wisents and other wildlife.

In the Belarusian part of Białowieża, a state game reserve was established in 1940, and a national park in 1991. However, the government of Belarus permits logging in the park. More than 100,000 people visit the Belarusian part of Białowieża Forest each year to see the "home" of Grandfather Frost and a nearby museum. Approximately 30,000 people live in the Belarusian part of the forested area, compared with about 3,000 in the Polish part.

Considering the history of human impact on Białowieża Forest, can any part of it truly be considered pristine? Prehistoric forests untouched by human beings—so-called primeval forests—consisted of a wide variety of plant species that grew to different heights, forming multiple stories (including canopy [top], understory, shrub, herb, and forest floor layers). The tallest trees were of great height, girth, and age. Primeval forests also contained large amounts of deadwood and decaying trees, as well as a variety of organisms—including lichens, mosses, and fungi—that grow on such materials. Characteristic species of animals lived in particular kinds of primeval forests.

Isolated parts of Białowieża Forest meet such primeval, or "old-growth," criteria today. Hundreds of trees in protected areas—particularly the oaks—are as old as 600 years, with trunks that are as much as 700 centimeters (275 inches) around. Scientists have measured oaks with heights of 36 meters (118 feet) or more. Areas containing such ancient, giant trees comprise only about 20 percent of the existing forest. These areas also contain the deadwood litter and associated organisms characteristic of an old-growth forest floor. Both the Polish and Belarusian parts of Białowieża Forest have thousands of species of fungi and hundreds of species of lichens and mosses.

Certain species of wild animals that live nowhere else—or in few other places—are found in Białowieża Forest. The most famous of these animals is the wisent. Although the last wild wisent in Białowieża was killed in 1919, Russian czars had sent several pairs of these animals to other countries as

Wisent Recovery

Two male wisents (European bison) butt heads in a test of dominance in Białowieża Forest. Although all wild wisents in the forest were exterminated by 1919, the breeding of captive individuals and their later release into the forest has led to limited recovery of the wisent herds. Today, hundreds of wisents live in Białowieża Forest, some roaming freely through the woods and others kept in breeding enclosures.

gifts in the late 1800's. After World War I, 54 wisents—the only remaining members of their species—lived in zoos around the world. In 1929, conservationists brought four of these wisents to Białowieża Forest, where they were kept in a breeding enclosure. Some descendants of these animals were set free in the forest in 1952. Today, about 300 wisents live in the breeding enclosure and 600 more roam free on both the Polish and Belarusian sides of the forest. However, all existing wisents are descended from only 13 animals, so scientists are concerned that they may be vulnerable to disease.

Białowieża Forest is also home to about 10 species of woodpeckers, whose survival is threatened by logging. Relatives of the tarpan, a species of small wild horse that became extinct in the late 1800's, are found in parts of the forest. These animals, called koniks, are the result of cross-breeding between tarpans and domestic horses prior to the tarpan's extinction.

Although some aspects of Białowieża's plant and animal life support the argument that this forest is a unique primeval remnant, other aspects highlight the forest's disturbance by human activities. Over the years, hunters, loggers, and miners have all changed the natural conditions of the forest in ways that continue to affect its ecology. A number of animal species that lived in Białowieża, such as the aurochs (wild ox) and European mink, were hunted to extinction or near extinction and cannot be restored to the forest.

Because populations of such native predators as the Eurasian lynx and gray wolf have been severely depleted in the forest, an overpopulation of red deer developed. Wildlife managers try to keep the deer in check through controlled hunting. Biologists note that it would be impossible to restore predator populations to their robust primeval conditions, because the protected areas of Białowieża are too small and fragmented. Predators typically require large hunting ranges in order to thrive and control prey populations.

Some types of animals and plants that never populated the ancient Białowieża Forest now find homes there. For example, American minks escaped into the forest from nearby farms, and seeds of certain crops spread from farms into the forest. These and other factors have permanently altered the Białowieża ecosystem.

Despite these ecological disturbances, conservationists point out that the surviving remnants of Białowieża Forest are as close as European forests come to primeval conditions today. In 2009, conservationists in Poland hoped that the country's Białowieża national park would be expanded to cover the entire Polish section of the forest. Logging would then be banned throughout this section. Belarusian scientists published a new management plan for the Belarusian part of the forest in 2009. The document included a recommendation to expand the strictly protected zone within Belarus's Białowieża national park, as well as plans to increase environmental monitoring, research, and educational activities in the park.

Białowieża Forest reached its 600th year as Europe's oldest nature reserve in 2009. With the combined efforts of Poland, Belarus, and international conservation organizations, future generations will continue to have the opportunity of experiencing the primeval beauty of Białowieża Forest.

■ Kristina A. Vaicikonis

Białowieża Biology

A biologist in the Polish part of Białowieża Forest uses tracking equipment to study the movement of pine martens, weasel-like mammals, that have been tagged with small radio transmitters. The sizes of marten home ranges vary in the forest, depending on the density of forest cover and the number of rodents available for food.

DEATHS OF SCIENTISTS

Notable people of science who died between June 1, 2008, and May 31, 2009, are listed below. Those listed were Americans unless otherwise indicated.

Bartlett, Neil (1932–Aug. 5, 2008), British-born chemist who founded noble-gas chemistry by proving that the noble gases are not *inert* (chemically inactive). The noble gases are the only elements that are made up of single atoms. Because they do not readily gain or lose electrons or share electrons with other elements, scientists once believed that noble gases could not be used to create compounds. Bartlett revolutionized this thinking by successfully creating xenon fluoride, the first compound made from a noble gas. His discovery is regarded as one of the most significant contributions to inorganic chemistry.

Michael E. DeBakey

Bennett, William R. (1930–June 29, 2008), physicist who helped construct the first gas laser. Bennett's team at Bell Laboratories (now part of Lucent Technologies) trapped helium and neon in a pressurized tube, charged their atoms with an electric current, and channeled the moving atoms into a concentrated, continuous beam of light. Medical technology has since developed eye-surgery techniques using the gas laser. The invention also led to the creation of such everyday products as compact-disc players and bar-code scanners.

Brück, Mary T. (1925–Dec. 11, 2008), Irish-born Scottish astronomer, teacher, and advocate for women in science. She is best known for her biography, *Agnes Mary Clerke and the Rise of Astrophysics* (2002). As an astronomer, she specialized in using sophisticated photographic techniques to measure the color and brightness of stars in order to determine their age.

Cover, Jack (1920–Feb. 7, 2009), aerospace scientist who invented the TASER (now called the Taser) stun gun, a device used by police officers and other law enforcers to temporarily immobilize a person with electric shocks. Cover invented the gun in 1974 and gave it the acronym TASER, which stood for *Thomas A. Swift Electric Rifle*. Tom Swift was Cover's childhood hero from a series of children's adventure stories.

Dannenberg, Konrad (1912–Feb. 16, 2009), German-born rocket scientist who helped lead a team in designing the propulsion system for NASA's Saturn 5 rocket. Saturn 5 was the launch vehicle that sent the Apollo 11 astronauts to the first United States moon landing in 1969.

DeBakey, Michael E. (1908–July 11, 2008), surgeon who pioneered surgery techniques on the heart and blood vessels. In 1966, DeBakey led a team that successfully implanted a heart pump into a patient. DeBakey's other medical achievements included surgically repairing *aneurysms* (ruptured blood vessels), creating synthetic blood vessels, developing techniques for by-passing blocked arteries, and performing heart transplants. During his lifetime, he performed more than 60,000 operations on heart patients.

Figueroa, Gonzalo (1931–May 20, 2008), archaeologist who accompanied Thor Heyerdahl on his famous expedition to Easter Island, Chile, in the mid-1950's. After the expedition, Figueroa continued to conduct research on the island to determine how its ancient sites and artifacts should be excavated, restored, and preserved. He served as the island's adviser to the Chilean government and to UNESCO, the United Nations agency that works to protect the world's cultural heritage.

Furchgott, Robert F. (1916–May 19, 2009), pharmacologist whose studies of the gas nitric oxide led to significant advances in the understanding and treatment of cardiovascular disease. His work showing that gases can perform important biochemical functions in the body earned him a share of the 1998 Nobel Prize for physiology or medicine.

Gonzalo Figueroa

Gajdusek, D. Carleton (1923–Dec. 11, 2008), medical researcher who, together with Baruch S. Blumberg, won the 1976 Nobel Prize in physiology or medicine for discoveries concerning the origin and spread of certain infectious diseases. Gajdusek concentrated his research on a disease common among the Fore people of Papua New Guinea, in which the brain cells are gradually destroyed. His findings led to progress in identifying the cause of such diseases of the nervous system as Alzheimer's, mad cow disease, multiple sclerosis, and Parkinson disease.

Gleason, Donald F. (1920–Dec. 28, 2008), pathologist who created the medical test for cancer of the prostate gland, an organ of the male reproductive system. Called the Gleason score, the test analyzes the tissue cells of the gland and grades the degree of abnormality from 1 (nearly normal) to 5 (most cancerous). Gleason devised his test in the 1960's, and it is still considered the most reliable tool not only for diagnosing cancer, but also for prescribing treatment and developing new therapies.

Goldsmith, Thomas T., Jr. (1910–March 5, 2009), television technology pioneer who, in the mid-1930's, along with others, perfected the cathode-ray tube (a precursor to the picture tube) in a way that allowed television sets to be mass produced. Goldsmith and a colleague also invented and, in 1948, received a patent for, the Cathode-Ray Tube Amusement Device, considered by some to be the first video game.

Joel, Amos E., Jr. (1918–Oct. 25, 2008), electrical engineer who invented the switching device that allows users of cellular telephones to pass from one *cell* (geographic area) to another without getting cut off. Joel patented his device in 1972. By the late 1970's, scientists had found a way to apply Joel's device to wireless telephones, which had been limited to just one cell. Joel's other inventions—more than 70 of them—led to such telephone advances as call waiting, caller ID, long-distance direct dialing, and touch-tone telephones.

Lamb, Willis E., Jr. (1913–May 15, 2008), atomic physicist who won the 1955 Nobel Prize in physics for his discoveries in the structure of the hydrogen atom. He shared the prize with Polykarp Kusch, a German-born American atomic physicist. Lamb found that the energy levels of electrons within a hydrogen atom are not identical. This phenomenon became known as the "Lamb shift." His discovery led to a better understanding of quantum mechanics and how electrons interact. His work also paved the way for a new discipline called quantum electrodynamics.

Lindauer, Martin (1918–Nov. 13, 2008), German zoologist and behaviorist whose research led to an understanding of how honey bees function in their colonies. Lindauer's observations included how bees respond to their colony's food and water needs, how a bee colony decides where to build its hive, and how bees use the sun to help them navigate.

Loyd, Paula (1972–Jan. 7, 2009), anthropologist stationed in southern Afghanistan to research the culture of the people living there. Loyd worked for the United States Army's Human Terrain System, a program intended to improve relations between U.S. troops and Afghans. She was completing an interview with an Afghan man on Nov. 4, 2008, when he doused her with cooking fuel and set her on fire. Loyd suffered burns over 60 percent of her body and died two months later.

Paula Loyd

Maddox, Sir John (1925–April 12, 2009), British science journalist and editor who is widely considered to have been a pioneer of modern science journalism. Maddox began his career as a lecturer in theoretical physics. Later, he became a science correspondent for the *Manchester* (England) *Guardian.* He served as editor of the prestigious science journal *Nature* from 1966 to 1973 and then again from 1979 to 1995, adding commentaries on the politics of science, introducing a peer review system for scientific articles, and increasing both the journal's circulation and its reputation.

Miles, Tim (1923–Dec. 11, 2008), British psychologist who led in the study of dyslexia. He reversed the assumption that dyslexia was a psychological disorder and diagnosed it instead as an abnormality in the way the brain processes information. With this new knowledge, Miles established guidelines and a training program for teachers of dyslexic students.

Noon, Carole C. (1949–May 2, 2009), primatologist and founder of the nonprofit

DEATHS OF SCIENTISTS continued

Carole C. Noon

organization Save the Chimps, based in Fort Pierce, Florida, and Alamagordo, New Mexico. An anthropologist who was inspired by British zoologist and chimpanzee expert Jane Goodall, Noon established the world's largest sanctuary for captive chimpanzees to house chimps that had been used in the aerospace, biomedical research, and entertainment industries and those originally sold as pets.

Palade, George E. (1912–Oct. 7, 2008), Romanian-born biologist who shared the 1974 Nobel Prize in physiology or medicine with American Albert Claude and Belgian Christian de Duve for their discoveries in cell biology. Palade helped develop a method—called cell fractionation—of separating the components of a cell to see how they function and interact. This method enabled him to learn how cells manufacture proteins, how the proteins move around within the cell, and how they are transported outside the cell. These discoveries provided the basis for later research into the cause of certain diseases.

Piatetski-Shapiro, Ilya (1929–Feb. 21, 2009), Russian-born Israeli mathematician whose research focused on modern number theory and algebraic geometry. He is best known for his analysis of two complex concepts, automorphic forms and L-functions. The theories he developed influenced scientists in many fields, including cell biology, geophysics, and computer science.

Selfridge, Oliver G. (1926–Dec. 3, 2008), British-born computer scientist and pioneer in the field of artificial intelligence. He was among the first to predict that computers would one day be able to replace—and even improve upon—human beings in performing everyday tasks. In a paper he presented in 1958, Selfridge explained how machines could be designed to recognize patterns and process them in much the same way that the human brain does.

Stent, Gunther (1924–June 12, 2008), German-born biologist who helped establish the field of molecular biology, the study of how living cells function and interact. Stent used leeches for much of his research, to show how the interactions of neurons affect learning and behavior and to demonstrate the process of evolutionary development. Stent was also a major force in the history and philosophy of science.

Weller, Thomas H. (1915–Aug. 23, 2008), virologist who shared the 1954 Nobel Prize in physiology or medicine with fellow Americans John F. Enders and Frederick C. Robbins. Together, they developed a method of growing the poliomyelitis virus on human tissues in test tubes. Weller also isolated the viruses of chickenpox, rubella (German measles), and shingles. The creation of vaccines for these diseases was possible, in large part, because of Weller's work.

Worzel, J. Lamar (1919–Dec. 26, 2008), ocean geophysicist who conducted research

Lamar J. Worzel

and invented devices that made it possible to view and measure the contours of the ocean floor and to study how sound flows through ocean waters. Working with his colleague, Maurice Ewing, Worzel opened the way for the United States to conduct undersea espionage against the Soviet Union during the Cold War.

Zhabotinsky, Anatol (1938–Sept. 16, 2008), Russian-born chemist who founded nonlinear chemical dynamics through his discovery of *oscillating* (fluctuating) reactions. (Nonlinear chemical dynamics is the area of chemistry that observes the unstable reactions that can occur when certain atoms or molecules are combined.) Building on the experiments of Russian chemist Boris Belousov, Zhabotinsky showed how a certain bromine-acid solution could produce reactions that oscillate under different conditions. Chemists call this the Belousov-Zhabotinsky (BZ) reaction.
　　　　　　　　　■ Cheryl Graham

DRUGS

The United States Food and Drug Administration (FDA) approved 24 new drugs in 2008 and 9 more in the first five months of 2009. Among these were the first drug ever produced in animals genetically modified to secrete the active ingredient in their milk as well as the first drug treatment for Huntington's disease. In 2008 and early 2009, the agency also approved four new vaccines for the prevention of infectious diseases.

In addition, the agency in 2008 approved 91 new *generic medications* (less-expensive copies of brand-name drugs whose patents had expired). The FDA approved another 46 generics in the first four months of 2009.

The FDA made history in February 2009 by approving the first drug manufactured with altered DNA (deoxyribonucleic acid, the material from which genes are made). The drug, recombinant antithrombin (sold under the brand name ATryn), is made with milk from goats genetically modified to produce copies of a human protein called antithrombin. Antithrombin acts as a blood thinner; people who are born with insufficient antithrombin are at higher risk for blood clots than the general population.

ATryn is used primarily in hospitals. It is injected into patients with hereditary antithrombin deficiency when they undergo surgical operations or childbirth.

To develop the drug, geneticists at GTC Biotherapeutics of Framingham, Massachusetts, combined human DNA for antithrombin with goat DNA so that the goats' milk glands would secrete human antithrombin. They chose goats because it takes only 18 months to bring a genetically engineered goat to maturity—a shorter time than for a cow to mature. Making human antithrombin in goats is faster and cheaper than making it synthetically or extracting it from donated human blood, and the animals are not harmed.

Some scientists advocate using genetically altered animals on a large scale to function as pharmaceutical factories. Animal rights activists, however, express ethical and other concerns about using animals in this way.

First drug for Huntington's disease. In August 2008, the FDA approved tetrabenazine (sold under the brand name Xenazine) for the treatment of *chorea* (involuntary jerky movements) in people with Huntington's disease. Tetrabenazine is the first drug ever approved to treat chorea, and the first treatment of any kind for Huntington's disease.

SEE ALSO THE SPECIAL REPORT, **THE TIMELESS SCOURGE OF MALARIA**, PAGE 88.

Huntington's is a rare, inherited disorder of the brain and nervous system that affects about 1 in 10,000 people in the United States. About 30,000 Americans have it, and another 200,000 are at risk of developing the disease because one parent has it.

The symptoms of Huntington's typically develop between ages 30 and 50. They include uncontrolled movements, loss of intellectual faculties, and emotional disturbance, all caused by the deterioration of brain cells.

Xenazine decreases the amount of dopamine in the brain. Dopamine is a chemical that communicates across synapses (microscopic spaces) between nerve cells in the brain. In Huntington's disease, this dopamine-enabled communications system is overactive, resulting in the abnormal movements called chorea.

Participants in the clinical studies of the drug reported a number of side effects. These included insomnia, depression, restlessness, nausea, and diminishment of *cognitive* (thinking) ability.

New cancer treatments. In December 2008, the FDA approved degarelix, an injectable drug for the treatment of hormonally sensitive, advanced prostate cancer. The drug suppresses production of the male sex hormone testosterone—which stimulates the growth of prostate cancer cells—and thus slows the growth of the cancer.

Degarelix belongs to a class of agents called gonadotropin-releasing hormone (GnRH) receptor inhibitors. Use of GnRH receptor inhibitors is one of the common treatments for prostate cancer, along with surgery, radiation therapy, and chemotherapy. In clinical tests, degarelix suppressed testosterone levels faster than previously approved medications, and matched long-term testosterone levels with the most effective of those medications.

Prostate cancer is one of the most common

DRUGS continued

cancers in the United States. About 190,000 new cases are diagnosed each year, and about 29,000 men die of the disease annually.

In March 2009, the FDA approved the drug everolimus (marketed under the brand name Afinitor) for treatment of people with advanced kidney cancer. Everolimus belongs to a class of drugs called kinase inhibitors, which interfere with cell communication and growth and, thus, disrupt the uncontrolled proliferation of tumor cells. The drug is intended for patients who have tried another kinase inhibitor that no longer exhibits significant therapeutic value.

In clinical trials, patients who took everolimus lived, on average, three months longer than patients who did not receive the drug. Because "targeted" drugs such as kinase inhibitors attack specific molecules in cancer cells, they usually cause fewer and gentler side effects than conventional chemotherapy agents, which attack all fast-growing cells. However, some patients in the everolimus clinical trials did experience such side effects as mouth sores, diarrhea, and coughing.

Antimalaria combination drug. In April 2009, the FDA approved a combination drug in tablet form to treat malaria. The tablet, incorporating artemether and lumefantrine, is sold under the brand name Coartem.

Artemether belongs to a class of antimalarial drugs known as artemisinins, which are medicines derived from a Chinese herb. Malaria parasites are less likely to mutate into drug-resistant forms in the presence of artemisinins than with other drugs, such as quinine-based drugs. The combination of an artemisinin-based drug with another drug delivers a one-two punch, note *epidemiologists* (scientists who study the spread of disease), that is more likely to be effective against malaria. The World Health Organization (WHO), an agency of the United Nations, strongly recommends artemisinin-combination drugs in preference to single-source antimalarial drugs to prevent the development and spread of drug resistance.

Treatment for gout. In February 2009, the FDA approved febuxostat (sold under the brand name Uloric) as a treatment for a painful form of arthritis known as gout. Febuxostat, taken in pill form, works by reducing levels of uric acid, a waste product of digestion and metabolism. If uric acid levels in the blood are too high, crystals may form in the big toe, foot, ankle, or knees. Pressure from these crystals causes symptoms of gout, including burning pain, stiffness, and swelling.

Previously, most gout patients have been treated with an older drug called allopurinol. In two of three clinical trials, patients who took febuxostat did better than those on allopurinol in controlling their uric acid levels.

FDA regulators approved febuxostat under the condition that the drug's manufacturer, Takeda Pharmaceuticals North America Inc. of Deerfield, Illinois, conduct a study to further assess the drug's cardiovascular safety. Results from the febuxostat clinical studies indicated a higher percentage of heart attacks, strokes, and other cardiovascular events in patients taking febuxostat than those taking allopurinol. FDA scientists could not determine, however, if these results were statistically significant.

Epilepsy. In November 2008, the FDA approved rufinamide (sold under the brand name Banzel) to treat the seizures associated with Lennox-Gastaut syndrome. Lennox-Gastaut is a severe form of epilepsy that usually begins before age 4. In most cases, it causes some degree of impaired intellectual functioning and behavioral disturbances.

Banzel is intended to be taken along with other antiseizure medications. Clinical studies demonstrated that subjects taking Banzel experienced a 20- to 40-percent improvement in seizure control compared with subjects taking a *placebo* (inactive substance). ■ Judy Peres

THERAPY AT THE CELLULAR LEVEL

Cells of the human immune system sport a biomolecular "backpack" (shown in green) attached by biochemists with the Massachusetts Institute of Technology (MIT). The "backpack" is actually a *polymer* (large chain-like molecule) that can carry a "payload." The MIT scientists reported that they could envision the "cell backpack" being used to deliver chemotherapy drugs directly to cancer cells in tumors or to align cells in a desired pattern for tissue engineering.

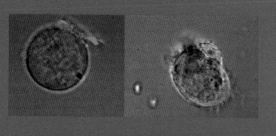

ECOLOGY

Two species of North American songbirds fly faster when migrating than previously thought, according to researchers led by Bridget Stutchbury of York University in Toronto, Canada. The researchers reported their findings in the Feb. 13, 2009, issue of *Science*. The songbirds—the wood thrush and purple martin—migrate thousands of miles between their summer homes in North America and winter homes in Central or South America.

Because small, rapidly moving songbirds are difficult to track, scientists have known relatively little about their migratory movements. However, increasing miniaturization of electronics has given scientists new tools. In summer 2007, the researchers captured wood thrushes and purple martins in Pennsylvania. They attached highly miniaturized devices called light-level geolocators to the birds and released them. The birds migrated to wintering grounds in Latin America and returned to Pennsylvania in spring 2008.

Each of the tiny geolocators, developed by engineers with the British Antarctic Survey, headquartered in Cambridge, the United Kingdom, contains a light sensor, a microprocessor, and a tiny data storage unit. The device weighs a little more than 1 gram (0.04 ounce) and can

SEE ALSO

THE SPECIAL REPORT, **MUTUALISM: THE PLEASURE OF YOUR COMPANY,** PAGE 58.

THE SPECIAL REPORT, **INVASION OF THE JELLYFISH,** PAGE 72.

be mounted on a bird's back so as not to disrupt balance or impede movement. The geolocator records the time of sunrise and sunset each day. From these data, scientists can determine approximate latitude and longitude, enabling them to identify the bird's daily location to within 300 kilometers (186 miles).

In 2008, Stutchbury and her colleagues retrieved geolocators in Pennsylvania from several returning birds. The data from the purple martins revealed that these birds had flown from Pennsylvania to Mexico's Yucatán Peninsula in five days. The birds flew an average of 500 kilometers (310 miles) per day on the 2,500-kilometer (1,550-mile) journey. Previously, scientists had believed the songbirds capable of flying no more than 150 kilometers (90 miles) a day.

ASIAN CARP BARRIER

An electric barrier built across the Chicago Sanitary and Ship Canal to prevent destructive Asian carp from entering Lake Michigan and other Great Lakes was switched on in April 2009 by the U.S. Army Corps of Engineers. The canal links the carp-infested Illinois River, a tributary of the Mississippi River, with the Chicago River, which flows out of Lake Michigan at Chicago. The carp, which invaded the Mississippi from flooded catfish farms, turn back when hit by an electric current.

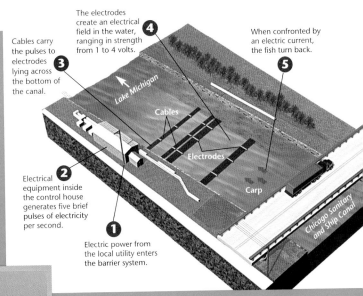

The electrodes create an electrical field in the water, ranging in strength from 1 to 4 volts. **4**

When confronted by an electric current, the fish turn back. **5**

Cables carry the pulses to electrodes lying across the bottom of the canal. **3**

Lake Michigan

Cables

Electrodes

Carp

Electrical equipment inside the control house generates five brief pulses of electricity per second. **2**

Electric power from the local utility enters the barrier system. **1**

Chicago Sanitary and Ship Canal

Asian carp leap wildly in the wake of a boat operated by a wildlife agent on the Illinois River. The invaders have decimated native fish in the Illinois and other tributaries of the Mississippi River. The large jumping fish have also injured sport fishers, boaters, and water skiers.

ECOLOGY continued

Populations of many species of migratory songbirds are experiencing steady declines. The ability to closely track the birds' migratory movements should help scientists understand the various risks these birds face and perhaps suggest ways to help stabilize songbird populations, the Stutchbury research team concluded.

Migratory movements of tuna. A study released in October 2008 yielded the most detailed information yet about spawning patterns of Atlantic bluefin tuna and their movements in the North Atlantic basin. Results of the study, led by marine biologist Jay R. Rooker of Texas A&M University at Galveston, appeared in the Oct. 31, 2008, issue of *Science*.

Atlantic bluefin tuna inhabit the Atlantic Ocean, the Gulf of Mexico, and the Mediterranean Sea. As adults, the tuna range widely in the Atlantic. To spawn, however, they return to the specific waters in which they were hatched—either the Mediterranean Sea or the Gulf of Mexico. Although the eastern (Mediterranean) and western (Gulf of Mexico) populations look the same, they are genetically distinct and do not usually interbreed.

The scientists sought to determine the hatching sites of Atlantic bluefin tuna caught in various locations. They used a technique involving chemical analysis of *otoliths* (ear bones) of captured fish. The scientists analyzed the relative amounts of two *isotopes* (variant forms of chemical elements) in the otoliths: carbon 13 and oxygen 18. Because the otolith tissue forms in the first year of the tuna's life, the ratio of these two isotopes provides a "signature" of the location of the fish's origin.

The scientists found that the rate of return to the tunas' birthplace to spawn was very high for both populations. Data revealed that 95.8 percent of eastern tuna returned to their Mediterranean Sea breeding waters and 99.3 percent of western tuna, to the Gulf of Mexico.

The data also revealed information about tuna ranges in Atlantic waters. The researchers found that the eastern and western tuna mix widely in the middle latitudes of the North Atlantic Ocean. However, populations in the Gulf of St. Lawrence and other northern waters were largely composed of western tuna.

The researchers emphasized the importance of gathering reliable data about Atlantic bluefin tuna in the face of the steep population declines of the species. According to the Inter-

national Commission for the Conservation of Atlantic Tunas, the 45-nation body that sets fishing quotas for tuna, the western Atlantic bluefin tuna has suffered a 90-percent decline in population since the 1970's. The eastern population has fared marginally better, experiencing a 50-percent decline. In its conclusions, Rooker's team recommended that the commission consider further restricting or banning the fishing of Atlantic bluefin tuna.

Self-organization of a population. In another study published in late 2008, scientists set out to determine how a population of animals organize themselves into a purposeful pattern, a process called spatial self-organization. Examples of spatial self-organization include the precise ways in which some species of birds fly in flocks or fish swim in schools.

Johan van de Koppel of the Spatial Ecology Department at the Netherlands Institute of Ecology and colleagues from the Netherlands, the United Kingdom, and France set out to study the process of spatial self-organization practiced by blue mussels—*bivalve* (two-shelled) water-living organisms related to oysters and clams. Blue mussels (*Mytilus edulis*) inhabit the intertidal zone, a section of seashore extending from the high-water to the low-water mark of daily tides.

The scientists observed that in nature, blue mussels organize themselves into small, regularly spaced clusters, each about 10 centimeters (4 inches) from nearby clusters. The scientists sought to replicate mussel patterning in laboratory conditions, placing individual mussels in evenly spaced configurations in laboratory test beds. In every test bed, the mussels self-organized into clustered groupings within 24 hours. In subsequent experiments, the researchers varied the number of mussels and such other factors as the availability of food and observed the results after 24 hours. With more food or higher densities, the clusters were larger.

Reporting in the Oct. 31, 2008, issue of *Science*, the van de Koppel team concluded that individual mussels, responding to various stimuli in their environment, move in ways that collectively result in predictable clustered patterning. The researchers asserted that spatial self-organization is an important factor in the structure and functioning of ecosystems, and they recommended further ecological studies along these lines. ■ Robert H. Tamarin

ENERGY

A *photovoltaic* (solar) cell with one of the highest efficiencies ever achieved was reported by scientists in Europe in November 2008. Photovoltaic cells produce electric current directly from sunlight, which causes electric charges to flow through layers of a conductive material. The efficiency of a photovoltaic cell refers to the percentage of the sunlight striking the cell that is converted into electric power.

Most conventional photovoltaic cells have conductive materials made of silicon crystals, which typically result in efficiencies as high as about 20 percent. These efficiencies can range as high as 35 percent with the use of special systems for concentrating sunlight. Researchers with the FULLSPECTRUM project, consisting of 19 research centers in several countries throughout Europe, developed a photovoltaic cell that boosted this efficiency even higher— to almost 40 percent.

The FULLSPECTRUM team created a so-called "multi-junction" photovoltaic system that was made of crystals of gallium, phosphorus, indium, and germanium arranged in panels. The panels included lenses to concentrate the solar energy onto the electricity-producing cells. Although similar technology had previously been used, the FULLSPECTRUM researchers made improvements in the structure of the network of thin metal wires that carry electric current in the cells.

The metal wires in multi-junction photovoltaic cells need to have high capacity and low resistance in order to effectively transport the sizeable electric current generated by concentrated sunlight. The European scientists tweaked the structure of the wire network to achieve the optimal efficiencies. They achieved an efficiency of 37.6 percent in 2006 and improved this to 39.7 percent in 2008.

Like conventional silicon-based photovoltaic cells, the improved multi-junction photovoltaic cells were expensive to produce. However, the team hoped that continued research on improving efficiency would lead to lower production costs.

Innovative electric car system. A test drive by South Korean President Lee Myung-bak in February 2009 highlighted an experimental system to power electric vehicles wirelessly. The innovative system was under development by scientists at the Korea Advanced Institute of Science and Technology

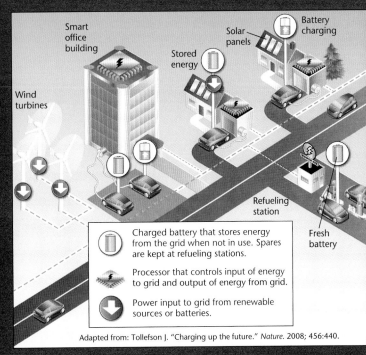

ELECTRIC CARS AS PART OF HIGH-CAPACITY GRID

Researchers in 2009 envisioned millions of battery-powered cars plugged into an electric grid with a distributed, high-capacity electric-power storage system. Cars would be able to recharge their batteries at home, work, and retail outlets by plugging into the grid. At special refueling stations, robotic arms could quickly replace used batteries with fresh ones. The grid would permit the storage of electric power during times of low demand and then draw power back when needed to meet peak demands. Electronic processors on houses and "smart" office buildings would regulate the input and output of electric power to meet needs and even out fluctuations. Renewable sources of energy, such as solar and wind power, would be incorporated into the grid.

Smart office building

Wind turbines

Solar panels

Stored energy

Battery charging

Charged battery that stores energy from the grid when not in use. Spares are kept at refueling stations.

Processor that controls input of energy to grid and output of energy from grid.

Power input to grid from renewable sources or batteries.

Refueling station

Fresh battery

Adapted from: Tollefson J. "Charging up the future." *Nature.* 2008; 456:440.

ENERGY continued

in Daedeok Science Town, South Korea. The scientists expected that their system, in which electric current is transferred wirelessly to vehicles from special strips embedded in roadways, would be tested with electric buses in a number of cities in South Korea by late 2009.

The Korean car power system was based on a technology called inductive charging, in which electric current is transferred between materials without wires. This is the same technology used to recharge batteries in some electric toothbrushes and shavers, which receive electric current through a magnetic connection while resting in a recharging cradle.

In the roadway version of this technology, power strips with electric current running through them from electrical stations are embedded in the tops of roads. Each strip in a working system, according to the researchers, would be from 20 centimeters (8 inches) to 90 centimeters (35 inches) wide and as long as several hundred meters. As cars or other vehicles pass over the strips, special magnetic devices on the undersides of the vehicles make connection with electromagnetic fields generated by the electric current in the strips—with no need for a physical contact with the strips. The electromagnetic energy is then converted back into electric current, which travels through cables to the battery in the vehicle.

The researchers said that their system was designed to allow electric vehicles to recharge their batteries during normal travel while driving over city roads. They noted that the system would make it possible to reduce the sizes of electric batteries in vehicles and to extend the ranges of such vehicles. The investigators estimated that by placing the power strips in approximately 10 percent of the roadway area in a city—particularly in places where vehicles slow down, such as near intersections—a practical system of recharging large numbers of electric vehicles could be maintained.

Improved coal gasification. An improved process of coal gasification, in which coal is tranformed into liquid fuels for cars and other vehicles, was reported in October 2008 by a team of scientists in Italy. The team was led by chemical engineer Maria Sudiro of the University of Padova in Italy.

The world's reserves of coal are much more abundant than reserves of crude oil, indicating that coal has the potential to meet energy needs for centuries. However, conventional methods of coal gasification are expensive and release large amounts of air pollutants and carbon dioxide, a greenhouse gas believed to contribute to global warming.

Sudiro's team revised a number of steps in the coal gasification process, including burning the coal in an environment of air, rather than pure oxygen, and using an *inert* (chemically unreactive) solid as a carrier of heat. Laboratory simulations of the new process indicated that it was 70 percent more energy efficient than conventional methods of coal gasification, and it yielded 40 percent more liquid fuel and released 32 percent less carbon dioxide.

"Spin battery" stores energy. In March 2009, the creation of a "spin battery" energy-storing device with potential applications in computers and automobiles was described by researchers at the University of Miami in Coral Gables, Florida, and the Universities of Tokyo and Tohoku in Japan. The team was led by University of Miami physicist Stewart E. Barnes. Energy experts praised the research for advancing the scientific study of magnets.

Most conventional batteries store energy through chemical reactions. Unlike these batteries, the spin battery created by the researchers stored energy with magnets. The battery was "wound up," or charged, through the application of a magnetic field to nanomagnets, tiny magnets that consist of only a few metal atoms. The nanomagnets induced an electromagnetic force, a force that an electromagnetic field exerts on electrically charged particles. As a result of this force, the magnetic energy of the device was converted directly into electrical energy—without the need for chemical reactions.

The device created by Barnes and his colleagues was extremely thin, with a diameter only about that of a human hair. The nanomagnets appeared as tiny microscopic dots on these "hairs."

The research team noted that its spin battery device had the potential to be used in electronic components of computers and other electronic devices, as well as in batteries that store power to run energy-efficient cars for many miles. The scientists said that further research was needed to clarify these and other potential practical applications of their spin battery technology. ■ Alfred J. Smuskiewicz

Energy—and Controversy— from Canadian Sands

An oil boom is taking place in Alberta in western Canada. Instead of producing gushers from oil derricks, however, operators in this oil boom are squeezing a thick, heavy, oil-like substance from sandy soil.

Oil sands (also called tar sands), are deposits of sand and soil that contain bitumen. Bitumen is a *viscous* (thick and sticky) oil that does not flow at room temperature and looks like cold molasses. Bitumen was formed in much the same way as crude oil. Over millions of years, the bodies of water-dwelling creatures accumulated in sediments on the bottoms of rivers, lakes, and seas. Subjected to great heat and pressure, this material eventually was transformed into petroleum. Over further eons, bacteria fed on the free-flowing crude, leaving behind heavy, glue-like bitumen.

The world's largest deposits of oil sands are in the Athabasca River Valley in northeastern Alberta. Geologists estimate that Alberta's sands may contain as much as 1.7 trillion barrels of oil. Other countries, including Russia, the United States, and Venezuela, also have sizable deposits of oil sands. However, only in Alberta has extraction of oil from oil sands been attempted on a large scale.

Extracting oil from oil sands is far more expensive than drilling oil wells. For bitumen-derived oil to be competitive on the world's oil market, the price of conventional oil must be high. The Canadian government, which has invested heavily in Alberta's oil sands, subsidizes the industry during times when oil prices dip sharply. With this support and rising world oil prices, Alberta's oil boom began in earnest in the 1990's.

To harvest near-surface deposits of oil sands, energy companies scoop out chunks of soil in what is essentially a strip-mining operation. Inside a processing facility, the oil-rich sand and soil is pulverized, then mixed with steam and hot water, producing a muddy substance called slurry. Eventually, the bitumen floats to the top and is extracted.

Operators next subject the bitumen to high heat in a furnace, converting it into lighter, less viscous petroleum. This petroleum can be refined into gasoline and other useful products.

Although mining is the most commonly used method for oil sands recovery, not all of the sands can be extracted in this way. In fact, most deposits are too deep in the earth to be dug out.

With deep deposits, the bitumen is recovered *in situ*—that is, while the sands remain in place. In the most common method of in-situ recovery, a network of pipes is embedded in the ground to the depth of the oil sands deposit. Operators pipe steam into the deposit, which heats the bitumen so that it becomes more liquid. Another pipe then sucks the hot bitumen slurry to the surface.

Oil sands have brought prosperity to Alberta. According to the Alberta Ministry of Finance and Enterprise, the province derives about

Digging for oil

Gargantuan shovels scoop up huge chunks of soil in the Athabasca region of Alberta in search of bitumen, a sticky, molasses-like substance related to petroleum and natural tar. The bitumen-soaked soil, referred to as "oil sands," harbors vast energy wealth. Petroleum is extracted from the oil sands—but at a high cost to the environment. Extracting the oil also requires high amounts of energy and water.

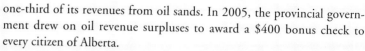

CONTINUED

one-third of its revenues from oil sands. In 2005, the provincial government drew on oil revenue surpluses to award a $400 bonus check to every citizen of Alberta.

Many environmentalists charge, however, that this prosperity comes at an unacceptably high cost. The environmental group Greenpeace has characterized Alberta's oil sands as "the world's dirtiest oil." They argue that the impact of oil-sands mining on local and global environments outweighs any benefits.

Mining involves creating huge pits in the landscape. From 7 to 17 liters (2 to 4 ½ gallons) of water are also needed to produce one barrel of synthetic crude oil, according to Alberta's ministry of energy. Processing facilities pump toxic *tailings* (the watery residue left after bitumen is extracted) into artificial holding ponds. Tailings ponds pose threats to water supplies as well as to wildlife. Among the by-products of oil sands processing are toxic chemicals called naphthenic acids. Environmental studies indicate that some leakage from tailings ponds into nearby soil and ground water is inevitable. Incidents of flocks of birds dying after landing on the ponds have been reported. Officials with energy companies active in Alberta's oil sands industry insist that the companies are committed to detoxifying and filling in tailings ponds to make them safe for people and wildlife, as required by Canadian law. As of mid-2009, however, no tailings ponds had been recovered.

Engineers estimate that recovering oil from oil sands introduces three to five times as much carbon dioxide (CO_2) into the atmosphere as drilling oil. Some environmentalists worry that if oil sands extraction proves profitable in Alberta, other regions will develop their oil sands reserves, increasing output of harmful greenhouse gases in the atmosphere.

In March 2007, Canadian Prime Minister Stephen Harper and Alberta Premier Ed Stelmach jointly endorsed a proposal to build a network of pipes and storage containers underground in Alberta to *sequester* (bury in a stable location) carbon from carbon dioxide emissions. The Canadian federal government provided a grant of $150 million to fund a feasibility study of the plan.

Energy companies are also investing in new, "cleaner" technologies for extracting and processing oil sands. Many environmentalists, however, continue to oppose oil sands operations, contending that there is no way to extract oil from oil sands in a manner that is acceptably safe to the environment.

Alberta's government estimates that the province has oil sands deposits capable of producing, by current technology, 173 billion barrels of oil. Given the world's insatiable thirst for oil, many analysts think it unlikely that either the Canadian federal government or the Alberta provincial government will apply brakes to expansion of the oil sands industry. These governments, analysts surmise, will prove reluctant to interfere with western Canada's oil-sands economic bonanza—despite environmental concerns. ■ Melissa White-Fournier

Oil-sands mining: before and after

As of 2009, 241 square kilometers (150 square miles) of forest in western Canada had been clear-cut for oil-sands mining. Clear-cutting involves the removal of all trees in an area.

ENGINEERING

A team of chemical engineers and materials scientists described in June 2008 a method for combating the growing problem of hospital patients becoming infected with dangerous bacteria, including strains that are resistant to the effects of antibiotics. Repeated exposure of bacterial populations to antibiotics can lead to antibiotic resistance as genetic *mutations* (changes) develop in certain bacteria and then spread throughout the microbe populations. When bacteria become resistant to an antibiotic, the drug can no longer kill the germs.

Each year in the United States, about 2 million patients become infected with hospital-acquired bacteria, and nearly 90,000 of these patients die from their infections. These numbers are increasing because many bacterial strains that cause hospital-acquired infections have developed resistance to antibiotics. Health experts estimate that about 70 percent of all hospital-acquired infections are caused by bacteria that are resistant to at least one drug.

The most common route for infection in hospital patients is transmission via the contaminated surfaces of medical devices, such as catheters. One way to combat these kinds of hospital-acquired infections is to design medical device surfaces that are resistant to bacterial attachment and growth.

Virginia A. Davis, Aleksandr Simonian, and their colleagues at Samuel Ginn College of Engineering at Auburn University in Alabama created a tough antimicrobial surface by combining one of the strongest known materials with one of nature's most powerful germ killers. For the strong material, they used

SEE ALSO

THE SPECIAL REPORT, **TELESCOPES: 400 YEARS OF STARGAZING,** PAGE 24.

SCIENCE STUDIES, **PLASTIC PLANET,** PAGE 114.

single-walled carbon nanotubes, tiny tubular structures made of carbon atoms. Such nanotubes have a diameter of only about 1 nanometer, or $\frac{1}{100,000}$ as wide as a human hair, but a length many times greater. The tight molecular structure of nanotubes makes them 100 times as strong as steel, which helped the antimicrobial surface made by the Alabama team resist wear. The germ-killer component incorporated into the antimicrobial surface was lysozyme, a natural enzyme-like substance found in most bodily fluids. Lysozyme damages cell walls of bacteria, causing the germs to die.

To build their antimicrobial surface, the researchers coated various supporting materials—including silicon, glass, and mica—with several alternating layers of carbon nanotubes

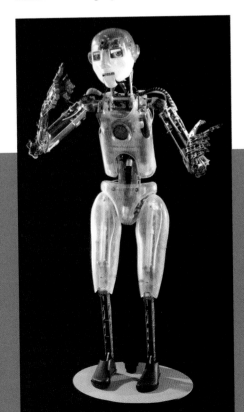

MEET ROBOTHESPIAN

So-called fluidic muscles enabled an interactive robot called RoboThespian™ to shake hands with people and perform song-and-dance routines at public events in 2008 and 2009. Manufactured by Engineered Arts Ltd. in the United Kingdom, the robot contains a network of electronic feedback sensors that cause muscle-like tubes filled with compressed air to contract and lengthen in response to touch. The robot is also programmed to speak various languages.

ENGINEERING continued

and lysozymes. In this technique, called layer-by-layer assembly, the material was repeatedly dipped in a solution of nanotubes and then a solution of lysozymes.

The researchers demonstrated that their antimicrobial surface prevented bacteria from attaching and growing. They concluded that catheters, intravenous bags, and other medical devices made with this surface could reduce bacterial infections, including infections with antibiotic-resistant germs in hospitals and clinics. Furthermore, they noted that the antimicrobial surface might have applications in other areas in which reducing the spread of infection is important, such as consumer appliances, public transportation, and sports equipment.

Engineered bacteria killer. In March 2009, biomedical engineer James Collins of Boston University in Massachusetts and colleagues reported that they had genetically engineered a bacteriophage called M13 to make bacteria more susceptible to antibiotics. Bacteriophages are viruses that infect bacteria. The team altered the genes of M13 so that the virus produced extra amounts of a protein that blocked the repair mechanisms of bacteria—thus helping antibiotics kill the germs.

Polymer coating for joints. More than 700,000 surgeries for total hip and knee replacements are conducted each year in the United States. Implants currently used in these replacements typically last about 15 years before wearing down and requiring the patient to undergo a second surgery. In July 2008, researchers announced that they had developed a method for potentially increasing the lifetime of artificial hips, knees, and other joints.

Bioengineer Andres Garcia, biochemist David Collard, and their team at the Georgia Institute of Technology in Atlanta created a surface coating for implants that improved natural bone growth around the implant—thus increasing integration of the implant into the bone and decreasing wear and tear on the artificial joint. The scientists coated the titanium surfaces of implants with a thin layer of special biopolymers, which are large molecules in biological systems consisting of repeating chemical units. The biopolymer used by the researchers was made with an engineered protein that mimicked fibronectin, a protein in the body that serves as a binding site for cells, including bone cells.

The biopolymer had a structure similar to a brush, with each fibronectin "bristle" able to bind with bone cells. By controlling the number of bristles, the scientists were able to control the amount of fibronectins that were exposed to the cells. This ability allowed the team to maximize bone growth on the coated implant, leading to the integration of the biomaterial with human tissue. "We designed a coating that specifically communicates with cells, and we're telling the cells to grow bone around the implant," explained Garcia.

The researchers demonstrated the success of the fibronectin-coated titanium by implanting it in rats. Four weeks after the implant surgery, researchers noted a 70-percent greater amount of bone matrix growing around the coated implants in the rats, compared with rats that received uncoated implants. The coated implants were also attached more strongly to the bones than the uncoated implants. The scientists hoped that testing in human subjects would eventually lead to the use of fibronectin-coated implants for joint replacements and for filling trauma-related gaps in bone.

Bendable laser scalpel. Laser-based surgeries are important in many areas of health care, including improving eyesight, destroying kidney stones, and removing spinal tumors. Nevertheless, the use of this technology has been limited by the fact that laser energy travels only in a straight line. Thus, a series of mirrors must be used to guide the laser beam to difficult-to-reach parts of the body, resulting in a weakening of the beam's energy.

An advanced laser technology coming under increasing use in surgery rooms in 2009 was the BeamPath CO_2 laser energy system, developed by engineers at OmniGuide, an optics company based in Cambridge, Massachusetts. This system consisted of hollow-core fibers delivering laser energy through a carbon-dioxide medium around bends for use as a tissue-burning scalpel. Carbon-dioxide lasers are among the most powerful lasers. The flexible fiber tubes were built with a so-called photonic bandgap structure, which is a reflective system in which light of all wavelengths can be reflected from all angles. This reflective structure, consisting of alternating layers of glass and polymer molecules, could safely direct the infrared energy of a high-intensity laser beam around bends through the human body without any loss in the beam's strength.

Human tissue is about 60 percent water, which absorbs carbon-dioxide laser energy well. This ready absorption allowed the Beam-Path laser scalpel to be more precise at cutting tissue than traditional metal scalpels. The precision also meant that surrounding healthy tissues suffered minimal heat damage. Furthermore, the bendable laser scalpel minimized bleeding because the burning of tissue by laser is a type of cauterization, which quickly stops bleeding. However, the high cost of the reflective fibers and the need to dispose of the fibers after use (because they could not be sterilized) limited application of this technology in 2009.

Since becoming available for surgical use in 2007, the BeamPath laser scalpel has been primarily used by *orthopedic* (bone and muscle), nose, and throat surgeons. OmniGuide researchers planned to continue improving the technology to promote its use in other surgical areas.

Dolphin-inspired swimming fin. Even Michael Phelps, the American swimmer who won eight gold medals and set world records in seven competitions at the 2008 Summer Olympic Games, would not have been able to exceed the speed of a swimmer wearing an engineering innovation named Lunocet. This swim fin, developed by inventor and engineer Ted Ciamillo of Athens, Georgia, was based on a dolphin's tail fin, or fluke. Ciamillo reported in late 2008 that swimmers wearing the fin on their feet reached speeds as high as 13 kilometers (8 miles) per hour, almost twice the speed

of Phelps at his fastest. Some Lunocet-wearing swimmers, according to Ciamillo reached such speeds that they almost breached out of the water, like dolphins.

The key to the Lunocet fin's speed and efficiency in water was its fluke-like shape and angle, as well as the material of which it was made. The fin—1.1 meters (42 inches) wide and 1.1 kilograms (2.5 pounds) in weight—was attached to the swimmer's aluminum footplate at a precise 30-degree angle. It was made from fiberglass and carbon fibers, which are thin fibers composed mostly of carbon atoms. The carbon atoms were bonded together in microscopic crystals aligned parallel to the long axis of the fiberglass. Together, these two materials conferred semi-flexible properties to the fin, helping it achieve excellent propulsion effects in the water.

The president of the U.S. Apnea Association, the leading competitive free-diving organization in the United States, noted that use of the Lunocet fin might produce significant outcomes in the sport of free diving, in which divers compete to reach the greatest depth in the shortest time while holding their breath. Besides being used in sports, the engineered fin might also be useful for the amphibious units of the U.S. Marine Corps, according to Ciamillo. The inventor said he planned to continue to improve the fin's efficiency and speed.

Advanced concrete bridge. An innovative new bridge opened to automobile traffic over the Mississippi River in Minneapolis in September 2008. The St. Anthony Falls Bridge, part of Interstate 35W, was a replacement for a

CUSTOMIZED CONCRETE

Traffic moves across the Mississippi River on the St. Anthony Falls Bridge, which opened in Minneapolis in September 2008. The bridge replaced an older Interstate 35W bridge that collapsed in August 2007, killing 13 people. The new bridge was constructed with various kinds of special mixtures of reinforced concrete, each of which was customized to suit the function of a particular bridge component. The concrete in tall wavy sculptures on the bridge was mixed with particles of titanium dioxide, a compound that can chemically break down stain-causing air pollutants.

ENGINEERING continued

bridge that collapsed in August 2007, killing 13 people. The new bridge featured 10 lanes of traffic supported by massive arching piers set in deep pilings. Engineers used advanced methods of mixing concrete in the construction of the bridge.

The 38,200 cubic meters (50,000 cubic yards) of reinforced concrete used in the bridge's construction were made with different mixtures, depending on the bridge component. Each mixture was tailored to the specific requirements of the particular bridge part. For example, engineers added silica fume, an industrial waste product, to the concrete in the box girders beneath the traffic lanes. The silica fume made the concrete less porous to road salt and reduced corrosion of the steel reinforcing bars ("rebar") inside the concrete. These characteristics were expected to increase the durability of the box girders.

Many components of the bridge were designed to reduce adverse impacts on the environment. Most concrete is made with portland cement, the manufacture of which generates large amounts of the greenhouse gas carbon dioxide, which is believed to contribute to global warming. In place of portland cement as a strengthening ingredient for the concrete in the St. Anthony Falls Bridge, engineers added fly ash and blast-furnace slag—two recycled industrial waste products.

At both ends of the bridge are tall, wavy sculptures designed as monuments to the people who lost their lives in the collapse of the previous bridge. The concrete in the sculptures was mixed with particles of titanium dioxide. This compound helps whiten the concrete by using the energy of sunlight to speed up natural oxidation reactions, which break down stain-causing pollutants in the air.

■ Irene Y. Tsai

See also **SPACE TECHNOLOGY.**

ENVIRONMENTAL POLLUTION

On Dec. 22, 2008, the packed-earth perimeter of a holding pond at the site of the Kingston Fossil (coal-burning power) Plant in eastern Tennessee broke open. From the breach surged 4.2 billion liters (1.1 billion gallons) of sludge consisting of coal fly ash and water. (Coal fly ash is a waste product of coal combustion. Coal-burning power plants continually produce the ash, which is mixed with water and channeled to on-site containment ponds.) The sludge, which overspread some 121 hectares (300 acres) of nearby land and entered the adjacent Emory River, traveled downstream and entered the Clinch River. Along these waterways, it threatened local public water supplies and severely disrupted the region's ecology, particularly that of river-dwelling organisms.

As the tidal wave of sludge spread onto surrounding land, it reached depths of 2 meters (6 feet) or greater, engulfing at least 15 homes. The wall of sludge also downed power lines, buried railroad tracks, and cut off a road. No fatalities were reported.

SEE ALSO

THE SPECIAL REPORT, **METHANE: ANOTHER GREENHOUSE TROUBLEMAKER,** PAGE 42.

THE SPECIAL REPORT, **INVASION OF THE JELLYFISH,** PAGE 72.

SCIENCE STUDIES, **PLASTIC PLANET,** PAGE 114.

Environmental experts warned of possible long-term threats from the sludge, even as crews armed with bulldozers and dump trucks began to clear away the muck. Trace heavy metals present in coal remained behind in the ash, becoming more concentrated. Such metals—all toxic to human beings and other animals—include arsenic, mercury, lead, selenium, and cadmium.

DISASTER IN A TENNESSEE VALLEY

Wet coal fly ash and washed-out soil engulf the first floor of a house near Kingsport, Tennessee (below), after a containment pond at the Kingston Fossil Plant broke open on Dec. 22, 2008. The avalanche of muddy sludge released when the packed-earth perimeter of the plant's containment pond gave way damaged at least 15 homes in the Emory River Valley.

Nearly half of the earthen wall of the Kingston Fossil Plant's containment pond (outlined in red, left) collapsed during the disaster. The breach of the wall sent a river of blue-gray coal sludge into the adjacent Emory River and over nearby land (above).

ENVIRONMENTAL POLLUTION continued

Sludge introduced into local river systems may spread such contaminants downstream, environmentalists cautioned, and rain may eventually wash contaminants into the local groundwater. In the wake of the disaster, the federal Environmental Protection Agency (EPA) reported high levels of arsenic in samples taken from river water near the site of the Kingston plant spill. Environmentalists reported a further concern: sludge that dries into a powdery consistency may introduce contaminants into the air.

The Kingston disaster focused media attention on the problem of waste disposal at coal-burning power plants. At the sites of many of the aproximately 700 coal-burning power plants in the United States, containment ponds have become, in essence, permanent storage facilities for coal fly ash. In addition to the risk of catastrophic spillage, environmentalists emphasize the danger of toxic chemicals leaching from such ponds into surrounding soil or groundwater.

According to industry experts, some coal-fired power plants bury their waste ash in landfills; some even transport the ash to abandoned coal mines for storage. Because the federal government does not classify coal fly ash as a hazardous waste, stringent rules that govern disposal of acknowledged hazards do not apply to it.

Prescription antidepressants in trace amounts in streams and rivers can disrupt normal fish behavior, according to studies reported in 2008. Human urine and leftover pills flushed down toilets introduce these common prescription medications into sewers. Sewage treatment plants pass such chemicals unchanged to outside waterways.

A research team led by biologist Heiko Schonfuss of St. Cloud State University in St. Cloud, Minnesota, studied the response of fathead minnows to the antidepressant venlafaxine (sold under the brand name Effexor). The researchers exposed the minnows as *larvae* (an immature form) to trace levels of the antidepressant. According to the team's findings, the venlafaxine-exposed minnow larvae responded less quickly to stimuli than unexposed larvae. In their report to the annual North America meeting of the Society of Environmental Toxicology and Chemistry in November 2008, the researchers concluded that such degraded response time could make larvae more vulnerable to predators and perhaps lead to an overall decline in minnow populations.

In another study reported at the meeting, researchers with the Institute of Environmental Toxicology at Clemson University in Clemson, South Carolina, found that exposure of hybrid striped bass to the antidepressant fluoxetine (sold under the brand name Prozac) also produced behavioral abnormalities. At lower concentrations, the bass appeared to behave normally. However, at higher concentrations of the drug, many of the fish exhibited such abnormal behaviors as slowed responses and floating in a vertical, rather than horizontal, position.

Researchers with both the St. Cloud study and the Clemson study noted that their experiments did not closely approximate conditions in the wild, where discharges from sewage plants would typically contain traces of a variety of medical drugs. According to the researchers, no one knows how a combination of various drugs might interact in the bodies of fish and other wildlife.

Herbicides harm frogs. Zoologists have in recent years reported widespread declines in populations of amphibians, including frogs. Scientists have theorized a number of possible causes for these declines, including exposure to chemicals not found in nature. In 2008, several reports based on scientific studies supplied new evidence that agricultural chemicals such as *herbicides* (weed-killing chemicals) are negatively impacting frog populations.

Toxicologist Val R. Beasley and colleagues from the University of Illinois at Urbana-Champaign discovered that a widely used agricultural herbicide called atrazine increases the population of snails in ponds by boosting the production of algae that the snails eat. Scientists have long known that freshwater snails act as a temporary host for a parasitic flatworm that infects frogs.

With algae-feeding snail populations exploding, the number of flatworms in the aquatic environment also increases, resulting in a high infection rate for frogs. The flatworm parasites weaken or kill frogs. Furthermore, atrazine suppresses the immune systems of young frogs, so these populations become especially vulnerable to flatworm infection. The parasites also endanger tadpoles, sometimes

FROG UNDER THREAT

The spotted northern leopard frog, common in parts of Canada and the United States, is among frog species threatened by agricultural pesticides, particularly atrazine, a herbicide used on corn and soybean fields, according to several studies reported in 2008. Researchers said the chemical promotes the growth of populations of a parasitic flatworm that infests the frogs. Atrazine also weakens the frogs' immune systems and feminizes male frogs (causes them to have feminine characteristics), interfering with mating.

causing severe deformities. The University of Illinois researchers reported their findings in the Oct. 30, 2008, issue of *Nature*.

Such agricultural chemicals as atrazine may be compromising frog populations in another way. A growing body of evidence suggests that chemicals in agricultural runoff are causing some male amphibians to undergo significant changes that effectively feminize them—that is, cause body changes that make them more like females. The more the male frogs are feminized, the less capable they are of mating. Such changes in male frogs could lead to declines in frog populations.

In the August 2008 issue of *Environmental Health Perspectives*, zoologist Krista McCoy and her colleagues at the University of Florida, Gainesville, reported on their study of Florida cane frogs collected from the wild. The researchers found that male cane frogs living near farms where heavy agricultural runoff occurred would be expected to experience significant reduction in levels of testosterone, the male sex hormone, as well as physical signs of feminization. Among the most startling of the

physical changes was the production of eggs within a normally *vestigial* (shrunken and nonfunctional) organ in the bodies of some male frogs.

Biologist Pamela Martin and her colleagues of Environment Canada reported similar findings in the July 30, 2008, issue of *Aquatic Toxicology*. In their study of leopard frogs collected from the wild in Ontario, the researchers documented higher rates of feminization in males taken from locales with intensive agriculture where they were likely exposed to atrazine and other agricultural chemicals.

Household products and fertility. Compounds in the original chemical formulations of two coatings used in common household products, Teflon and Scotchguard, may interfere with fertility in women—that is, make it more difficult for them to become pregnant. Researchers led by epidemiologist Chunyuan Fei of the University of California at Los Angeles reported this finding in the January 2009 issue of the medical journal *Human Reproduction*. (Epidemiologists study the causes and the spread of disease.) In their study, the research team analyzed data from a Danish medical database of new mothers.

Teflon is applied to cookware to prevent food from sticking. Scotchgard is applied to carpets, clothing, and upholstery to reduce soiling. Older versions of these products contain two chemicals, perfluorooctanoic acid (PFOA) and perfluorooctane sulfonate (PFOS). Although these chemicals have been phased out in recent years because of concerns over potential health effects—manufacturers of Teflon and Scotchgard now use other chemicals—products containing PFOA and PFOS are still present in many homes.

The University of California researchers compared women with relatively high blood concentrations of PFOA and PFOS with those who had lower concentrations of the chemicals. They found that women with high levels of PFOA and PFOS took longer, on average, to become pregnant than the women with lower levels.

PFOA and PFOS are persistent chemicals—that is, they resist breakdown into simpler compounds. Products containing PFOA and PFOS were first marketed in the 1950's, and the chemicals have been accumulating in the environment ever since. ■ Daniel D. Chiras

FOSSIL STUDIES

A well-preserved, nearly complete fossil of a monkey-like creature reported in May 2009 shed light on the early evolution of primates, the group that includes lemurs, monkeys, apes, and human beings. A team led by paleontologist Jorn Hurum of the University of Oslo in Norway described the fossil, which had been unearthed in 1983 from 47-million-year-old sediment inside a shale pit near Frankfurt, Germany. The divided fossil had been in two private collections before the team put the parts back together and analyzed it with computed tomography and other imaging techniques.

The creature, *Darwinius masillae*, dated to around the time that primate ancestors are thought to have begun branching into two main evolutionary lines—prosimians (including lemurs and certain other "primitive" primates) and anthropoids (monkeys, apes, and human beings). Hurum's team reported that the cat-sized *D. masillae* had some characteristics of lemurs, such as general body shape, though it appeared to be more closely related to monkeys. The fossil indicated that, like most modern primates, the animal had fingers and toes with nails, and thumbs and big toes that were *opposable* (positioned opposite of other digits). It lacked the foot "grooming claw" and fused row of lower teeth characteristic of lemurs.

Paleontologist Jens Franzen of the Senckenberg Research Institute in Germany—a member of Hurum's team—said that *D. masillae*

SEE ALSO

THE SPECIAL REPORT, **FASCINATING FACTS FROM FOSSIL FECES**, PAGE 12.

THE SPECIAL REPORT, **MUTUALISM: THE PLEASURE OF YOUR COMPANY**, PAGE 58.

likely belonged to a group of animals that was ancestral to anthropoids. However, he added, the species itself may not have been a direct ancestor of the line.

Early whales. Two discoveries reported in 2008 provided new insights into the biology of early whales. In February 2009, paleontologist Philip Gingerich of the University of Michigan in Ann Arbor described the fossil skeleton of a small whale, 2.6 meters (8.5 feet) long, from 47-million-year-old marine deposits in Pakistan. Gingerich named the fossil *Maicetus inuus* (meaning *fertile mother whale*) in recognition of the fact that the skeleton contained within its abdominal cavity a skeleton of a fetal whale—the first report of a fossilized whale pregnancy.

The unborn whale was oriented such that its head pointed toward the mother's *pelvic* (hip) area. This indicated that the young of this early whale were born headfirst. That type of birth is typical of modern land mammals. In

MUTUALISM IN AMBER

A fossilized termite with its gut ripped open (far left), perhaps by a bird, is seen inside a piece of *amber* (hardened tree sap), where it became trapped 100 million years ago in a forest in Myanmar (Burma). Insect expert George Poinar, Jr., of Oregon State University in Corvallis reported in May 2009 that he had found fossilized *protozoans* (one-celled organisms) (left) in the gut. The protozoans helped the termite break down and digest wood. The find was the earliest known example of mutualism, a relationship between species in which each species benefits.

modern whales and other fully aquatic mammals, by contrast, the young are born tailfirst. Gingerich said that this finding provided further evidence that early whales were amphibious—like seals—spending much of their time in the sea, such as for hunting, but emerging on land at times, including for birthing.

Evidence of unique swimming behavior in early whales was reported in September 2008 by paleontologist Mark D. Uhen of the Alabama Museum of Natural History in Tuscaloosa. The fossil whale, named *Georgiacetus vogtlensis*, was found in 40-million-year-old deposits in the southern United States.

The fossil showed that this early whale had large, paddle-like hind limbs. Because the pelvis was not anchored to the spine, however, the whale would not have been able to paddle strongly with these limbs. In addition, unlike modern whales, *Georgiacetus* lacked a *fluke* (tail fin). Uhen theorized that these whales were intermediate in form between earlier species, which paddled with well-anchored hind limbs, and modern whales, which use undulations of their flukes to swim. He said that *Georgiacetus* might have swum by undulating its hips to swing its hind limbs from side to side.

Hairy heterodontosaur. A previously unknown species of "feathered" heterodontosaurid dinosaur was described in March 2009 by paleontologist Xiao-Ting Zheng of the Shandong Tianyu Museum of Nature in China and three colleagues. Heterodontosaurs are classified as ornithischians—the so-called "bird-hipped" dinosaurs, which were *herbivorous* (plant-eating) reptiles with hipbones similar to those of modern birds. The specimen, named *Tianyulong confuciusi*, was discovered in sediment in China dating from early in the Cretaceous Period (145 million to 65 million years ago).

The fossil preserved skin impressions of filamentous or hairy extensions, which appeared to be much like the filaments of feather-like structures seen in certain other dinosaur fossils, as well as the feathers of modern birds. All of the other dinosaurs in which paleontologists had discovered such feather-like filaments were classified as saurischians—the so-called "lizard-hipped" dinosaurs, which had hipbones similar to those of modern lizards.

Paleontologists believe that modern birds are descended from saurischians—not ornithis-

HALF-SHELLED, TOOTHED TURTLE

An artist's rendition of the earliest known turtle, *Odontochelys semistestacea*, shows two individuals swimming in the sea 220 million years ago. Fossils of this turtle, discovered in China, were reported in November 2008 by paleontologist Chun Li of the Chinese Academy of Sciences and colleagues. The fossils revealed that *Odontochelys* had a pointed snout with teeth—unlike modern turtles, which have untoothed beaks—and a shell covering its belly but not its back.

chians. Thus, the finding of feather-like structures in both of these groups suggested to paleontologists that feathery or hairy coatings on the body may have been present in the common ancestors of all dinosaurs, not just dinosaurs that were ancestral to birds.

Jawed vertebrate origins. A previously unknown and well-preserved fossil gnathostome (jawed *vertebrate* [animal with a backbone]) was described in March 2009 by a team led by paleontologist Min Zhu of the Institute of Vertebrate Paleontology and Paleoanthropology in Beijing, China. The jawed fish, named *Guiyu oneiros*, was discovered in limestone beds in southern China dated to late in the Silurian Period (444 million to 416 million years ago). Its age, 419 million years, made it the oldest known well-preserved gnathostome fossil.

Unlike most previously described Silurian

FOSSIL STUDIES continued

fish fossils, which consist of little more than piles of scales, the new specimen displayed detailed characters of the fish's skeleton. These details revealed that the fish was a type of sarcopterygian, or lobe-finned fish—a group that also includes modern lungfish and coelacanths, as well as the ancestors of amphibians. The fossil extended the known appearance of this group back more than 20 million years.

Paleontologists have long believed that lobe-finned fish and the more numerous ray-finned fish—which include most modern fish—share a common ancestor from which they later branched into the two main groups of *osteichthyans* (bony fish). The *Guiyu* fossil implied that the branching of these two groups occurred far earlier than previously thought.

Chains of Cambrian arthropods. Some modern *crustaceans* (shellfish) engage in group behavior at times, such as making migrations in long chains in which individuals maintain physical contact with one another. Such "collective" behaviors, however, have rarely been seen in fossil crustaceans. In October 2008, paleontologist Hou Xian-Guang of Yunnan University in China and three British colleagues described one of the first known examples of this type of behavior in a prehistoric species of *arthropod* (the group of jointed animals that includes crustaceans, insects, and spiders).

The fossils were discovered in 525-million-year-old sediment, from early in the Cambrian Period (543 million to 490 million years ago), in the Chengjiang shale beds of China's

PREDATOR X

Workers pull a plaster jacket containing part of the skull of a prehistoric marine reptile called a pliosaur from the ground on the Norwegian island of Spitsbergen in the Arctic Ocean (right, top). Paleontologist Jorn H. Hurum of the University of Oslo in Norway reported in February 2009 that the 150-million-year-old remains indicated that the creature—nicknamed "Predator X"—was the largest marine reptile ever discovered. He estimated that this pliosaur grew to at least 15 meters (50 feet) in length and weighed some 41 metric tons (45 tons). Predator X, shown in an illustration (right, bottom), had massive jaws that could easily crush the bodies of its marine prey.

Yunnan Province. Slabs of shale showed chains of 2 to 20 shrimp-like individuals in which the *telson* (tail spike) and rear appendages of each individual were locked beneath the *carapace* (back covering) of the individual following behind. According to the researchers, such body-locking contact suggests that these creatures may have swum in long, chain-like arrays to remain in contact in the dark, deep-sea environment. The scientists said that these specimens provided a unique glimpse into social behavior in early marine communities.

Correction resolves paradox. Evidence presented in 1999 indicated that certain advanced single-celled organisms appeared on Earth as early as the Archean Eon (more than 2.5 billion years ago)—much earlier than previously thought. However, information strongly challenging that view was published in October 2008 by geochemists Birger Rasmussen of Curtin University in Western Australia, Jochen J. Brocks of Australian National University, and colleagues. The reanalysis restored the date of the oldest known *cyanobacteria* (blue-green algae) to about 2 billion years ago, and that of *eukaryotes* (organisms consisting of cells that have *nuclei* [center parts] and internal organelles) to about 1.7 billion years ago.

In 1999, Brocks and a team of researchers had reported on their analysis of biomarkers found inside rocks that were dated to 2.7 billion years ago. Biomarkers are *organic* molecules (molecules containing carbon-to-carbon bonds) that are characteristic of the tissues of particular types of organisms. Biomarkers found in rocks are evidence of the ancient organisms that left them behind. Brock's team said that some of these biomarkers were characteristic of cyanobacteria and others of eukaryotes—suggesting that these two life forms appeared on Earth hundreds of millions of years earlier than indicated by previous evidence.

In the new study, Rasmussen, Brocks, and their co-investigators compared the ratios of two carbon *isotopes* (different forms of an element) in the biomarkers versus the ratios of these isotopes in other organic material—petroleum—inside the same rocks. This analysis revealed more precise time estimates than the earlier analysis for the period when the organisms that produced the biomarkers lived, as well as the time that the petroleum in the rocks was formed. This dating technique showed that the ages of the biomarkers were younger than that of the rocks in which they were found. The researchers concluded that the biomarkers contaminated the rocks sometime after 2.2 billion years ago.

The restoration of the more recent dates for the appearance of cyanobacteria resolved a paradox created by the 1999 study. Cyanobacteria are photosynthetic, meaning that they produce their own food by using the energy of sunlight, releasing oxygen as a by-product. The dates from the 1999 study implied that cyanobacteria appeared some 300 million years before an abrupt rise in atmospheric levels of oxygen, as recorded in geological evidence. Scientists did not understand why there would have been such a long time lag between the beginning of photosynthesis and the rise of oxygen in the atmosphere. The new report settled this confusion by revealing that the earlier dates were incorrect.

Giant protozoa solve mystery. The possible resolution of another mystery regarding early organisms was published in November 2008 by biologist Mikhail V. Matz of the University of Texas at Austin and colleagues. A number of researchers had previously reported finding preserved trails in marine sediment dated from 1.8 billion to 1 billion years ago. These fossilized trails seemed to indicate that some form of crawling animal life existed on the sea floor during those ancient times. However, that conclusion presented a problem because other fossil evidence suggested that such animal life did not exist until after 600 million years ago.

Matz and his colleagues reported that they had discovered a living single-celled, grape-sized organism—a protozoan named *Gromia sphaerica*—on the sea floor at a depth of 800 meters (2,600 feet) in the Bahamas. Photographs showed these giant ameba-like protozoans at the ends of grooves or trails in muddy bottom sediments. Because of the stillness of the deep-sea environment, the researchers concluded that the blob-like cells had not been rolled on the sea floor by currents. Rather, the scientists proposed that the cells propelled themselves slowly along the sea floor using small finger-like projections called pseudopods.

These modern trails, which were as long as 50 centimeters (1.5 feet), closely resembled the trails found in the ancient marine sediments. Thus, this new report suggested that the ancient grooves were not made by complex, multicellular animal life. Instead, the trails may have been left by giant single-celled organisms, which are more likely to have existed at that time.

■ Carlton E. Brett

GENETICS

Individuals carrying variant forms of certain genes are much more likely than other individuals to become heavy smokers with strong dependence on nicotine, according to a December 2008 report by a team of researchers led by epidemiologist Victoria L. Stevens of the American Cancer Society in Atlanta. The genes the researchers examined make up a cluster of three genes (named CHRNA5-CHRNA3-CHRNB4) that are important in regulating the body's response to nicotine in the brain.

The researchers analyzed the chemical makeup of the gene cluster in 1,452 heavy smokers, defined as people who smoked at least 30 cigarettes per day for at least five years. The scientists compared these results with the makeup of the same genes in 1,395 people who were classified as light smokers, individuals who smoked less than five cigarettes per day. The researchers were most interested in determining whether chemical *variants* (different versions) known as single nucleotide polymorphisms, or SNP's (pronounced "snips"), were more common in one group than the other. Such SNP variants are changes in the sequences of chemical units, called bases, that make up deoxyribonucleic acid (DNA), the molecule of which genes are made.

The sequence of bases in a gene provides instructions for the production of a particular protein. Various proteins are needed by the body to build body parts and to carry out other functions. The SNP's in the gene cluster examined by Stevens and her team code for a type of protein known as a receptor. Receptor proteins, located on the outer surfaces of many cells, bind to certain molecules, causing certain biochemical reactions to occur. The function of the receptor protein studied by the researchers is to bind to nicotine molecules, especially in the cells of the brain.

The researchers first identified two groups of SNP's that were more common among the heavy smokers. They then analyzed the effects on smoking behavior of having various combinations of these SNP's. They found that the odds of being a heavy smoker were up to two times as great in people with particular SNP combinations, compared with other combinations. This finding suggested to the scientists that genetic tests might be used to identify these genetic variants in patients—thus helping

SEE ALSO THE SPECIAL REPORT, **THE TIMELESS SCOURGE OF MALARIA,** PAGE 88.

to predict the likelihood of a person becoming a heavy smoker. In such cases, early treatment interventions might help prevent the development of heavy smoking.

Physical activity trumps genetic risks. Physical activity can overcome health risks associated with variants of a gene linked to obesity, according to a study published in September 2008. The study was conducted by a research group headed by public health expert Evadnie Rampersaud of the University of Maryland in Baltimore.

As an indicator of obesity, the researchers evaluated body mass index (BMI), which is a measurement representing the proportion between an individual's weight and height. In adults, a BMI from 25 to 29.9 indicates that the individual is overweight, and a BMI of 30 or more indicates that the individual is obese. The scientists evaluated BMI in members of the Old Order Amish community in Lancaster County, Pennsylvania. Individuals in this community have similar genetic characteristics and similar dietary habits, making any effects of physical activity relatively easy to identify.

The investigators obtained blood samples for genetic analysis from 704 Amish adults. In the analysis, the researchers looked for variants of a gene, known as FTO, that had previously been shown to be associated with fat mass and obesity. To record levels of daily activity in the participants, the scientists had each person wear an accelerometer, a device that measures the intensity of physical activity by sensing the amount of motion. The researchers performed a statistical analysis of the relationship between BMI and daily activity levels in individuals carrying different variants of the FTO gene.

The genetic and statistical analyses revealed that individuals having low levels of daily activity also had—as expected—high BMI values and FTO variants that are strongly related to having high BMI. However, in individuals having high levels of daily activity, the relationships between these FTO variants and BMI disappeared. In fact, although the BMI values were lower for all individuals in the high-activity group, those individuals with FTO variants normally associated with high risk for obesity also had the greatest decrease in BMI if they maintained high levels of daily activity.

From this finding, Rampersaud's team concluded that regular physical activity could reduce risks of health problems—potentially even among individuals who have a genetic predisposition to obesity.

Human genome studies. Announcements by three independent teams of researchers in November 2008 heralded a new era for deciphering the genome sequences of individual people. The human genome is the complete set of genetic material making up a person's DNA. The genome sequence of each individual consists of approximately 3 billion chemical bases.

Two of the research teams focused on individuals representing specific ethnic groups. The first team, led by David R. Bentley, chief scientist at Illumina Cambridge LTD, a biotechnology company in England, *sequenced* (deciphered the order of bases in) the genome of a male member of the Yoruba tribe in Nigeria. The second team, led by Jun Wang, director of the Beijing Genomics Institute in China, sequenced the genome of an individual of Han Chinese ethnicity. (Previously, the genomes of two Caucasian men were the only whole sequenced genomes of individual human beings.)

The genomes of the Yoruba and Han Chinese individuals were obtained by using a new, faster approach to genome sequencing called reversible terminator chemistry. This approach, representing the "next generation" of sequencing technology, produces three to four orders of magnitude more genetic information than methods used to complete the initial human genome sequence in the 1990's. In traditional sequencing methods, lengthy sequences of bases must be analyzed in a time-consuming process. In the reversible terminator chemistry technique, by contrast, the DNA from an individual is first broken into relatively small pieces. Copies are then made of each DNA piece, in which different chemical bases are labeled with differently colored fluorescent "tags." Powerful computers monitor when each tagged base is incorporated into the copies. Finally, to complete the genome sequencing, the computers combine the information obtained from each of the separate DNA pieces.

The analysis of the genome information from these two individuals yielded large numbers of previously unknown genetic variants.

For example, in the Asian individual alone, more than 300,000 new SNP variants were discovered. A large number of novel SNP variants were also found in the DNA of the Yoruban individual. However, both teams of researchers noted that the primary value of their studies was to demonstrate the practicality of using the reversible terminator chemistry method to sequence the whole genomes of individuals.

The third team of researchers, led by physician Timothy J. Ley and biochemist Elaine R. Mardis, both of Washington University School of Medicine in St. Louis, sequenced the genome of an individual who had been diagnosed as having a type of cancer known as acute myeloid

BLACK WOLF MYSTERY SOLVED

A genetic *mutation* (change) inherited from domesticated dogs may explain why nearly half of North American wolves are black, according to a study reported in February 2009. Geneticists at Stanford University in California and other institutions analyzed the genetic makeup of black- and gray-coated wolves in Yellowstone National Park (below). Their analysis revealed that black wolves have a mutation inherited from ancestors that were domesticated black dogs, which apparently mated with North American wolves thousands of years ago. By contrast, in Europe, where no such mating took place, there are almost no black wolves.

GENETICS continued

leukemia. These scientists added a new twist to genome research by *sequencing* (determining the order of) genetic material from two types of cells taken from this individual—a normal cell from the patient's skin and a cancerous cell from the patient's blood. (Genome sequencing typically focuses on genetic material from a single type of cell.) The scientists hoped to discover genetic *mutations* (changes) that were unique to the cancerous cell.

The team discovered 10 genes in the cancer cell genome that had mutations not found in the DNA from the skin cell. Two of these mutations were in genes that were previously known to be involved in the development of cancer. The other eight mutations were previously unknown. Although the functions of the eight new genes were not known, the two-cell approach used by Ley and Mardis was shown to be a practical technique for sequencing genomes of individuals and yielding new genetic information.

Neandertal genome. Preliminary results from the first rough draft of the genome of Neandertals were announced at a scientific meeting in February 2009 by an international team of investigators. Neandertals were relatives of modern human beings who lived in Europe and parts of Asia from approximately 150,000 to 30,000 years ago. Some scientists classify Neandertals as a subspecies of modern human beings, *Homo sapiens*. Other scientists classify them as a separate species, *H. neanderthalensis*.

Evolutionary geneticist Svante Pääbo of the Max Planck Institute for Evolutionary Anthropology in Germany led the team, which also included scientists at 454 Life Sciences Corporation, a developer of DNA sequencing technology in Branford, Connecticut. The team sequenced minute amounts of fragmentary genetic material extracted from fossil bones of a Neandertal skeleton that was unearthed inside a cave in Croatia. The scientists also sequenced some DNA fragments from Neandertal bones found at other sites. The DNA fragments that were analyzed— from less than half a gram (0.02 ounce) of bone tissue—were believed to represent about 60 percent of the entire Neandertal genome.

To avoid contamination of the small amounts of prehistoric genetic material with that of the investigators, the researchers used specially developed "clean-room" precautions and techniques. They also used their knowl-

edge of ways that DNA chemically changes inside fossils over time to distinguish the Neandertal DNA from that of microbes that contaminated the bones. Finally, the scientists relied on various modifications in genome sequencing technology to allow for the analysis of the fragmentary genetic material.

Pääbo's team reported that preliminary results of the analysis indicated that although most of the Neandertal genome was similar to that of modern human beings, some parts of the Neandertal genome were more similar to that of chimpanzees. The researchers concluded that any interbreeding between Neandertals and modern-type human beings was minimal—though the two types of human beings coexisted for a time in the same areas.

The team planned to publish their complete findings later in 2009. These findings were to provide details of comparisons of Neandertal and modern human DNA, focusing on genes of interest related to human evolution. Such genes include those related to speech, language, and brain development.

Stem cell advances. Two important advances in research using adult stem cells were reported in late 2008. Stem cells are immature cells that may be useful in medical treatment because some stem cells, known as pluripotent stem cells, have the potential to develop into any desired type of tissue. Tissue grown from such stem cells might be used to replace damaged body parts in patients who have diseases characterized by the degeneration of tissue. Most pluripotent stem cells must be derived from destroyed human embryos—a technique that many people object to. The new research built upon previous studies that demonstrated how mature cells from adults could be "reprogrammed" to develop into induced pluripotent stem cells (iPS cells).

In August 2008, a research team led by biologist Kevin Eggan of Harvard University in Cambridge, Massachusetts, announced that it had created iPS cells from the skin cells of an elderly woman who had amyotrophic lateral sclerosis (ALS), also called "Lou Gehrig's disease" from the name of a baseball player who died from the illness. In ALS, nerve cells in the spinal cord and brain are progressively destroyed, leading to paralysis and death.

Eggan's team reprogrammed the skin cells by using a modified virus to deliver four particular genes into the cells. Researchers in Japan had previously identified these genes as being able to cause skin cells to change into iPS cells. However, the Japanese research left unanswered the question of whether this technique could be applied to cells from human beings with *chronic* (long-term) health conditions, such as ALS. Eggan's group showed that its iPS cells could be grown in the laboratory into nerve cells of the type needed to control motor activity in patients with ALS.

Although the researchers did not determine if the laboratory-grown nerve cells could serve as replacement cells to "cure" patients with ALS, the work by Eggan's group was the first to show that it was possible to use body cells from a patient with a chronic disease to produce iPS cells. At the very least, scientists noted, this genetic reprogramming method could be used to produce new tissue for laboratory studies to improve the understanding of ALS and other chronic degenerative conditions.

In September 2008, a research group led by pediatrician and biologist George Q. Daley of Harvard Medical School in Boston announced that it had used a genetic reprogramming method similar to that used by Eggan's team to produce iPS cells from skin and bone marrow cells taken from patients who had a wide range of degenerative diseases. These diseases included Becker and Duchenne muscular dystrophy, Down syndrome, Gaucher's disease, Huntington's disease, Lesch-Nyhan syndrome, Parkinson disease, and Type 1 diabetes mellitus.

As with Eggan's research, it was not clear if the iPS cells developed by Daley's team might help in providing new treatments for individuals with these various diseases. Nevertheless, genetics researchers expected that the iPS cells would provide new opportunities for detailed studies of the basic mechanisms of these diseases, as well as opportunities for testing new treatment options under controlled laboratory conditions.   ■ David S. Haymer

GEOLOGY

Research published in 2008 and 2009 shed light on the complex geological processes involved in a powerful earthquake that struck the city of Wenchuan in western China in 2008. The earthquake, which occurred on May 12, killed tens of thousands of people.

With a magnitude of 7.9, the Wenchuan earthquake was as powerful as the San Francisco earthquake of 1906. However, the Wenchuan earthquake occurred in a very different geological setting. The San Francisco earthquake was caused by horizontal movement along the San Andreas Fault, which separates the North American and Pacific *tectonic plates* (large slabs that make up Earth's outer shell). During that quake, the Pacific Plate slid approximately 6 meters (20 feet) northward. By contrast, the Wenchuan earthquake occurred in the middle of Asia, where the edge of the Tibetan Plateau—marked by the Longmen Shan mountain range—meets the lowland of the Sichuan Basin. This site also marks the boundary between the Indian subcontinent and the Asian continent, which collided 50 mil-

SEE ALSO THE SPECIAL REPORT, **THE SEARCH FOR WATER ON MARS,** PAGE 100.

lion years ago. As a result of that collision, much of India was forced beneath Asia, lifting the Himalayas and the Tibetan Plateau.

Some of the crust involved in this ancient collision was squeezed out to the east to form the Longmen Shan mountain range, which rises some 6,000 meters (20,000 feet) above the plains of Sichuan. Geologists have long debated the exact methods by which the Longmen Shan formed. The study published in March 2009 provided important information regarding this dispute.

In the study, geologists Judith Hubbard and John H. Shaw of the Department of Earth and Planetary Sciences at Harvard University in Cambridge, Massachusetts, reported the results of their analysis of the geology of the

GEOLOGY continued

Longmen Shan region and the seismic record of the Wenchuan earthquake. They found that the upper crust in this region is broken into a series of sheets. These sheets are sliding one over another toward the east, and the fractures separating the sheets, called thrust faults, slope gently upward toward the east. As a result of these movements, the upper crust is horizontally compressed by as much as 40 percent, and this compression led to the lifting that produced the mountain range.

Hubbard and Shaw also created a detailed picture of the thrust faults in this area, from 3 kilometers (2 miles) to 15 kilometers (9 miles) below the surface. The geologists identified movement along two of these faults as the cause of the Wenchuan earthquake, as well as of its many strong aftershocks.

In the study published in July 2008, seismologists Tom Parsons of the United States Geological Survey in Menlo Park, California; Chen Ji of the University of California at Santa Barbara; and Eric Kirby of Pennsylvania State University in University Park analyzed the *geological stresses*—the straining, or bending, of blocks of rock—related to the Wenchuan earthquake. They found that, although the earthquake had relieved stresses that had built up on some of the faults, the movement of the sheets of rock created new stresses in the adjacent terrain. These new stresses set the stage for future earthquakes. The seismologists warned that in such

conditions, destructive aftershocks may occur several years after the initial earthquake.

Past Indian Ocean tsunamis. The *tsunami* (series of huge ocean waves caused by an earthquake or landslide) in the Indian Ocean on Dec. 26, 2004, killed more than 228,000 people in Southeast Asia, South Asia, and East Africa. This catastrophic event took geologists by surprise, because such powerful tsunamis had not been known to happen before in the Indian Ocean. The tsunami prompted geologists to examine coastal deposits for geological records of any previous large tsunamis in the Indian Ocean. Two studies published in October 2008 described newly found evidence of earlier tsunamis in this region.

The wavelength—that is, the distance from the crest of one wave to that of the next—in a tsunami may be 160 kilometers (100 miles) or more in the open ocean. The speed with which waves of a tsunami travel depends on the depth of the water. Over the deep ocean, tsunamis typically have a speed of 500 kilometers (310 miles) per hour. As the waters become more shallow closer to shore, the waves move more slowly. Because of the long wavelength, however, the back of a wave continues to travel fast even as the front of the

SUMATRA TSUNAMIS

Geologist Katrin Monecke of Kent State University in Ohio (right, top [on left]) and a colleague examine sedimentary deposits on a marshy plain near Meulaboh, Sumatra, along the coast of the Indan Ocean. Monecke reported in October 2008 that cores (cylindrical samples) drilled from these deposits revealed evidence of three tsunamis (series of huge ocean waves) that happened in this area before the devastating tsunami of 2004. The evidence was in the form of three layers of sand deposited by the tsunamis on top of the normal marshland deposit (right, bottom). The layering indicated that these tsunamis happened around 1000, again around 1290 to 1400, and in 1907.

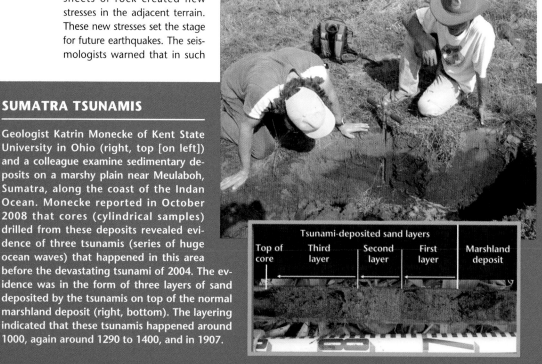

Tsunami-deposited sand layers

| Top of core | Third layer | Second layer | First layer | Marshland deposit |

wave slows. As a result, the water piles up, making the wave higher and higher. The main wave at Aceh, at the northern tip of Sumatra, in the 2004 tsunami was approximately 35 meters (115 feet) high as it reached the shore, and it traveled about 1.6 kilometers (1 mile) inland.

A tsunami wave breaks as it comes on shore, ripping sand from the beaches and carrying it inland. This sand is left behind as a layer of sediment, marking the extent of the tsunami. If the sand layer becomes buried and preserved, it provides a permanent geological record of the tsunami event.

Geologist Katrin Monecke of Kent State University in Ohio and an international team of co-investigators reported in October 2008 on their search for records of such sand layers near the town of Meulaboh, Sumatra. They collected *cores* (cylindrical samples) from peat deposits on the marshy coastal plain, from the shore to 2 kilometers (1.2 miles) inland. While examining the cores, the scientists found three layers of sand. The youngest of these layers was estimated to be from a tsunami in 1907, which was much smaller than the 2004 tsunami. Of the two older sand layers, one was deposited around 1290 to 1400 and the other, around 1000. These were both extensive layers, indicating large tsunamis.

In a separate study reported in October 2008, geologist Kruawun Jankaew of Chulalongkorn University in Bangkok, Thailand, and colleagues described a similar search for sand sheets on Phra Thong Island, off the western coast of southern Thailand. They found a single sand layer, indicating that the last substantial tsunami on the Thai coast occurred between 1300 and 1450.

Icebergs off the Carolinas? Geologists know from sedimentary evidence found on the North Atlantic Ocean floor that during the last ice age, which ended roughly 11,500 years ago, large numbers of icebergs broke off from the Laurentide Ice Sheet that covered eastern Canada. These icebergs drifted south through the Labrador Sea, into the North Atlantic, and across the ocean toward Europe. As they melted and released their loads of rocky debris, the icebergs left a record of rock fragments and pebbles on the deep sea floor. These deposits are known as Heinrich events, after the German geologist—Hartmut Heinrich—who discovered them. The deposits date from roughly 60,000 to 17,500 years ago.

Marine geologists had believed that all the icebergs associated with the Heinrich events

GIANT CRYSTAL CAVE

A geologist examines several of the world's largest known crystals in a cave in Chihuahua, Mexico. The crystals, which are made of a form of gypsum called selenite, measure up to 12 meters (39 feet) in length and 1.8 meters (6 feet) in diameter. In September 2008, geologist Stein-Erik Lauritzen of the University of Bergen in Norway reported that the largest of the crystals began forming about 400,000 years ago. Scientists had previously determined that the crystals, which were discovered in 2000, grew as the cave was flooded with hot, mineral-rich water.

drifted eastward across the Atlantic. However, research published in June 2008 indicated that some of the icebergs drifted southward toward Florida. This was the first evidence of icebergs occurring this far south in the North Atlantic.

The research was conducted by marine geologists Jenna C. Hill and Paul T. Gayes of Coastal Carolina University in Conway, South Carolina, and their colleagues from the Scripps Institution of Oceanography in La Jolla, California, and the National Oceanic and Atmospheric Administration (NOAA) in Savannah, Georgia. These scientists carried out a detailed mapping survey of the upper part of the continental slope off the Carolinas. Using the sonar mapping system of a NOAA research vessel, they discovered many longitudinal furrows gouged into the stiff sediments of the sea floor

GEOLOGY continued

in this area. When an iceberg touches the sea bottom, its lowest part, called the keel, acts like a plow to produce a nearly straight track. The track has a central trench bordered on either side by low ridges, where the sediment was pushed aside. When the iceberg finally runs aground and is stopped, a mound of sediment is left behind at the end of the track.

The iceberg tracks found by the investigators run parallel to the Carolina coast from the northeast toward the southwest, indicating that the icebergs were carried by a cold, southward-flowing coastal current. Unfortunately, the geologists were unable to precisely date these tracks. However, they noted that the tracks appeared to be only slightly altered by bottom currents. They theorized that the tracks represented the last two Heinrich events, which occurred about 25,200 and 17,500 years ago.

Oldest rock on Earth. In September 2008, the oldest known rock on Earth was described by a team of scientists led by geologist Jonathan O'Neill of McGill University in Montreal, Canada, and geochemist Richard W. Carlson of the Carnegie Institution of Washington (D.C.). The rock was from the Nuvvuagittuq greenstone belt on the northeastern side of Hudson Bay in Quebec. Rocks from this site are, as the name of the site suggests, generally green. However, the rock discovered by the scientists stood out because it was light gray.

Using radioisotope dating methods, the scientists estimated the age of the rock to be approximately 4.28 billion years. This great age made the specimen the oldest sample of solid rock from the Hadean Eon, which lasted from the time of Earth's formation, about 4.6 billion years ago, to the beginning of the Archean Eon, 3.8 billion years ago. The Nuvvuagittuq rock was 300 million years older than any other rock previously discovered on Earth.

■ William Hay

MEDICAL RESEARCH

In December 2008, doctors at the Cleveland Clinic in Cleveland, Ohio, performed the first face transplant surgery in the United States. The surgical team was led by Maria Siemionow, professor of surgery at the Cleveland Clinic Lerner College of Medicine of Case Western Reserve University.

Three previous face transplant surgeries had been performed—in France in 2005 and 2007 and in China in 2006. However, none was as extensive as the surgery performed by Siemionow's surgical team.

That surgery replaced about 500 square centimeters (78 square inches) of surface area of the patient's face, which had been largely destroyed by gunshot. The transplanted facial tissue included skin, arteries, veins, nerves, muscles, and some bone. The only original features remaining were the woman's upper eyelids, forehead, lower lip, and chin.

On May 6, 2009, at a press conference at the Cleveland Clinic, Siemionow's patient revealed herself as Connie Culp, a 46-year-old woman from Ohio. Culp, whose face almost destroyed by a shotgun blast, gratefully acknowledged her donor, thanked the hospital staff, and occasionally cracked jokes and laughed.

Researchers have established stringent standards for candidates for face transplants, medical analysts report. Patients must be severely disfigured and have exhausted all other reconstructive procedures. They must be informed of the risks of the procedure, including the risk of tissue rejection. In tissue rejection, the recipient's immune system recognizes the transplanted tissue as foreign and attacks it. In addition, recipients are required to take *immunosuppressive drugs* (drugs that reduce the activity of the immune system) for the rest of their lives.

Medical professionals also emphasize the need for careful psychological screening of candidates for face transplants. The face-transplant recipient must be prepared to see him- or herself with a new, unfamiliar face and be comfortable with the knowledge that it has been donated by a dead person. Nevertheless, a face transplant may offer the last hope of a normal life for a person suffering from severe facial disfigurement.

New approach to food allergies. In March 2009, a research team led by pediatric allergist Wesley Burks of Duke University in Durham, North Carolina, reported preliminary results of a study investigating a new treatment for children with peanut allergies. The treatment involved giving children tiny amounts of peanut flour to *ingest* (eat or drink) daily over a period of several years. The researchers slowly increased the daily dosage over time. By the end of the testing period, some of the children appeared to have overcome their peanut allergy.

This approach to allergy treatment is called desensitization. By being exposed to tiny amounts of the *allergen* (allergy-producing substance), the patient gradually becomes less and less sensitive to it. Allergists have long used injections of tiny amounts of allergenic material to achieve desensitization, but oral treatment (by eating or drinking) has not been used.

Food allergies occur when the immune system mistakenly mounts an immune response to a protein in an ingested food. Foods most likely to provoke an allergic reaction include milk, eggs, peanuts, tree nuts, wheat, soy, fish, and shellfish. According to the Centers for Disease Control and Prevention (CDC) in Atlanta, 4 out of every 100 children in the United States suffer from food allergies.

Mild symptoms of an allergic reaction may include rashes, hives, itching, swelling, and a runny nose. More serious reactions may include wheezing and difficulty breathing. The most serious allergic reaction is anaphylaxis, a life-threatening condition that causes extreme difficulty breathing and a dangerous drop in blood pressure. From 2004 to 2006, about 9,500 children were hospitalized for anaphylaxis triggered by allergic reactions to food, according to the CDC.

In the Burks study, which began in 2004, researchers gave children who suffered from peanut allergies daily doses of peanut flour, starting with 0.1 milligrams (equivalent to $\frac{1}{1,000}$ of a peanut). A control group of children were given a *placebo* (inactive substance).

Over the next 10 months, the doses were gradually increased until they reached 300 milligrams a day, a dosage participants continued to receive for another 24 months. At the end of the treatment period, some of the participants were able to tolerate 3,900 milligrams of peanut protein (equivalent to about 13 peanuts); others tolerated lesser amounts before exhibiting any symptoms of allergic reaction. In all, 27 out of 33 children were able to ingest from 300 to 3,900 milligrams of peanut protein without experiencing serious allergic reaction.

These results suggest that oral desensitization therapy, like injection therapy, can raise the threshold at which allergic reactions begin. Acknowledging that the approach is still experimental, the researchers cautioned that the therapy should be tried only under close medical supervision.

BLOOD PRESSURE FROM THE INSIDE

In January 2009, researchers with the Fraunhofer Institute for Microelectronic Circuits and Systems, based in Duisburg, Germany, announced the development of a nanotech blood-pressure sensor that surgeons will be able to implant inside a patient's artery. The device, when commercially available, will enable patients and their doctors to monitor blood pressure continuously around the clock. The sensor is designed to be implanted inside the femoral artery in the groin. Medical analysts suggested that the nanotech sensor would prove a boon for patients who suffer from irregular, difficult-to-control blood pressure, who now must wear cumbersome pressure-taking devices.

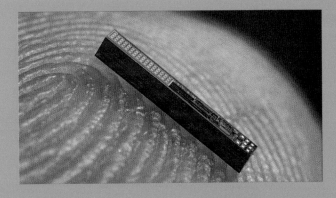

MEDICAL RESEARCH continued

Cholesterol-lowering drugs help prevent heart attack, stroke, and death from these conditions in apparently healthy people who have normal cholesterol levels but high levels of high-sensitivity C-reactive protein (CRP). An international team of researchers, led by Paul M. Ridker from the Center for Cardiovascular Disease Prevention and Division of Cardiovascular Medicine at Brigham and Women's Hospital in Boston, reported this finding in November 2008.

CRP, which the body produces in response to inflammation, can be an indicator of damage to arteries leading to the heart caused by the accumulation of plaque—the waxy buildup caused by the gradual depositing of cholesterol. This condition increases the risk of heart attack.

Physicians have long gauged blood levels of low-density lipoprotein (LDL), the artery-clogging "bad cholesterol," to determine whether people should start taking statins, drugs designed to lower LDL levels. However, physicians do not typically take CRP levels into account when considering statin therapy.

For the study, funded by AstraZeneca, the London-based maker of the statin drug rosuvastatin (sold under the brand name Crestor), researchers selected 17,702 men and women from 26 countries. Study participants had no known coronary disease and relatively low LDL cholesterol levels but high CRP levels.

Participants received either a daily dose of rosuvastatin or a placebo for two years. The researchers tracked the incidence of heart attack, stroke, bypass surgery, *angioplasty* (a technique used to open partially clogged arteries), and *angina* (chest pain caused by reduced blood flow to the heart), as well as deaths from cardiovascular disease.

In the group that received rosuvastatin, CRP levels dropped by nearly 50 percent, and the risk of heart attack, stroke, and cardiovascular death was reduced by nearly half. (Stroke occurs when arteries leading to the brain become narrowed or clogged.) Compared with the placebo group, the rosuvastatin group experienced 55 percent fewer nonfatal heart attacks and 48 percent fewer strokes; they also required 46 percent less bypass surgery or

A QUESTIONABLE QUEST FOR WHITENESS

The use of ultraviolet (UV) radiation to whiten teeth is not only ineffective but also potentially damaging to skin and eyes, according to a study reported in February 2009 by researchers with the Norway-based Nordic Institute of Dental Materials. Conventional tooth-whitening treatments use the bleaching agent hydrogen peroxide. However, some dentists suggest that exposure to UV radiation enhances the action of hydrogen peroxide. The researchers stated that the radiation, which may be four times as strong as sunlight, provides no benefit and may damage teeth. They reported that the enamel of teeth exposed to UV had higher numbers of exposed grooves, which weaken teeth, making them more likely to crack or chip.

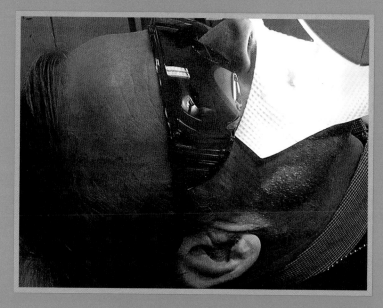

angioplasty than the placebo group. The researchers speculated that other statin drugs could produce similar results.

The investigators recommended routine CRP screening and statin therapy for people with high CRP levels, regardless of their cholesterol levels. Officials with the American Heart Association (AHA) said the organization would take these findings into account when next revising AHA prevention guidelines.

Stem cell advances. In June 2008, a 30-year-old Colombian woman with disabling breathing problems received a transplanted *trachea* (windpipe) made of her own body's stem cells that had been cultured on a "scaffold" derived from a donor's trachea. (A stem cell is a cell that has the ability to develop into any of the specialized cells that form various tissues in the body.) In the November issue of the London-based medical journal *The Lancet*, surgeon Paolo Macchiarini of the Department of General Thoracic Surgery at the Hospital Clinic in Barcelona, Spain, described the medical procedure that he and his colleagues had used to perform the transplant.

Before the surgery, the woman, Claudia Castillo Sánchez, had been disabled by severe shortness of breath resulting from damage to her left lung and left *bronchial tube* (the airway leading from the windpipe into the left lung) from tuberculosis infection. (The infection itself was eventually cured.) It was this left bronchial tube that the surgeons sought to replace with the donor trachea.

Macchiarini and his assisting surgeons began the therapy by removing a 7-centimeter (2.8-inch) section of trachea from a donor, a woman who had died suddenly. They then submerged the trachea in a special solution to strip it of its cells, leaving a tube of connective tissue that could be used as a scaffold on which to culture Sánchez's own cells. The researchers theorized that the removal of the donor cells would minimize the possibility of rejection in their transplant patient.

Simultaneously, the research team removed *epithelial* (surface-layer) cells from the inner lining of Sánchez's healthy right bronchial tube and grew them in a special culture solution. They also extracted stem cells from her bone marrow and induced these cells to grow into chondrocytes, cells that make up cartilage.

The researchers put the stripped-down trachea into an instrument called a bioreactor. They seeded the outside of the tracheal scaffold with Sánchez's stem-cell derived chondrocytes and the inside, with her harvested bronchial cells. After 96 hours of cell culture, the newly engineered tissue was ready to be transplanted. The surgical team cut away the patient's damaged left bronchial tube and replaced it with the bioengineered organ.

After one month, the surgeons removed a tissue sample from the transplanted bronchial tube and found that blood vessels were spreading through the tissue, a sign of health. Four months after the transplant, the patient's new airway functioned normally and she was living an active life. Because the tissue had been engineered from her own cells, Sánchez did not need to take immunosuppressive drugs.

Analysts noted that the Sánchez case marked the first time that tissue engineering had been used to replace a defective airway in a patient's *pulmonary* (lung) system. They speculated that similar procedures could prove especially beneficial to patients with weakened immune systems, such as people suffering from various cancers.

Diabetes studies. Intensively controlling *glucose* (blood sugar) in people with Type 2 diabetes may not reduce the risk of heart attack and stroke as much as controlling cholesterol levels and blood pressure. Several studies revealed these findings in 2008 and 2009.

Diabetes is a disease that disrupts the body's ability to produce or use insulin, the *hormone* (chemical messenger) necessary for cells to derive energy from glucose. In the United States, diabetes affects about 8 percent of the population, according to the CDC.

There are two major forms of diabetes. Type 1 diabetes occurs when the body does not produce insulin. This form of the disease usually begins in childhood and always requires treatment by insulin injection.

Type 2 diabetes develops when people lose the ability to produce enough insulin or to efficiently use their insulin. This form of diabetes occurs most commonly in middle age. According to the CDC, Type 2 diabetes accounts for more than 90 percent of all diagnosed diabetes. It is often treated by oral drugs.

Without effective insulin, glucose builds up in the blood. Because high glucose levels gradually damage blood vessels that nourish body tissues, people with diabetes are at increased risk for cardiovascular disease, blindness, kidney failure, amputations, and other health problems.

MEDICAL RESEARCH continued

3-D ARTIFICIAL BONE PRINTING

An artificial bone formed using 3-D printing technology fits perfectly inside the skull it was made for. Doctors at the University of Tokyo in Japan reported their development of the method in November 2008. The replacement bone is made by squirting a solidifying liquid onto a layer of calcium phosphate powder in the desired shape, much as an ink-jet printer squirts ink droplets onto paper.

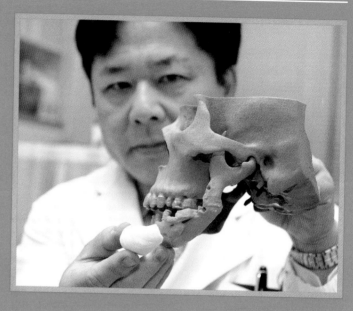

In January 2009, a research team led by William Duckworth of the Phoenix Veterans Affairs Health Care Center in Phoenix reported on their study of 1,791 military veterans with long-standing Type 2 diabetes. Investigators examined the effects of intensive glucose control on such cardiovascular events as heart attacks. The research appeared in the Jan. 8, 2009, issue of the *New England Journal of Medicine*.

Intensive glucose control involves prescribing relatively high dosages of oral drugs to maintain glucose levels at near-normal levels. Many diabetes patients on standard dosages of oral drug therapies, in contrast, have above-normal glucose levels that are considerably improved from the dangerously high levels they would experience without treatment.

Participants in the study received either intensive or standard glucose control. Those receiving intensive therapy attained, on average, a long-term blood glucose level of 6.9 percent; those receiving standard therapy, 8.4 percent. A level in the range of 4.3 to 5.9 percent is considered normal, and physicians generally recommend to their diabetic patients a

level of 7.0 or lower. (Long-term blood glucose level, also called the A1C test, measures the bonding of glucose molecules to a particular blood protein and is expressed as a percentage. This value indicates the average blood sugar level for the two or three most recent months.)

The researchers tracked heart disease, stroke, and amputations among the participants, following them for an average of 5.6 years. They found no significant difference between the two groups.

Other studies reported in 2008, including studies based in the United States, the United Kingdom, and Australia, reported similar findings. Taken together, these studies suggest that in people with long-standing diabetes, intensive control of blood sugar levels with drug therapy does not reduce the risk of heart disease. Blood pressure and cholesterol levels appear to be more important factors in reducing the risk of heart disease. However, researchers cautioned that none of the studies undermined the importance of controlling glucose levels, especially in people newly diagnosed with diabetes. ■ Renée Despres

See also **DRUGS; PUBLIC HEALTH.**

NOBEL PRIZES

The 2008 Nobel Prizes in science were awarded for the discovery and development of a protein that has become an important tool in bioscience, for insights into the properties of subatomic particles, and for the discoveries of two viruses, one of which causes cervical cancer in women and the other, AIDS. Each prize was worth about $1.4 million.

The Nobel Prize in chemistry was awarded jointly to three American scientists: Japanese-born Osamu Shimomura of the Marine Biological Laboratory in Woods Hole and Boston University Medical School, both in Massachusetts; Martin Chalfie of Columbia University in New York City; and Roger Y. Tsien of the University of California, San Diego. Shimomura discovered and isolated the green fluorescent protein (GFP), a molecule in the jellyfish *Aequorea victoria* that glows when exposed to ultraviolet light. Chalfie demonstrated how to link GFP to other proteins, "tagging" them so they can be viewed under a microscope. Tsien used DNA technology to extend the range of colors in which GFP glows and its intensity. (DNA—deoxyribonucleic acid—is the molecule genes are made of.)

Using GFP, researchers can see inside cells and observe biological processes that have previously been invisible. Such processes include the damage caused to nerve cells by Alzheimer's disease, the growth of new blood vessels as cancer tumors spread, and the growth of disease-causing bacteria.

The Nobel Prize in physics also went to three scientists. Japanese-born American physicist Yoichiro Nambu of the University of Chicago was awarded half the prize, and Japanese scientists Toshihide Maskawa of Kyoto University and Makoto Kobayashi of the High Energy Accelerator Research Organization in Tsukuba, both in Japan, shared the other half.

TOOLS FROM THE SEA

The 2008 Nobel Prize in chemistry went to three American scientists for their research on the green fluorescent protein (GFP), a molecule that glows when exposed to ultraviolet light. GFP can be used to "tag" other proteins, allowing scientists to see inside cells (right, inset) and observe biological processes. Martin Chalfie of Columbia University in New York City (right, below) discovered how to link GFP to other proteins. Japanese-born Osamu Shimomura of the Marine Biological Laboratory in Woods Hole and Boston University Medical School, both in Massachusetts, isolated the molecule from the jellyfish *Aequorea victoria* (right, above). Roger Y. Tsien of the University of California, San Diego, extended the range of colors in which GFP glows and its intensity.

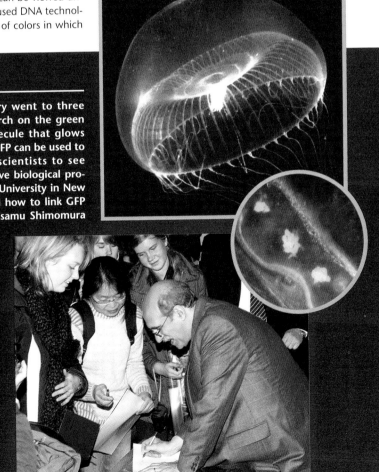

NOBEL PRIZES continued

NOBEL PRIZE IN PHYSIOLOGY OR MEDICINE

Three European researchers—French scientists Luc Montagnier (left) and Françoise Barré-Sinoussi (center), both of the Pasteur Institute in Paris, and German scientist Harald zur Hausen of the German Cancer Research Center in Heidelberg (right)—shared the Nobel Prize in physiology or medicine. Montagnier and Barré-Sinoussi shared half the award for their discovery that the human immunodeficiency virus (HIV) causes AIDS. Zur Hausen received the other half for his discovery that human papillomavirus (HPV) causes cervical cancer.

Nambu was honored for his discovery of spontaneous broken symmetry, an important property of *subatomic particles* (pieces of matter smaller than atoms). Physicists had long theorized that the universe exists because at some time after the big bang, the perfect symmetry that would have resulted in matter and antimatter annihilating each other was broken. (The big bang is a cosmic explosion that most scientists believe occurred about 14 billion years ago and started the expansion of the universe. Matter is the substance of which all things are made; it is composed of subatomic particles. Antimatter resembles ordinary matter but with some of the properties of its particles—such as electric charge—reversed. When identical amounts of matter and antimatter come into contact, they usually destroy each other.)

Nambu developed a mathematical calculation to describe broken symmetry that occurs spontaneously after studying an example of the phenomenon called *superconductivity* (the sudden flow of electric currents without any resistance). He later showed that spontaneous broken symmetry occurs among subatomic particles as well. Nambu's calculations contributed to the development of the Standard Model, the leading fundamental theory of physics.

Kobayashi and Maskawa identified the particles that must exist for Nambu's theory to work. They proposed the existence of a new family of quarks, a type of subatomic particle. Some time later, scientists discovered the proposed quarks, confirming the theory and providing yet more support for the Standard Model.

The Nobel Prize in physiology or medicine was shared by three European researchers. Harald zur Hausen, a German scientist at the German Cancer Research Center in Heidelberg, was awarded half of the prize for his discovery in the 1980's that human papillomavirus (HPV) causes cervical cancer. The finding led to the development of vaccines to help prevent the second most common cancer in women worldwide.

The other half of the prize was awarded to French scientists Françoise Barré-Sinoussi and Luc Montagnier, both of the Pasteur Institute in Paris. The scientists were honored for their discovery in the mid-1980's that the human immunodeficiency virus (HIV) causes AIDS. Their work led to the development of methods to diagnose AIDS and to screen blood products for AIDS, as well as drugs that have "substantially decreased the spread of the disease and dramatically increased life expectancy among treated patients." ■ Kristina Vaicikonis

See also **CHEMISTRY; MEDICAL RESEARCH; PHYSICS.**

NUTRITION

Children choose high-sugar, high-fat, high-salt foods over more healthful options, and they eat more food when exposed to television ads promoting such foods. Furthermore, obese children appear to be more responsive to the ads than children who are not overweight. A research team at the University of Liverpool in the United Kingdom, published these findings in the September 2008 issue of the journal *Public Health Nutrition*.

The team, led by psychologist Jason Halford, selected 59 British children, ages 9 to 11, for the study. The test group included children who were of normal weight or overweight or obese. According to statistical averages for their age and height, 56 percent were of normal weight, 25 percent were overweight, and 19 percent were obese. Of the 59 participants, 32 were male and 27 were female.

The study was structured so that each child attended two sessions, several weeks apart. In one session, the children viewed five minutes of toy ads followed by a popular television cartoon. In the other session, they viewed five minutes of standard TV ads for popular high-calorie, high-salt snack foods (which critics call "junk food") followed by the same cartoon.

SEE ALSO

THE SPECIAL REPORT, FASCINATING FACTS FROM FOSSIL FECES, PAGE 12.

CONSUMER SCIENCE, VITAMIN D: IS IT A MIRACLE VITAMIN?, PAGE 143.

After completing each "show," the children were offered a variety of snacks. The snacks ranged from such low-fat foods as grapes and rice-cake to such sugary foods as gumdrops, known as jelly sweets in the United Kingdom, and from high-fat chocolate candy to high-fat, high-salt potato chips. The researchers recorded and evaluated what each child ate after each session.

Halford and his colleagues found that the children ate an average of 300 calories of snacks after seeing the program with toy commercials, with little difference among weight groups. After the program with snack commercials, however, children consumed significantly more calories, and the heavier the child, the

CALORIES COUNT— IN PUBLIC PLACES

In the summer of 2008, New York City restaurants that are part of restaurant chains began posting calorie counts for each food item they sell. The New York City Board of Health in late 2007 passed an ordinance calling for the postings, but implementation of the law was held up for several months by court challenges. Many nutritionists applauded the city's action and predicted that public demand for information about food calories would encourage other municipalities or states to pass similar laws. Some health officials urged the federal government to follow suit.

BREAKFAST WRAPS

SPINACH FETA WRAP $3.25
WITH EGG & ROASTED TOMATO
240 CALORIES

BACON AVOCADO WRAP $3.25
WITH EGG & AGED CHEDDAR CHEESE
380 CALORIES

oven-toasted

NUTRITION continued

more he or she ate. On average, the normal-weight children consumed about 550 calories. The overweight children consumed about 600 calories. The researchers observed that the obese children ate snacks with about 775 calories after the TV snack commercials.

They found that the children consumed more calories after watching the TV food commercials. More of the children also chose higher-fat foods, such as chocolate and potato chips, or the high-sugar gumdrops (jelly sweets). They typically rejected the more healthful snacks—the grapes and the rice cakes. The researchers concluded that commercial advertising of breakfast foods, candy, snacks, and fast foods on television causes children to eat more and, specifically, to seek calorie-rich and high-salt food. Furthermore, the incentive to eat these foods appears to be more pronounced in overweight than in normal-weight children.

Diet and bone health in adolescents. Researchers with the High Spanish Council for Scientific Research in Granada, Spain, found that a so-called Mediterranean diet helps promote the body's efficient use of calcium in adolescent boys aged 11 to 14. Calcium intake and utilization are of crucial importance to the formation of healthy bones in children, especially during such periods of rapid growth as early adolescence. The study, led by nutritionist Isabel Seiquer, was reported in the August 2008 issue of the *Journal of the American College of Nutrition.*

A Mediterranean diet is high in vegetables, fruits, cereals, and legumes (beans). These foods provide vitamins, minerals, fiber, and other beneficial substances. Fats in this diet include a high proportion of such "healthy" fats as olive oil and canola oil and a low proportion of such saturated fats such as butter, nondiet margarine, and animal fat. (Saturated fats contribute to an individual's risk for heart disease, among other illnesses.)

The Mediterranean diet also emphasizes fish over red meat. Many kinds of fish provide health-promoting omega-3 fatty acids and—unlike many meats—are low in saturated fat. On the other hand, diets in many northern European countries and in North America tend to minimize fruit, vegetable, and whole-grain intake and favor foods high in saturated fat. In these societies, many adolescents tend to have diets low in minerals and vitamins and high in calories, sugar, and fat.

The children selected for the Seiquer study were 20 boys, ages 11 to 14 years. For the first three days of the study, the boys ate their usual diet while keeping food journals and weighing everything they ate and drank. At the end of the three days, they began eating a supervised, Mediterranean-style diet. The boys continued on this diet for 28 days. Data about calcium content and such other factors as calories, fat, carbohydrates (starch), vitamin content, and mineral content in foods from both diets were carefully analyzed and recorded.

The scientists measured calcium levels as well as levels of phosphorus and sodium in the boys' blood, urine, and feces. They calculated calcium retention in the participants' bodies by subtracting the amount of calcium eliminated in urine and feces from the amount consumed in food and beverages. (The researchers noted that this calculation represented a slight underestimate of actual absorbed calcium, because some calcium is naturally secreted in digestive fluids and thus adds to the amount in feces.)

The researchers then assessed bone-building activity by measuring blood levels of parathyroid hormone and alkaline phosphatase. Parathyroid hormone is a protein that regulates the amount of calcium in the blood; alkaline phosphatase is an enzyme indicating active bone growth.

Of the 16 vitamins and minerals evaluated in the meals during both diet periods, all but 4 nutrients—calcium, iron, vitamin B1, and vitamin B12—measured higher in the Mediterranean diet than in the standard diet. Although calcium intake was about the same for both of these diets, calcium absorption and bone-building activity increased markedly during the Mediterranean diet phase.

The scientists concluded that a Mediterranean-style diet may boost the body's ability to absorb and utilize calcium consumed in food. Such a diet would, therefore, better support the growth of strong, healthy bones, they reasoned, than the typical eating habits of adolescents in northern European and North American societies.

Children in the United States are generally not meeting recommended daily allowances (RDA's) of fruits and vegetables, according to a study led by dietitian Barbara Lorson of Ohio State University in Columbus. In the United

States, RDA's are defined by the Food and Nutrition Board of the National Academy of Sciences, based in Washington, D.C.

Lorson and her colleagues accessed data on the dietary habits of U.S. children and youth from the National Health and Nutrition Examination Survey (NHANES) for the period of 1999 to 2002. (The National Center for Health Statistics of the Centers for Disease Control and Prevention in Atlanta conducts the continuous NHANES survey and publishes statistics every two years.) The researchers found that, overall, young people tend to consume the bulk of their fruit and vegetable intake in the form of energy-dense 100-percent fruit juice and French fries and that they consume fewer green leafy and orange vegetables than recommended. On average, the typical child ate a total of one cup of fruit or drank just under one-half cup of fruit juice and ate one cup of vegetables daily.

Among the scientists' specific findings were revelations that younger children consumed more fruit and fewer vegetables than older children, Mexican Americans consumed more fruit than non-Hispanic white children, and overweight children consumed less fruit and more French fries than other children.

In summary, Lorson's team reported that at least 50 percent of 2- to 5-year-olds, 70 percent of 6- to 11-year-olds, and 80 percent of 12- to 18-year-olds did not meet their recommended daily intake for fruit. The investigators further reported that 80 percent of the children did not meet the RDA for daily vegetable intake.

■ Catherine J. Klein and Amy Schweitzer
See also **AGRICULTURE; MEDICAL RESEARCH; PUBLIC HEALTH.**

RANKING CANCER-FIGHTING VEGGIES

Researchers have long known that eating plentiful amounts of fruits and vegetables can lower the risk for certain types of cancer. But a study published in 2008 suggests that certain vegetables may be more effective cancer fighters than others.

Biochemist Dominique Boivin at Québec University in Québec, Canada, and colleagues analyzed extracts from 34 vegetables to determine their effect on cells from eight different types of cancerous tumors—brain, breast, kidney, lung, pancreas, prostate, skin, and stomach. The researchers found that cruciferous vegetables—

including broccoli, Brussels sprouts, curly cabbage, and kale— and vegetables in the genus *Allium*—including garlic, onions, and shallots—significantly inhibited the growth of cancer cells in the laboratory. The most commonly eaten vegetables—lettuce, carrots, potatoes, and tomatoes—had less effect on the cancer cells. According to the researchers, the types of vegetables people choose to eat may be more important than previously thought.

OCEANOGRAPHY

Scientists with the Census of Marine Life announced in February 2009 that they had identified 235 species that live both in the waters surrounding the continent of Antarctica, which lies at the South Pole, and in the waters of the Arctic Ocean near the North Pole. Among the shared species were humpback whales and birds. Most of the species, however, were *invertebrates* (animals without backbones) including worms, crustaceans, and sea butterflies—a snail species that has wing-like projections to aid in swimming. The census is a massive 10-year project to identify all *marine* (ocean-living) species of organisms.

"This raises a whole bunch of evolutionary questions," observed oceanographer Ross Hopcroft of the University of Alaska at Fairbanks, one of the scientists leading the census effort. Hopcroft pointed out that the Arctic and Antarctic regions are approximately 11,000 kilometers (nearly 7,000 miles) apart and that no one knows for sure how some of the species could have dispersed from one pole to the other.

In the cases of whales and birds, which are capable of long migrations, the process of dispersion is not hard to imagine. However, most invertebrate species typically do not range far. Scientists theorized that multiple generations of these species may have traveled gradually along deep-sea currents that link the poles, perhaps during the height of the last ice age, about 20,000 years ago, when ice covered much more of the two polar regions than it does now.

Hopcroft noted that scientists planned to perform DNA testing on all 235 of the mutual-polar species. The results of these tests, he predicted, would clarify whether the north and south polar specimens are genetically identical or *divergent* (different) and would offer insights into the evolutionary pasts of the species.

The Census of Marine Life, which began in 2000 and involves 2,000 researchers from 82 countries, is funded by the United Nations (UN) Environment Programme, among other international agencies, and by governments and private conservation groups. As of early 2009, the census had recorded at least 120,000 marine species, including 7,500 species in Antarctic waters and 5,500 in Arctic waters.

To identify polar species, 18 expeditions

SEE ALSO

THE SPECIAL REPORT, **METHANE: ANOTHER GREENHOUSE TROUBLEMAKER,** PAGE 42.

THE SPECIAL REPORT, **INVASION OF THE JELLYFISH,** PAGE 72.

explored Antarctic waters and 14 expeditions investigated Arctic waters. Biologists observed herds of roving sea cucumbers, meadows of sea lilies, dumbo squid (so-named for their elephant-like "ears"), and masses of a sea spider species, each the size of a human hand. (Sea spiders are related to crustaceans, such as crabs, as well as to insects.) Most newly discovered species have been invertebrates.

Dearth of big fish. The "trophy fish" that anglers are catching off Key West, Florida, are markedly smaller than those caught 50 years ago, according to a study released in January 2009. The average weight of a trophy fish from Key West was 20 kilograms (44 pounds) in 1956, compared with a mere 2 kilograms (about 4 ½ pounds) in 2007. The study, led by marine biology graduate student Loren McClenachan of the Scripps Institution of Oceanography in San Diego, further documented a drop in the average length of Key West trophy fish from 92 centimeters (3 feet) in 1956 to 42 centimeters (17 inches) in 2007.

The basis of McClenachan's historical analysis was a collection of hundreds of old photographs of trophy fish, visual records of the largest fish in daily catches, hung on drying racks at the local Key West dock. The photos, found in a library archive, spanned a three-decade period beginning in the 1950's; many were black-and-white prints by local professional photographer Charles Anderson. McClenachan supplemented the archival photos with a series of photos she took at the Key West dock in 2007. From the collection of vintage and modern photos, she was able to identify and measure more than 1,200 fish.

McClenachan's study is representative of an emerging field called *historical marine ecology*, in which scientists sift through old photographs, archives, and newspaper articles for information on what the ocean used to be like. These anecdotal data provide useful scientific evidence in the absence of the kind of data obtained at a later time from more technologically advanced methods and tools for monitoring the oceans.

In addition to differences in scale, McClenachan identified differences in species caught over the 50-year period. From 1956 to 1960, people hooked huge groupers and other large predatory fish, including sharks. In 2007, the main catch was small snapper—fish that would have been discarded in the 1950's heyday of Key West sports fishing.

The McClenachan study provides evidence in the Florida Keys of a trend that has been widely observed over much of the world in the last 25 years: the disappearance of some desirable food fish species and the serious reduction in size of other species. Experts in marine biology attribute much of the decline to overfishing by the world's highly industrialized fishing fleets.

Google Earth adds "Ocean." The online mapping service Google Earth no longer stops at the shoreline. On Feb. 2, 2009, Google chief executive officer (CEO) Eric Schmidt unveiled Google Earth 5.0, which features a new service called "Ocean in Google Earth." Ocean enables users to explore the depths of the Earth's oceans from their desktops.

A worldwide network of scientists contributed satellite and sonar imagery, underwater photographs, and other scientific data to Google for its Ocean feature. Users of Ocean in Google can explore the sea depths through the eyes of a dolphin, "diving" through coral reefs, kelp forests, and old shipwrecks. They can also obtain reports from ongoing scientific ocean expeditions as well as details of the world's best surfing spots.

"There's been a complete disconnect between our land-based lives and the oceans," said Arctic explorer and Ocean contributor Pen Hadow at the product launch. "What this service is doing is engaging everybody in a better understanding of how oceans work, what they are ... and what the dangers are for all of us."

Crabs feel and learn from pain. It does not take a complex mammalian brain and nervous system to experience pain and retain memories of it. Crustaceans—the invertebrate group that includes lobsters, shrimp, and crabs—also feel pain and try to avoid it. In

DIMINISHING TROPHIES

Photographs from three different eras—the 1950's, the 1980's, and the 2000's—dramatically illustrate changes in Florida fisheries in the past 50 years. According to an analysis performed by oceanographer Loren McClenachan, the most highly desired large predatory fish, common in daily sportsfisher catches in the 1950's, had all but disappeared from the Florida waters around Key West by 2007.

1950

1980

2000

OCEANOGRAPHY continued

support of these conclusions, biologists Bob Elwood and Mirjam Appel of Queen's University Belfast in Northern Ireland presented findings from their experiments with hermit crabs in the March 2009 issue of *Animal Behavior*.

A hermit crab does not produce its own shell. Instead, it finds an abandoned shell, crawls inside, and carries its new home around on its back for shelter. Hermit crabs are known to have strong preferences for certain species of shells.

In their experiments, Elwood and Appel attached wires to some hermit crab shells and delivered small shocks to the animals' abdomens. Electric shocks were not applied to individuals in a control group. The biologists observed that the only crabs to leave their shells were those that had been shocked. The researchers interpreted this behavior as an indication that being shocked is unpleasant for the crabs.

In addition, shocked crabs were more likely to leave their least favorite than their favorite shells. The researchers surmised that the crabs made a value judgment, weighing the merit of the shell against the unpleasantness of the shock. The researchers asserted that this evidence of evaluative behavior in response to

the experience of the shock indicated that the crabs felt pain and were not merely exhibiting a reflex to the shock.

The scientists took their experiment a step further with crabs already conditioned by previous shocks. The researchers placed new shells close to crab subjects and shocked the crabs but at levels lower than those previously found to motivate crabs to leave their shells. These crabs now abandoned their shells and moved quickly toward the new shells, investigating them briefly and then occupying them. The behavior strongly suggested to Elwood and Appel that the crabs remembered being shocked and learned from it.

Candidate for oldest animal. Also in March, Brendan Roark, a geosciences professor at Texas A & M University in College Station, announced the discovery of what may be the oldest living animal on the planet: a 4,265-year-old deepwater black coral found on a *seamount* (underwater mountain) in the Pacific Ocean about 160 kilometers (100 miles) south of the Hawaiian island of Oahu. Among living things on Earth, only one, the bristlecone pine of California, is known to be old enough to rival the longevity of the deepwater black coral, known by the scientific name *Leiopathes*.

NEW UNDERWATER SPECIES

A newly discovered species, the orange bamboo coral, lives 1,751 meters (5,745 feet) below the surface in the Papahanaumokuakea Marine National Monument in the northwestern Hawaiian Islands. The coral grows to a height of 1.5 meters (5 feet). It is one of seven new species reported in March 2009 by scientists with the U.S. National Oceanic and Atmospheric Administration (NOAA).

Corals are simple sea creatures whose bodies are similar to the bodies of jellyfish. Many species of coral, including *Leiopathes*, form large colonies consisting of individual organisms called polyps. Each polyp secretes a cup-shaped hard shell of calcium carbonate around the lower half of its body. Over time, individual polyps die, but their shells accumulate to form extensive limestone structures. In shallow-water coral species, these are often called reefs. In deepwater coral species, such as *Leiopathes,* they are typically called coral beds.

Although a coral bed is populated by thousands or even millions of polyps, the colony itself is considered the organism, rather than individual polyps. This is because the polyps are genetically identical and they share critical life functions. Therefore, living polyps can be considered to carry on the life processes in the organism, exactly as the original, long-dead polyps did.

The Roark team used carbon 14 dating (also called radiocarbon dating) to determine the age of calcium carbonate in the skeletal structure underneath the living polyps. (Radiocarbon dating is a dating method based on the amount of radioactive carbon in a specimen.) They concluded that the living polyps themselves were only a few years old but that these polyps had been continuously replaced for more than 4,200 years. The research, funded by several United States federal agencies, appeared in the March 23, 2009, early online edition of the *Proceedings of the National Academy of Sciences.*

The number of shark attacks around the world in 2008 dropped to its lowest level since 2003, despite population growth during this period, according to data from the International Shark Attack File. There were 59 reported shark attacks in 2008, compared with 71 in 2007 and 57 in 2003. The International Shark Attack File is a compilation of shark attack statistics maintained by the Florida Museum of Natural History in Gainesville, Florida, and the American Elasmobranch Society, a nonprofit organization devoted to the study of sharks, rays, and skates.

About two-thirds of the world's shark attacks occur in the United States, mostly along Florida beaches, where warm water attracts surfers, swimmers—and sharks. George Burgess, the director of the International Shark Attack File, attributed the 2008 decline in shark attacks to the downturn in the economy, which resulted in fewer beach vacations and, thus, fewer people splashing about in ocean waters. ■ Christina Johnson

The *carnivorous* (meat-eating) sea squirt (left) lives off the coast of Tasmania, Australia, at a depth of more than 4,000 meters (13,000 feet). The previously unknown species was reported in January 2009 by a joint American and Australian team using a remotely operated vehicle from Woods Hole Oceanographic Institution in Massachusetts.

The same scientific team discovered a new waffle cone sponge (right) in deep Tasmanian waters southeast of the Australian mainland. The creature measures 0.5 meter (1.6 feet) wide and 2 meters (6.5 feet) tall.

PHYSICS

The Large Hadron Collider (LHC), the world's most powerful particle accelerator, began operation on Sept. 10, 2008, at the international CERN laboratory near Geneva, Switzerland. Particle accelerators are devices that speed up subatomic particles to high energies and collide them to reveal information about properties of matter. The LHC was designed to produce beams of *protons* (positively charged particles belonging to a large family of particles called hadrons) with energies as great as 7 trillion electron volts. This energy level was seven times as great as the energy produced by the previous particle accelerator recordholder—the Tevatron at Fermi National Accelerator Laboratory near Batavia, Illinois.

The LHC was built in a circular tunnel 27 kilometers (17 miles) in circumference, straddling the French-Swiss border. This tunnel previously housed the Large Electron-Positron (LEP) accelerator. Reusing an existing tunnel led to substantial savings in the cost of building the LHC for the group of 20 European nations that support and operate CERN. Although the LHC is operated by these 20 nations, scientists throughout the world have access to the particle accelerator for research.

At the heart of the LHC are two pipes kept at near-perfect vacuum conditions—with an atmospheric pressure that is one-tenth as dense as the pressure at the surface of the moon. These conditions allow particles to circulate through the LHC for days without colliding with an atomic *nucleus* (central part). The particles are held on course by 9,300 powerful superconducting magnets, which conduct electric current with no loss of energy when operating at extremely low temperatures. To keep them superconducting, they are cooled with liquid helium to a temperature of 271 °C (456 °F).

The two pipes carry beams of particles circulating in opposite directions. The two beams cross at eight points around the ring, where head-on collisions of particles can result. Each beam contains trillions of particles traveling at 99.99 percent of the speed of light (299,792 kilometers [186,282 miles] per second), whizzing around the ring 11,245 times per second. Most of the particles avoid collisions, but at full power the LHC was expected to produce as many as 600 million collisions of subatomic particles per second.

SEE ALSO THE SPECIAL REPORT, **TELESCOPES: 400 YEARS OF STARGAZING,** PAGE 24.

The goal of the LHC's initial tests was to transfer proton beams from CERN's Super Proton Synchrotron to the LHC and to let the protons coast around in stable orbits. This delicate process required synchronizing the beams from the two machines to within a fraction of a *nanosecond* (billionth of a second).

Celebrations were held at physics laboratories around the world when this goal was achieved within hours after the LHC began operating. This elation turned into disappointment a few days later, when a connection carrying electric current from one magnet to another failed. The failure produced a pressure pulse that damaged nearby magnets, resulting in the shutdown of the LHC for repairs.

In February 2009, technicians estimated that LHC operations would resume in September. However, for the first few months of operation, the energy level of the LHC was to be restricted somewhat.

Once the LHC becomes fully operational, the researchers' most immediate goal was to be the production and detection of a theoretical particle called the Higgs boson. British physicist Peter Higgs proposed the existence of this particle in 1964 as the source of the *mass* (amount of matter) that nearly all known subatomic particles carry. Without the Higgs boson, physicists believe, the existence of matter would not be possible because it would have no mass.

The detection of the Higgs boson was expected to help physicists better understand the relationship between gravity and other forces in nature—a relationship that is one of the major mysteries in physics. Until the start-up of the LHC, particle accelerators could not attain the energy believed to be needed to produce the Higgs boson in detectable quantities.

Another major goal of the LHC was to detect unstable theoretical particles called supersymmetric particles. Some physicists believe that every particle of matter has a supersymmetric "shadow" force-carrying particle, and every force-carrying particle has a supersymmetric "shadow" matter particle. The detection of such particles would likely lead to a more unified understanding of matter and forces, according to physicists.

Yet another goal of the LHC was to shed light on the nature of dark matter and dark energy. Together, dark matter and dark energy are believed to make up more than 90 percent of the universe.

Dark matter is an invisible substance thought to be present in every galaxy. Although dark matter itself cannot be seen, the influence of its gravity on the motion of stars has been observed by astronomers. Without the added gravity supplied by the mass of dark matter, the gravity of stars themselves would be insufficient to hold galaxies together. Scientists estimate that the total mass of dark matter in the universe is five times as great as that of ordinary, visible matter.

Physicists believe that dark energy makes up about 70 percent of the universe, filling the cosmos with a "negative" antigravity pressure that is causing the expansion of the universe to speed up. Much less is known about dark energy than about dark matter.

When two particles collide at high energies inside a particle accelerator, hundreds of new particles are created during the conversion of energy of motion into mass. Scientists track these particles with complex arrays of detectors. The detectors generate immense streams of data, from which computers can reconstruct the paths of all the particles emerging from the collision points. To analyze these data, CERN created an ultrafast worldwide computer network that can be accessed by thousands of scientists at hundreds of institutions around the globe. Use of this network for LHC research represented the largest coordinated international effort in the history of science.

Einstein's foresight on dark energy. In March 2009, the National Aeronautics and Space Administration (NASA) reported that an analysis of cosmic radiation detected by its

LARGE HADRON COLLIDER REPAIRS

A cylindrical unit containing a superconducting magnet is raised from inside the Large Hadron Collider (LHC), in a tunnel on the French-Swiss border, to the surface for repairs. The LHC, the world's most powerful particle accelerator, was shut down for these repairs in September 2008—only a few days after beginning operation. Particle accelerators are devices that speed up subatomic particles and collide them to reveal information about matter. Repairs were needed to correct technical problems with electrical connections and associated magnets. Physicists hoped the LHC would resume operation by late 2009.

PHYSICS continued

Chandra X-ray Observatory satellite suggested that dark energy has properties similar to that of the "cosmological constant." German-born physicist Albert Einstein introduced the concept of the cosmological constant in 1917 as he was struggling with problems posed by his theory of gravity, known as the general theory of relativity. However, he later rejected the idea.

According to the general theory of relativity, gravity is a distortion, or curve, in the fabric of space-time. This distortion is caused by massive objects, such as the sun, resulting in less massive objects, such as Earth, getting trapped in a space-time curve around the more massive objects. The general theory also states that time moves more slowly closer to a massive object than it does farther away. Because the general theory of relativity combined space, time, and gravity, it provided scientists with a comprehensive understanding of space-time throughout the universe.

When applied to the universe as a whole, the general theory of relativity implied that a static, unchanging universe was not possible. Rather, the relationship between gravity and mass suggested that the universe must be either expanding or contracting. However, Einstein—like most scientists in the early 1900's—maintained that the universe must be static and unchanging. To resolve this dilemma, Einstein inserted the cosmological constant into his relativity equations as a negative-pressure "pushing" force to oppose and balance the positive-pressure "pulling" effects of gravity. The cosmological constant provided a mathematical means of maintaining the static nature of the cosmos.

In the 1920's, United States astronomer Edwin Hubble discovered that the universe was expanding. In the wake of this discovery, Einstein repudiated his cosmological constant, calling it "my biggest blunder."

Many scientists assumed that the pulling effects of gravity would gradually slow the expansion of the universe. However, in the late 1990's, two teams of astronomers discovered—based on careful analyses of the bright-

ness levels of exploding stars called type Ia supernovae—that the universe is actually expanding at an accelerating rate. This discovery suggested that a force something like the cosmological constant must be at work to counter the effects of gravity, though the exact nature of this force remained a mystery.

The key to understanding the effects of dark energy is understanding the relationship between the pressure it exerts and its energy density—that is, the amount of energy per unit volume. The rate of change in cosmic expansion is proportional to this relationship, which can be expressed with a mathematical equation incorporating Einstein's concept of the cosmological constant. For the cosmological constant to lead to a static universe, the value of dark energy's pressure in this equation would be 1. In other words, pressure would be equal to 1 times the energy density. By contrast, if dark energy's pressure was a negative value less than 1, this would provide evidence that the cosmological constant is causing the universe to expand at an accelerating rate.

The Chandra scientists, led by Alexey Vikhlinin of the Harvard-Smithsonian Center for Astrophysics in Cambridge, Massachusetts, studied X rays emitted by hot gases in 86 distant clusters of galaxies. Galaxy clusters, which are the largest assemblies of objects held

UNIVERSAL PHYSICS OF COILING

Universal physical principles of coiling are represented by something as simple as rolled-up sheets of paper (far right), according to a June 2008 report by physicist Enrique Cerda of the University of Santiago in Chile. Cerda noted that in all coiled rolls—regardless of material—the innermost part of the roll always straightens away from the rest of the roll, making an angle of about 24.1 degrees (α [alpha] in the diagram at right) with the coil. In addition, the end of the innermost part of the roll always makes an angle of about 125.2 degrees (β [beta]) with the point at which the sheet first detaches from the roll's inner face. Cerda demonstrated that these angles occur in rolled-up paper, carpet, metal strips, mica sheets, and other materials. The physicist also noted that these principles of coiling might be important for understanding the packing of genetic material inside viruses, as well as certain other biological structures.

together by gravity, each contain hundreds to thousands of individual galaxies.

The temperature of the gas located between individual galaxies in clusters depends on the strength of gravity within the cluster, which, in turn, arises from the amount of mass contained in the cluster. Measurements of the wavelengths and intensity of X rays emitted by the gas provide estimates of the temperature of the gas, thereby permitting assessments of the total amount of mass within the cluster.

As we look deeper into space, we are also looking further back in time. Most galaxy clusters formed when the universe was young, and they later tended to merge with one another. Thus, the farthest, oldest clusters generally have less mass than closer, younger clusters. However, the repulsive effects of dark energy can theoretically inhibit the merger of clusters. Therefore, X-ray analysis to measure differences in mass between younger and older clusters can provide an estimate of the pressure generated by dark energy.

After performing this type of X-ray analysis of the galaxy clusters, the Chandra researchers estimated the pressure exerted by dark energy to be equal to 0.991 times the energy density. Plugged into the previously mentioned mathematical equation for an accelerating universe, this negative value coincided with Einstein's idea of the cosmological constant.

The researchers noted that the accuracy of this estimated pressure required additional refinement. Nevertheless, the estimate provided strong evidence that the mysterious force of dark energy is, in fact, Einstein's once-discarded cosmological constant.

Biggest, brightest explosion ever. In September 2008, astronomers and astrophysicists working with NASA's Swift Gamma Ray Burst Mission orbiting telescope published their observations of the brightest, most energetic explosion ever recorded. The explosion was a gamma-ray burst (GRB) approximately 7.5 billion light-years away. A light-year is the distance traveled in one year by a pulse of light—9.46 trillion kilometers (5.88 trillion miles). The burst was so bright that it was visible to the unaided eye for about 40 seconds—despite being approximately halfway across the universe.

A GRB is thought to happen when a massive star depletes its fuel supply, causing the star to collapse into a *neutron star* (a small, extremely dense star) or a *black hole* (a region of space in which the gravitational pull is so strong that nothing, not even light, can escape). After the star collapses, a powerful, bright jet of gas shoots outward. Collisions of high-speed particles in the jet generate beams of gamma rays and X rays. These rays are the two forms of electromagnetic radiation with the greatest energy, with gamma rays being more energetic than X rays. (Forms of electro-

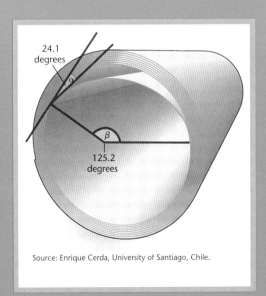

Source: Enrique Cerda, University of Santiago, Chile.

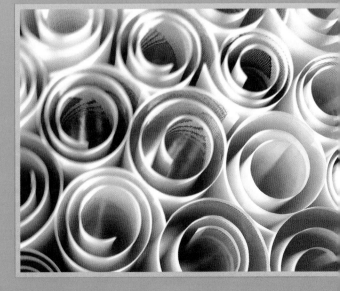

PHYSICS continued

magnetic radiation with lesser energy are ultraviolet rays, visible light, infrared light, microwaves, and radio waves.)

The GRB, which was designated as GRB 080319B, occurred on March 19, 2008. The radiation blast was so intense that it temporarily "blinded" the X-ray and visible-light detectors on the Swift satellite. Fortunately, the satellite was linked to an electronic network that quickly alerted a number of ground-based telescopes to point to the GRB and begin observations. These observations, combined with the resumed Swift surveillance, allowed scientists to make the most detailed portrait of GRB astrophysics ever produced. The published report on GRB 080319B covered all aspects of the electromagnetic spectrum from 30 minutes before the GRB occurred to several months afterward.

The scientists concluded that the *luminosity* (rate at which energy is emitted) of the GRB was 2.5 million times as great as the most luminous *supernova* (exploding star) ever recorded. They said the GRB was also the most intrinsically bright object ever observed— meaning its actual brightness, as opposed to just its brightness as seen from Earth.

One reason the GRB appeared to be so bright and powerful to Earth-based telescopes was that its gas jet was pointed almost directly toward Earth. The researchers discovered that the jet contained a narrow, highly energetic component within a wider, less energetic component. They noted that such narrow components had not been seen in most other GRB jets, but these components might have been found had other GRB's been as carefully studied as GRB 080319B.

The intense energy of GRB 080319B made it by far the most distant object ever visible to the unaided eye. Most stars that we see in the night sky are from hundreds to thousands of light-years away. Previously, the most distant object seen with the unaided eye was the Triangulum Galaxy (M33), which is about 3 million light-years away. The incredible brightness and distance of GRB 080319B made this cosmic event truly extraordinary in the eyes of astronomers and astrophysicists.

More electricity from sunlight. In July 2008, scientists at the National Renewable Energy Laboratory (NREL) in Golden, Colorado, described research in which they substantially improved the efficiency with which sunlight is converted into electric energy by certain kinds of *photovoltaic* (solar) cells. Not only were the solar panels more efficient than many standard photovoltaic cells, but they also promised to be relatively inexpensive to manufacture.

In a photovoltaic cell, *electrons* (negatively charged particles) that are normally attached to atoms absorb energy from sunlight, causing them to become independent and free to move around. Inserting the photovoltaic cell into an electric circuit allows the electrons to flow as an electric current.

Most photovoltaic cells are made of crystals of silicon or other semiconductors, the same types of materials used to make computer chips. Such cells are efficient—that is, they convert large amounts of the sunlight striking the cells into electric energy. However, the crystals used in these cells are expensive to produce.

Photovoltaic cells can also be made of less expensive polycrystalline materials, sheets comprised of multiple small crystals. However, such cells are inefficient, because when an electron crosses a boundary between crystals, it is likely to be recaptured by an atom. The key to making a more efficient photovoltaic cell out of polycrystalline materials is to keep the electrons free long enough to allow them to move out of the cell to create the current.

The NREL researchers reported that they made photovoltaic cells out of thin films of the polycrystalline material known as CIGS (copper, indium, gallium, and selenium), sandwiched between layers of cadmium sulfide and zinc oxide. Illuminating their cells at low light levels, they measured the time that individual electrons remained free. They found that the electrons in their cells had a free "lifetime" of about 250 nanoseconds.

Although this time may appear to be short, it is long enough to allow many electrons to travel to the edge of a reasonably large photovoltaic cell and enter the electric circuit. However, the researchers noted that their cells must be sealed to prevent contact with air, because oxygen atoms would capture the electrons and reduce their lifetime. Some analysts with the solar-power industry believed that CIGS materials would make solar power more competitive with traditional sources of electric power.

■ Robert H. March

■ PSYCHOLOGY

A combination of cognitive behavioral therapy (CBT) and an antidepressant medication is the most effective treatment for children and adolescents who suffer from anxiety disorders, according to a stu°dy reported in the October 2008 issue of the *New England Journal of Medicine* (NEJM). Researchers conducted the study, called The Child/Adolescent Anxiety Multimodal Study (CAMS), at multiple sites across the United States. Psychiatrist John T. Walkup of Johns Hopkins University in Baltimore, Maryland, authored the report in NEJM.

Anxiety disorders are a related group of behavioral disorders characterized by excessive worry or unwarranted fears. Examples of childhood anxiety disorders include separation anxiety, the fear of being separated from parents or caregivers; social anxiety disorder, the fear of being negatively evaluated by others, especially peers; and generalized anxiety disorder, a state of nearly continuous worry over any of a variety of everyday events. Patients with an anxiety disorder have difficul-

ty controlling their anxiety, despite being able to understand intellectually that the fear behind it is unreasonable.

Typically, an individual with an anxiety disorder feels compelled to avoid activities associated with the fear at the root of his or her anxiety. Eventually, a repeating cycle of fear and avoidance may guide the individual's actions and interfere with the activities of daily life. If left untreated, an anxiety disorder can undermine a young person's success in school and cause problems in his or her relationships with family or friends.

The CAMS researchers randomly assigned 488 children and adolescents, ages 7 to 17 years, to one of four treatments for a 12-week period. All of the participants had previously been diagnosed with moderate to severe anxiety disorders. The four treatments included CBT, a behavioral-based therapy that helps patients overcome their disabling anxiety by guiding them gradually through structured encounters with what they fear; sertraline (sold under the brand name Zoloft), an

THREE DEGREES OF HAPPINESS

Happy friends or relatives living nearby increase a person's chances of being happy, researchers James Fowler of the University of California at San Diego and Nicholas Christakis of the Harvard Medical School in Cambridge, Massachusetts, reported in December 2008. The "happiness network" extends to three degrees of separation— to a friend of a friend of your friend, for example. A diagram (right) created by Fowler and Christakis shows the happiness effect in social networks. For the study, the researchers used data gathered from participants in the long-running Framingham Heart Study.

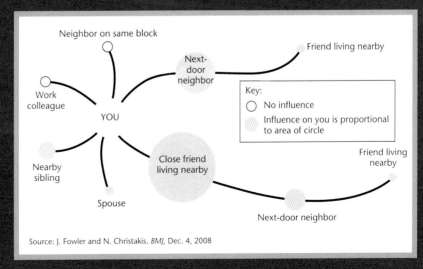

Neighbor on same block

Next-door neighbor

Friend living nearby

Work colleague

YOU

Key:
○ No influence
▨ Influence on you is proportional to area of circle

Nearby sibling

Close friend living nearby

Friend living nearby

Spouse

Next-door neighbor

Source: J. Fowler and N. Christakis. *BMJ,* Dec. 4, 2008

PSYCHOLOGY continued

antidepressant belonging to a class of drugs known as selective serotonin reuptake inhibitors (SSRI's); CBT combined with sertraline; and a placebo (inactive substance).

At the end of the 12-week treatment period, the researchers found that 81 percent of the combination treatment group reported improvement. Among the participants in the CBT-only group, 66 percent reported improvement; in the sertraline-only group, 55 percent of participants reported improvement. Of those taking the placebo, only 24 percent reported improvement.

The results further indicated that the three effective treatments were safe. Children in the sertraline-only group showed no more side effects than did the children taking the placebo. Additionally, no participant taking sertraline had attempted suicide, a rare side affect of SSRI's previously observed in children and adolescents.

The CAMS research team concluded that combination treatment is the most effective therapy for children diagnosed with anxiety disorders, but that either sertraline alone or CBT alone demonstrates significant effectiveness. The researchers noted that these findings reiterate results obtained in previous CBT studies and SSRI studies showing that each of these treatments is effective in treating childhood anxiety disorders.

Psychologist Philip Kendall, a senior investigator in the study, speculated that further analysis of the study data and new studies could yield information to help therapists predict which type of treatment would be most effective for an individual child. In the meantime, he acknowledged, therapists can be assured of the effectiveness of all three of the nonplacebo treatments.

Research may lead to new drugs. A specific group of brain *neurons* (nerve cells) in a part of the brain called the amygdala appear to be critical to the body's response to fear and may prove a useful target for future antianxiety medications. A team of researchers led by neuroscientist Denis Paré of Rutgers State University in Newark, New Jersey, reported this conclusion in the July 31, 2008, issue of the scientific journal *Nature*. The scientists based their findings on studies of laboratory rats.

The neurons, called intercalated (ITC) neurons, are believed to play a role in relaying

DOGS UNDERSTAND FAIRNESS

Dogs note which other dogs receive a treat after performing a trick, exhibiting their sensitivity to fair play, according to a study of 43 dogs reported in January 2009 by Friederike Range of the University of Vienna, Austria, and colleagues. Dogs who are repeatedly overlooked for treats eventually refuse to perform tricks or perform them less frequently, the researchers said. They theorized that dog ancestors evolved a sense of fairness to ensure that all animals in the pack contribute to the common good.

sensory information (information conveyed by any of the five senses of sight, smell, touch, taste, and hearing) between various parts of the amygdala. Scientists have long known that the amygdala plays an important part in the body's response to fear: for example, it initiates the so-called "fight or flight" response in people. However, the pathways through which sensory-based communications travel within and beyond the amygdala are poorly understood.

The Paré team trained rats to associate the sound of a particular musical tone with a shock administered each time the tone was played. With this training—technically termed classical conditioning and sometimes referred to as the Pavlovian response (after the famous Russian psychologist Ivan Pavlov)—the rats acquired a fear of the tone. They showed physical signs of fear by becoming immobile and trembling.

Typically, researchers can reverse the effects of the classical conditioning by repeatedly exposing the subjects to the same tone without any accompanying shock. In this process, called fear extinction, the subjects learn through repeated hearing of the tone without any shock that the tone is no longer a signal for pain, and they cease to be afraid of it. When they have sufficiently "unlearned" the conditioned behavior, they no longer exhibit physical signs of fear.

In human beings, behavioral therapies to treat anxiety disorders are somewhat similar to the fear extinction process in laboratory subjects. These therapies desensitize patients to fear-causing stimuli, such as when a person who is deathly afraid of spiders is gradually desensitized to spiders in carefully controlled sequences of increasing exposure.

To examine the role of ITC neurons in the fear extinction response, the Paré team introduced into the brains of some of their rat subjects a chemical toxin that binds with an ITC-specific neurotransmitter. (A *neurotransmitter* is a chemical that relays messages between nerve cells.) The attached toxin prevents the neurotransmitter from transferring information at the receptor site of the receiving ITC neuron, effectively blocking the signal carrying sensory information.

The researchers then performed standard fear extinction training on all the rats to desensitize them to the tone. Afterward, the researchers found that the rats receiving the toxin were more likely to exhibit the physical signs of fear than rats whose ITC neurons were working normally. In other words, the rats with disrupted ITC neurons still feared the tone, despite having gone through the extinction procedure.

These results suggested to the researchers that ITC neurons are specifically involved in fear extinction, and the scientists recommended further research on them. Compounds designed to enhance the working of amygdala-based ITC neurons could offer a whole new class of medications with which to treat human anxiety disorders, the researchers speculated. Such medications might include drugs to aid specifically in behavioral therapies of desensitization.

Autism. In June 2008, researchers with the University of Washington Autism Center in Seattle reported that adults with autism have an abnormally low concentration of neuron connections in regions of their brains that are involved in processing social and emotional information. The ability to recognize faces comprises one such processing task.

Autism, which appears in childhood and persists throughout life, is characterized by a limited ability to communicate and interact with other people. The University of Washington research team, led by Elizabeth Aylward, used magnetic resonance imaging (MRI) to compare brain activity in participants who had autism with brain activity in participants who did not have autism. Participants were prompted to view a succession of images of faces and to press a button when they saw a repeat image—all while the MRI imaging was occurring.

The MRI data revealed that in participants with autism, connections between the brain's *fusiform* area and adjacent areas of the *limbic system* were relatively weak, as compared with results obtained from other participants. The fusiform area is involved in face recognition, and the limbic system is a group of brain structures that process social and emotional information. According to the authors of the study, the results indicated that these regions in the brains of participants with autism were not working together effectively.

In another study, released in July, researchers at Harvard University in Cambridge, Massachusetts, announced their discovery of several previously unknown genetic mutations in patients with autism. The findings indicated that different individuals have different sets of mutations that cause autism.

◾ Timothy J. Bruce

PUBLIC HEALTH

The greatest public health concern of 2009, both in the United States and throughout the world, was the outbreak of a new influenza virus. Public health officials originally referred to the illness as "swine flu" but later designated it as "2009 H1N1 flu."

The flu first appeared in Mexico in February. People who became ill reported such symptoms as chills, fever, cough, sore throat, body aches, headache, and fatigue. Some people also reported nausea, vomiting, and diarrhea. Researchers determined that the fast-moving virus was a novel form, containing genes from viruses that originate in swine, birds, and human beings. However, the illness spread through person-to-person contact as people coughed or sneezed, rather than from contact with pigs or birds.

By April, public health authorities at the U.S. Centers for Disease Control and Prevention (CDC) in Atlanta and at the World Health Organization (WHO), an agency of the United Nations headquartered in Geneva, Switzerland, became concerned that the illness could become a *pandemic* (a disease that spreads throughout the world). Schools and other places where large numbers of people gather were closed in some countries. Some nations also screened travelers at their borders and quarantined or turned away those who appeared ill.

By May 12, at least 3,000 people in 45 U.S. states and the District of Columbia had contracted the disease, and 3 people had died from it.

SEE ALSO

THE SPECIAL REPORT, **THE TIMELESS SCOURGE OF MALARIA,** PAGE 88.

SCIENCE STUDIES, **PLASTIC PLANET,** PAGE 114.

Throughout the world, more than 5,000 people in 30 countries became infected, and laboratory testing confirmed 56 deaths from H1N1. Many more deaths from the virus were suspected. On June 3, the CDC reported 11,054 confirmed or suspected cases and 17 deaths in the United States; at the same time, WHO reported 19,273 confirmed cases and 117 deaths worldwide.

Baby boomlet. Federal researchers reported in March 2009 that in 2007 (latest year for which statistics were available), 4,317,119 babies were born in the United States—the highest number of babies born in a single year. That figure surpassed even the peak year of the baby boom, 1957. (The baby boom was a time of increased birth rates that occurred after World War II, from 1946 to 1964.) The 2007 number primarily reflected an increase in the population of reproductive-age women; however, birth rates also increased for every category of women aged 15 to 44 years. For teenage women aged 15 to 19 years, the increase in birth rate, which began in 2005, interrupted a 34-percent decline that ranged from a high of 61.8 live births per 1,000 teenage women in 1991 to a low of 40.5 live births per 1,000 teenage women in 2005.

The birth rate among unmarried women also reached historic levels in 2007. The rate of 52.9 births per 1,000 women that year rose 21 percent from 2002 and 5 percent from 2006. Overall, 39.7 percent of all births in 2007 occurred among

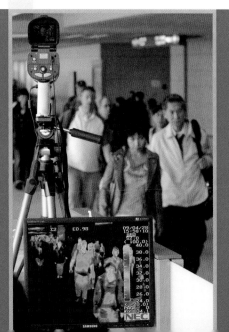

SCANNING FOR FLU

A thermal scanner at Incheon International Airport in South Korea registers the body temperature of travelers as part of an effort to prevent the spread of H1N1 flu. The scanners screened for an elevated temperature, a possible sign of fever. The spread of the flu virous around the globe in April 2009 alarmed world leaders and caused some nations to quarantine or turn away people who appeared to be ill.

unmarried women, another historic level. The greatest increase of nonmarital births occurred among women aged 25 to 39 years. As nonmarital births among women of all ages rose, the proportion accounted for by teenagers dropped. In 1975, more than half of all nonmarital births occurred among teens; in 2007, teens accounted for 23 percent of all such births.

Peanut butter threat. From September 2008 to April 20, 2009, 714 people in 46 states became ill after eating peanut butter and peanut-associated products tainted with *Salmonella typhimurium.* Public health officials at the CDC reported those figures in April 2009. Eight people died of their illness and 116 were hospitalized.

S. typhimurium is a bacterium that can cause gastroenteritis, a condition whose symptoms include diarrhea, vomiting and nausea, abdominal pain, and fever. Although the illness is generally mild, it can be severe in people who are young, elderly, or whose immune system has been weakened by another condition.

After many of the sickened people said that they had eaten peanut butter before becoming ill, Minnesota state health officials tested an open container of peanut butter from a nursing home. The investigators found that the peanut butter contained the same strain of *S. typhimurium* found in specimens from residents who became ill. Investigators in other states found the same strain of *S. typhimurium* in unopened containers of the same brand of peanut butter, King Nut.

The investigators traced the tainted peanut butter to a Peanut Corporation of America processing plant in Blakely, Georgia. The plant manufactured King Nut peanut butter and peanut paste, which was used by many companies to make such products as cookies, crackers, cereal, and pet treats. The products were sold to such institutions as nursing homes and other long-term-care facilities, hospitals, and cafeterias. None of the tainted foods had been sold directly to consumers. On January 9, the processing plant ceased production and the next day recalled all of its peanut products manufactured since Jan. 1, 2007.

Milk formula scandal. Six infants in China died and nearly 300,000 others became ill after drinking milk formula tainted with melamine. China's ministry of health announced that determination in December 2008.

Melamine is a chemical used in fertilizers, wood adhesives, flame retardants, and other industrial products. It was responsible for the deaths of thousands of pets in the United States in 2007, after cats and dogs were fed melamine-tainted pet food made in China. In 2008, 22 Chinese dairy producers used the chemical to thicken raw milk used in baby formula. The milk had been thinned by water to increase its volume. The watered-down milk had a lower protein concentration than regular milk. By adding melamine to the formula, the dairy producers increased the product's nitrogen content, making the formula appear to contain more protein in certain laboratory tests.

In the Chinese infants, the tainted formula caused kidney stones and, in some cases, kidney failure and death. Chinese officials ordered all tainted dairy products removed from store shelves and arrested a number of persons involved in the scandal. Three dairy executives received death sentences, and others were imprisoned for periods of two years to life.

Circumcision and common STI's. Circumcision among heterosexual men reduces the risk for contracting two common sexually transmitted infections (STI's), according to a study published in a March 2009 issue of the *New England Journal of Medicine.* The study was conducted by researchers at the Rakai Health Sciences Program and Makerere University in Uganda; Johns Hopkins University Bloomberg School of Public Health in Baltimore; and the U.S. National Institutes of Allergy and Infectious Diseases.

Researchers recruited 3,393 heterosexual men between the ages of 15 and 49 in Uganda who were not circumcised and who tested negative for HIV (the virus that causes AIDS), herpes simplex virus type 2 (HSV-2), and syphilis. A subgroup of the subjects who tested negative for human papillomavirus (HPV) was also chosen. About half of the men underwent surgical circumcision, and the other half did not.

After 24 months, the researchers found that circumcision in adolescent boys and men reduced the likelihood of acquiring HSV-2 by 28 percent and of acquiring HPV by 35 percent. HSV-2 causes genital herpes. HPV causes genital warts, and in women, some strains of the virus can cause cervical cancer. Previous studies have shown that circumcision also reduces the risk of acquiring HIV by 50 percent or more.

In their report, the researchers noted that circumcision does not completely prevent infection. Also, the incidence of another STI—syphilis—was the same in both circumcised and uncircumcised men. Thus, the scientists recommended that public health officials continue to promote safe-sex practices.　■ Deborah Kowal

SCIENCE AND SOCIETY

The inauguration of Barack Obama as president of the United States on January 20, 2009, brought major changes to the nation's scientific community. In his inaugural address, the new president gave a strong boost to science and technology: "We will restore science to its rightful place and wield technology's wonders to raise health care's quality and lower its costs. We will harness the sun and the winds and the soil to fuel our cars and run our factories. And we will transform our schools and colleges and universities to meet the demands of a new age."

Science had been a key part of Obama's campaign for the presidency. The candidate advocated a "competitiveness agenda"—an economic plan that embraced, among other things, a doubling of federal funding for scientific research.

In mid-February, Congress passed and President Obama signed the $787-billion

SEE ALSO THE SPECIAL REPORT, **METHANE: ANOTHER GREENHOUSE TROUBLEMAKER,** PAGE 42.

THE SPECIAL REPORT, **THE TIMELESS SCOURGE OF MALARIA,** PAGE 88.

American Recovery and Reinvestment Act—the "stimulus" bill—which allocated more than $20 billion for research and development (R&D) programs. Specific allocations included $10.4 billion to the National Institutes of Health (NIH) for biomedical research; $3 billion to the National Science Foundation for fundamental research, mainly to be carried out at universities; and $3.5 billion to the Department of Energy for energy-related R&D.

Key scientific appointments. On Dec. 15, 2008, President-elect Obama nominated Steven Chu as secretary of energy in his incoming administration. Obama declared that the appointment of Chu, a past recipient of the Nobel Prize in physics, would "send a signal to all that my administration will value science...." Chu shared the 1997 Nobel Prize in physics with Claude Cohen-Tannoudji and William Daniel Phillips for developing a technique of trapping atoms—that is, greatly slowing down atoms so they can be more easily studied.

Beginning in 2004, Chu served as director of the Lawrence Berkeley National Laboratory, a Department of Energy-funded facility that has sponsored pioneering research in such alternative energy technologies as solar and biofuels. Chu served on the faculties of both Stanford University in Stanford, California, and the University of California at Berkeley.

On Dec. 20, 2008, President-elect Obama nominated physicist and climate expert John Holdren of Harvard University in Cambridge, Massachusetts, a key advisor during the presidential campaign, as his science adviser. The president's science adviser heads the Office of Science and Technology Policy and provides the president with scientific advice and information needed to carry out federal policies.

Holdren, a frequent critic of environmental policies of the administration of former

OBAMA SIGNS STIMULUS BILL

United States President Barack Obama signs the American Recovery and Investment Act on Feb. 17, 2009, as members of Congress look on. The massive appropriation, popularly known as the "stimulus bill," was designed to boost the recession-ridden U.S. economy. Substantial funds were allocated to scientific research, particularly in the field of energy research.

President George W. Bush, warned in 2008 that global warming "is already well beyond dangerous and is careening toward completely unmanageable." Analysts interpreted the Holdren appointment as a signal that Obama intended to embrace policies to reduce the U.S. carbon footprint—that is, the production of carbon dioxide and other gases believed to cause global warming.

Also in December, Mr. Obama nominated Jane Lubchenco, a marine ecologist from Oregon State University in Corvallis, to serve as administrator of the National Oceanic and Atmospheric Administration (NOAA). NOAA includes the National Weather Service and the National Marine Fisheries Service, among other agencies. Lubchenco has led research into stressed ecosystems in Pacific waters along the Oregon coast and has served on several important commissions on the health of the oceans. Political observers noted that her selection as head of NOAA, the first ever of a professional marine ecologist for the post, suggested that Obama intended to elevate the condition of the oceans to a major policy priority.

Chu, Holdren, and Lubchenco were all confirmed by the U.S. Senate in early 2009. Commentators noted that the three scientists' advocacy of a large role for the federal government in combating climate change signaled a major shift in environmental policy from that of the Bush administration.

Turnaround on EPA policy. In April, the U.S. Environmental Protection Agency (EPA) formally stated that six greenhouse gases contribute to air pollution, which may endanger public health or welfare. The development was in response to a January 26 memo issued by President Obama directing the EPA to revisit its earlier rejection of the policy.

Under Bush-era EPA Director Stephen Johnson, the agency had declined to issue the greenhouse "danger finding" in July 2008, after the director announced that he opposed EPA regulation of greenhouse gases. The impetus for studying the potential danger to health of such greenhouse gases as carbon dioxide, methane, nitrous oxide, and others was an April 2007 ruling by the U.S. Supreme Court. In that ruling, a majority of the justices charged the EPA with determining whether greenhouse-gas emissions endanger human health.

At issue ultimately was whether the federal government and state governments have the authority, under the Clean Air Act, to enforce regulations that specifically address the output of greenhouse gases, such as minimum gas mileage standards for automobiles. (Congress passed the Clean Air Act in 1970; it expanded the law in 1990.) Many analysts regarded the EPA turnaround as another sign of the Obama administration's clear break with the environmental policies of the Bush administration.

Greenhouse gases are suspected of causing global warming, which according to data collected by scientists, has been occurring on Earth for more than a century. These gases have the property of trapping the heat from sunlight within Earth's atmosphere. When in balance, greenhouse gases keep the Earth relatively warm and hospitable to life. However, increases in these gases due to such human actions as burning coal and oil, driving automobiles, and many other activities have in recent years caused Earth's atmosphere to retain more and more heat. Many scientists believe that the process of global warming will accelerate if ways are not found to reduce greenhouse-gas emissions.

The issue of global warming continued to be divisive among the American public, according to polls conducted in 2008 and 2009. Polls taken by the Gallup organization, CNN/Opinion Research Corporation, and others indicated that a substantial majority of Americans believe that global warming is indeed happening, though a smaller majority believe that the cause of global warming is such human-influenced activities as driving automobiles and manufacturing goods in factories. However, a minority of Americans reject the premise that global warming poses a threat to Earth and its population. Some polls, moreover, showed the percentage of skeptics, though small, growing between 2007 and 2009 in the United States.

Stem cell research shift. On March 9, 2009, President Obama issued an executive order reversing an earlier decision by President George W. Bush to restrict federal funding of embryonic stem cell research to cell lines that were already in existence. While lifting the stem cell ban, the president's order instructed the NIH to issue new guidelines, including safeguards to ensure that scientists conduct stem cell research responsibly. In his remarks at the signing, President Obama called on Congress to provide additional funding for the research.

Stem cells are unspecialized cells that are capable of developing into any of the hundreds of different kinds of cells that comprise tissues in the human body. Researchers around the world are experimenting with stem cells,

SCIENCE AND SOCIETY continued

many of them seeking treatments or cures for human diseases. Although some stem cells exist in human beings of all ages, stem cells contained in human embryos have special properties that make them uniquely useful. (An *embryo* is a very early stage of a fetus in a woman's womb.) Researchers experiment on stem cells only after an embryo has been discarded, usually from a fertility clinic.

In 2009, most polls indicated that a majority of Americans favored an expanded federal role in stem cell research, but the issue continued to be controversial. In Congress, House Minority Leader John Boehner (R., Ohio) accused President Obama of rolling back "important protections for innocent life." In March, the Georgia Senate passed a bill to ban most forms of stem cell research. Also in March, the Mississippi House of Representatives approved a budget that prohibits the use of state money for "research that kills or destroys an existing human embryo."

Evolution wars continue. In March 2009, the Texas Board of Education voted to remove from state science teaching standards a provision requiring that students examine the "strengths and weaknesses" of scientific theories. Such wording has been widely used by proponents of intelligent design theory to encourage educators to cast doubt on the merits of the classic theory of evolution developed by British naturalist Charles Darwin.

Intelligent design is a theory that ascribes the creation of life to a supreme intelligence. The Supreme Court and other federal courts have ruled that teaching intelligent design as science in public schools violates the separation of church and state prescribed in the First Amendment to the Constitution.

Darwin's theory of evolution, first published in 1859, states that all life on Earth arose from a single original life form and that species evolve over time through natural selection, giving rise to new species. The theory is supported by considerable scientific evidence, such as the vast fossil record illustrating slow and gradual change of species as well as the extinction of some species and the appearance of new ones.

In its March ruling, the Texas board gave some leeway to social conservatives by incorporating wording into other science curriculum standards that could be used to encourage skepticism about other widely held scientific theories. Among such theories is the big bang—the theory that the universe came into being in a huge explosion about 14 billion years ago.

According to educational publishing experts, Texas curriculum standards have an enormous impact on U.S. public education. Texas represents the second largest textbook market in the United States, after California, and its standards influence textbooks sold throughout the country.

Although debate in the Texas Board of Education attracted the most national attention, similar battles over the teaching of evolution were being fought in several other states during 2008 and 2009. In Oklahoma, the state legislature passed a bill in early 2008 that would have allowed students to express their religious opinions about the origin of life while forbidding science teachers to oppose these views with science-based evolutionary theory by, for example, downgrading test answers. Governor Brad Henry, after intense lobbying from both sides of the issue, vetoed the bill on June 6.

■ Albert H. Teich

TRANSPLANT TOURISM

A man in the Philippines shows his scar from a surgical incision made to remove his kidney for transplant to another person. The man sold his kidney to provide for his family. Although illegal in most countries, international trafficking in transplantable organs flourishes in black-market commerce, as wealthy people in need of a transplant travel to various locales to purchase their organs. Such commerce is known as "transplant tourism."

The Threat of Near-Earth Objects

On June 30, 1908, a massive explosion shook the remote Tunguska River wilderness of Siberia. Eyewitnesses forty miles distant saw a brilliant white light split the sky. A few moments later, they heard a series of thunder-like peals and were thrown to the ground by a shockwave.

In the 100 years since what has become known as the Tunguska Event, investigators have worked to piece together what happened. Scientific evidence points to a chunk of asteroid or comet that exploded under the extreme heat and pressure of entering Earth's atmosphere.

No human beings are known to have died in the Tunguska blast, which flattened trees over about 2,000 square kilometers (775 square miles). But the explosion packed enough energy to level a major city and potentially kill millions. Such destructive power has fueled worries about the danger presented by collisions of near-Earth objects (NEO's) with Earth. NEO's are comets and asteroids that have been tugged by the gravitational attraction of nearby planets into orbits that carry them near Earth. Scientists in 2009 were studying the Tunguska Event and similar occurrences in an effort to track and, perhaps, deflect threatening NEO's.

How big was the Tunguska NEO? The question is important because there are many small objects in space but relatively few large ones. If a giant asteroid caused the blast, there is little chance that another such object will hit Earth anytime soon. But if the object was small, Tunguska-like events may be worryingly common.

Recent studies suggest that the damage at Tunguska was caused not by the NEO's explosion, but by the still-plummeting fireball and the shockwave it produced. The scientific evidence suggests that the destruction was caused by an object as small as 30 meters (100 feet) in diameter. Astronomers estimate that an NEO of this size strikes Earth, on average, once every 300 years.

Evidence of large impacts by celestial objects can be found in Earth's rocky crust. In the 1980's, scientists identified a layer rich in iridium in rocks laid down 65 million years ago. Iridium is rare in Earth's crust but is found in relatively high concentrations in some asteroids and comets. The scientists theorized that the thin iridium-rich band represented a layer of debris that settled out of the air after a huge asteroid or comet impact.

Scientists now suspect that the asteroid or comet responsible for the iridium deposits crashed into Earth on or near Mexico's Yucatán Peninsula. They have found a large crater encompassing part of the peninsula and the surrounding sea floor. This feature, known as the Chicxulub (CHEEK shoo loob) Crater, measures 180 kilometers (112 miles) in diameter.

Such a huge impact undoubtedly threw billions of tons of dust and debris into the atmosphere. Heat from the impact probably triggered global

Tunguska impact

Trees flattened in a single direction attest to the power of the June 30, 1908, blast above the Tunguska River basin of Siberia. The blast, now believed by scientists to have been caused by the explosion of a relatively large asteroid or chunk of comet entering Earth's atmosphere, sent out shockwaves in every direction from "ground zero." Only the remote location of the impact site spared the world from a disaster of major proportions.

fires. Clouds of smoke and impact debris would have blocked out sunlight for many months, causing temperatures to plummet. Many plants—and the animals that depended on them for food—would have died out. Many scientists believe that these effects led to the extinction of the dinosaurs.

Impactors the size of the one that made Chicxulub Crater are extraordinarily rare. But even a much smaller asteroid can cause global damage. The impact of an asteroid 1 kilometer (0.6 mile) in diameter—a thousand times as small as the Chicxulub impactor—would still kick huge amounts of dust into the atmosphere. The dust would block sunlight, causing crop loss and starvation. Such effects could threaten civilization itself.

Tracking such dangerous NEO's has become a growing priority for scientists and governments. In the 1990's, the United States Congress initiated the Spaceguard project to coordinate U.S. efforts to identify and track NEO's. Congress charged NASA with identifying, by 2008, 90 percent of all NEO's 1 kilometer (0.6 mile) in diameter or larger within about 50 million kilometers (30 million miles) of Earth. (In 2007, NASA scientists reported that they could not meet the 2008 deadline; NASA officials projected that scientists would achieve the 90-percent goal in 2010.) Scientists estimate that about 1,000 objects may fit this description.

Congress later expanded its directive to NASA, instructing the agency to identify, by 2020, 90 percent of NEO's from 150 meters (500 feet) to 1 kilometer (0.6 mile) in diameter. There may be 400,000 NEO's in this size range. Similar projects have been undertaken in other countries.

A major reason for tracking NEO's is that impacts from space are one of the few types of natural disasters that may be preventable. In general, scientists agree that we already have the technology needed to deflect an asteroid. The challenge is to select the best response to a particular threat.

Some experts propose destroying a threatening NEO with nuclear weapons, but planners worry that the NEO might simply be broken into smaller fragments headed for Earth. A safer approach would be to use explosives to push the asteroid off course. Alternatively, a space probe could be sent to fly alongside the NEO; over time, this "gravity tractor" would drag the NEO off course through mutual gravitational attraction.

Many scientists judge that a combined approach would probably prove safest and most effective. For example, an asteroid could be nudged off course with a non-nuclear explosion; then a gravity tractor could make additional adjustments as necessary. Any such correction would rely on early warning: the earlier a collision is predicted, the more slightly an NEO's path must be changed for the object to miss Earth.

Our ability to divert a dangerous impactor will depend in no small part on determining its composition. A large explosion might deflect a dense asteroid, for example, while shattering a more porous one. This is one reason scientists are so interested in determining what caused the Tunguska Event.

For many years, scientists thought the Tunguska blast left no impact crater. But in the late 1990's and early 2000's, a group of Italian scientists began an intense study of Lake Cheko, a small lake near the center of the

Tunguska blast zone. The location of the lake and the unusual patterns in the layers of sediment in it led them to suspect that it is actually an impact crater, left by a fragment of the Tunguska object that reached the ground.

In 2008, seismic studies revealed a rock-like object 1 meter (3 feet) in diameter buried in the lake bottom. The scientists hope eventually to unearth the fragment, which may be a piece of the Tunguska asteroid or comet.

A meteorite from Tunguska would be a find of rare importance. But rarer still is the opportunity to track an object from space and later recover samples for study in the lab. This scenario occurred in October 2008, when the U.S. astronomer Richard Kowalski spotted an NEO 1 meter or less (a few feet) in diameter on a collision course with Earth. After further observations, Kowalski and colleagues were able to predict the time of impact to within 15 seconds and the point of impact to within a few kilometers in the desert of Sudan. The object shattered in a series of explosions seconds after entering the atmosphere. Later, a team of scientists led by U.S. astronomer Peter Jenniskens located and recovered 280 meteorites, fragments of the NEO. The fragments, determined to belong to an F-class asteroid, added to our scientific knowledge about this poorly understood asteroid group. The astronomers' success in so accurately predicting the NEO's impact suggested that watching for such objects is beginning to pay off.

In April 2009, an NEO roughly the size of the Tunguska impactor was observed as it passed near Earth. Its closest approach was 72,000 kilometers (45,000 miles) away, about one-fifth the distance to the moon and only twice the altitude of many artificial satellite orbits. This "near miss" added urgency to such efforts as Spaceguard and prompted scientists to sound a call for increased international cooperation. Getting nations to cooperate on the threat posed by NEO's and persuading governments and other agencies to provide funding for relevant scientific research pose large challenges, analysts agree. Some of the difficulty may stem from a widely held perception that the danger is remote. Scientists have put the odds of a civilization-ending strike in any one lifetime at about 1 in 100,000. Tunguska-sized objects strike far more often. But two-thirds of the planet is covered in water, and some of the landmass is sparsely populated or wilderness.

Scientists counter, however, that a serious or catastrophic collision between Earth and a significant celestial object will eventually occur; it is only a matter of time. When the threat becomes real, will human beings mobilize to act—or will we share the fate of the dinosaurs? The answer will depend on both science and politics. ■ Jeff De La Rosa

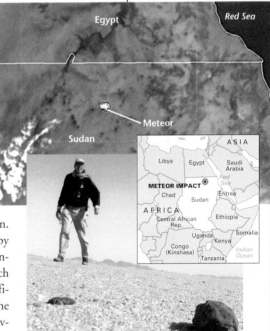

U.S. astronomer Peter Jenniskens (above) of the SETI Institute in Mountain View, California, in December approaches fragments of the meteor that landed in the Sudan. A recovery team led by Jenniskens found nearly 280 pieces of the NEO.

SPACE TECHNOLOGY

The spacefaring nations of the world conducted a variety of piloted and unpiloted missions in mid- to late 2008 and early 2009. The National Aeronautics and Space Administration (NASA) of the United States used space shuttle missions to prepare the International Space Station (ISS) to house a complete crew of six astronauts, which began occupying the station in late May 2009. Japan opened its large ISS laboratory module, named Kibo, with an "astronaut dance party," and the European Space Agency (ESA) successfully demonstrated its first Automated Transfer Vehicle (ATV), a craft designed to carry supplies to the ISS after NASA retires the shuttle (expected to happen in about 2010). In addition to these ISS-related missions, a *taikonaut* (astronaut from China) performed his country's first spacewalk in 2008.

The most prominent unpiloted, robotic space mission was NASA's Phoenix Mars Lander, which touched down near the north pole of Mars in May 2008. Phoenix confirmed the presence of water ice on the red planet in June, and photos taken by a camera on the lander provided tantalizing—though controversial—clues that salty, liquid water may also exist on Mars. Deeper in our solar system, NASA's nuclear-powered Cassini probe plowed through ice geysers erupting from the surface of Enceladus, a tiny frozen moon of Saturn, and the Messenger spacecraft took revealing close-up photographs of the surface of Mercury. Other robotic space missions included India's first lunar probe as well as launches of U.S. and European satellites to study Earth and to search for Earth-like planets circling other stars.

International Space Station. After 10 years of assembly, the ISS was near completion in early 2009. In March, astronauts on the space shuttle Discovery and the ISS finished a mission that allowed the ISS to support its full crew size of six astronauts. The main task of that mission had been the delivery and installation of the fourth and final pair of solar arrays, along with the final section of the station's main *truss* (structural backbone). The ISS's solar arrays, each of which is 73 meters (240 feet) in length, convert sunlight into electricity to power the station's life-support systems, communications gear, and scientific experiments.

The pair of solar arrays and the truss section delivered in March weighed 14,088 kilo-

SEE ALSO

THE SPECIAL REPORT, **TELESCOPES: 400 YEARS OF STARGAZING,** PAGE 24.

THE SPECIAL REPORT, **THE SEARCH FOR WATER ON MARS,** PAGE 100.

grams (31,060 pounds) on the ground and completely filled the shuttle's payload bay. In orbit, however, the influence of gravity is so slight that the equipment was essentially weightless, making it fairly easy for the astronauts to manipulate. Astronauts aboard Discovery and the ISS used two of the three available robotic arms in a series of maneuvers to remove the arrays and truss from the payload bay and to move them into position for assembly and attachment to the station.

After the hardware was moved into position, astronauts Steve Swanson and Richard Arnold used power tools to bolt the truss sections together. Once the new truss piece was firmly in place, the two spacewalkers connected the cables that carried power from the new solar arrays to the station's electricity grid and relayed instructions from the station's computers to the arrays.

The first test of these cable connections came the following day, when ISS astronauts used their laptop computers to enter commands for the unfurling of the new solar array panels. The astronauts, monitored by mission engineers at the Johnson Space Center in Houston, unfolded the solar array panels carefully and gradually. The gradual unfolding allowed enough time for sunlight to warm the plastic panels so that the panels would not stick together—a problem that had occurred during previous assembly missions.

The unfolding and deployment of the new solar arrays proceeded without a hitch. The functioning of these arrays doubled the amount of electric power available for ISS scientific experiments—from about 15 to 30 kilowatts. The added electric power could also be used to operate the station and keep its crew comfortable.

Water recycling. In addition to the solar arrays and truss section, Discovery also delivered a less visible, though equally important, piece of equipment to the ISS in March—a new device for recycling water from the urine of the station's crew. The new Urine Processing Assembly, which was necessary to obtain drinking water for six-astronaut crews on long missions, was a replacement for a device that the space shuttle Endeavour delivered in November 2008. That device malfunctioned and could not be properly used.

As long as the space shuttle was available to dock at the ISS, station crew members could draw water from the shuttle's fuel cells, which combined hydrogen and oxygen into water. After the retirement of the shuttle, however, the station's crew will have to conserve every drop of water by recycling moisture in the air from breathing and perspiration, as well as water used for cleaning. The new urine processing device was an important part of the ISS water recycling system.

After ISS commander Mike Fincke installed the Urine Processing Assembly replacement, the device worked so well that he was able to

ORION CREW EXPLORATION VEHICLE

Work continued in 2008 and 2009 on Project Constellation, NASA's planned replacement for the aging U.S. space shuttle fleet. The new spacecraft system was to consist of an Atlas rocket and the Orion Crew Exploration Vehicle. Orion, depicted in this artist's rendering, was to carry four to six crew members to the International Space Station and to the moon. NASA hoped to begin piloted missions using Orion as early as 2015.

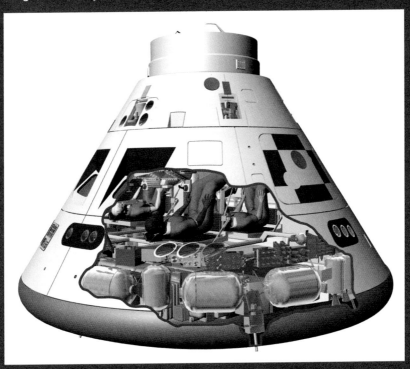

SPACE TECHNOLOGY continued

process about 32 kilograms (70 pounds) of stored urine into water. However, this first sample of recycled water had to be tested in laboratories on Earth to make sure that all harmful impurities and bacteria were removed.

Kibo module. In June 2008, Discovery carried the final and main part of Japan's Kibo laboratory module to the ISS. Astronauts berthed Kibo, which means "hope" in Japanese, on the station's Harmony pressurized node, opposite the ESA's Columbus laboratory.

Kibo, measuring 11 meters (36 feet) in length, was the largest pressurized module on the ISS. It weighed so much that it had to be launched empty, without its experiment racks in place. (The racks had been delivered to the ISS aboard Endeavour in March and stored in a small module dubbed "Kibo's attic.") After Discovery's crew carefully checked for air leaks and tiny floating debris that could have been inhaled or caused eye damage, Japanese astronaut Akihiko Hoshide dedicated the new module in a brief ceremony. Many viewers in Japan watched the ceremony via video transmission. Following the ceremony, the astronauts enjoyed a weightless half-hour in Kibo's spacious open interior—pushing off the walls, flipping head over heels, or just floating motionless. Johnson Space Center Mission Control Capcom (the individual in charge of communication with the crew) Alvin Drew referred to this celebration in microgravity as an "astronaut dance party."

Japanese scientists and their counterparts in the United States, Canada, Europe, and Russia planned to use Kibo to conduct research into the microgravity conditions of space on new drugs and materials. They also hoped that medical observations of astronauts in Kibo would lead to a greater understanding of methods for keeping the human body healthy in space.

Endeavour mission. Astronauts in the shuttle Endeavour, during their November 2008 mission to the ISS, performed a number of tasks besides delivering the urine recycling device that later had to be replaced. They spent much of their time painstakingly cleaning and lubricating the mechanisms that rotate the ISS's solar array wings to capture the most sunlight as the station travels through its 90-minute orbit of Earth. The astronauts hoped that their efforts would make it unnecessary to perform repair work on one of the rotary mechanisms, which was damaged.

Automated Transfer Vehicle. In September 2008, the ESA deorbited its first ATV after a successful five-month test that included docking with the ISS. The ATV, named Jules Verne (after the pioneering French science-fiction author), was directed to burn up in the atmosphere. Like Russia's Progress resupply capsules, the ESA ATV's were designed to be pilotless cargo crafts for delivering food, fuel, air, and other supplies to the ISS. In addition, the ISS could use engines on docked ATV's for boosting itself to higher orbits and maneuvering to avoid space debris, thereby saving fuel.

ESA engineers studied possible upgrades to the ATV design in 2009. Some of these upgrades included equipping the ATV's with heat shields so that the vehicles could survive reentry into the atmosphere to return cargo to Earth. Other upgrades would allow the ATV's to carry human passengers—giving the ISS partnership another route to space for its astronauts and cosmonauts in case problems develop with the Russian Soyuz capsules (currently used to deliver crew members to the ISS) or the Orion capsule under development by NASA.

In addition to the Progress vehicles and ATV's, another unpiloted craft that was expected to resupply the ISS after the retirement of the shuttle fleet was Japan's H-II Transfer Vehicle. Project managers described this vehicle at a December 2008 press conference in Japan.

Hubble's final servicing. Astronauts on the shuttle Atlantis conducted the fifth and final scheduled servicing mission to the Hubble Space Telescope in May 2009. The astronauts installed new parts and equipment upgrades to the orbiting telescope that were designed to study the large-scale structure of the universe and the evolution of galaxies. The servicing mission was expected to keep Hubble functioning to at least 2014.

First spacewalk by China. In September 2008, Chinese taikonaut Zhai Zhigang donned a new spacesuit developed in China and clambered outside the hull of his Earth-orbiting Shenzhou 7 spacecraft while two crewmates waited inside. One of the crewmates wore a Russian-made spacesuit in case Zhai experienced trouble with his untested suit and had to be rescued. The rescue proved to be unnecessary, however, as the Chinese-made spacesuit functioned appropriately.

This spacewalk, part of China's spaceflight with a three-person crew, set the stage for the launch of China's Tiangong 1 space station, which was expected to take place by late 2010. Western space experts believed that Tiangong, which means "heavenly palace" in Chinese, would likely be used for military reconnaissance, as well as docking exercises and space habitation experience.

China was working alone in the early development of its human spaceflight program. However, Chinese experts were also working with the ISS partners and other nations in 2009 to develop international strategies for future exploration of the moon.

Water on Mars. NASA's Phoenix Mars Lander provided new data in the "follow-the-water" strategy that scientists are using to learn if life could exist on the red planet—or if life existed there in the past. The lander radioed data to Earth from its May 2008 touchdown until November, when dropping temperatures ended the craft's ability to function.

In July 2008, Phoenix provided scientists with the first direct evidence of current water ice on Mars when its robotic arm scooped up a white substance from the soil and deposited it into a sensitive analytical instrument. The instrument heated the substance and analyzed the chemical components in the resulting vapor. The analysis revealed the hydrogen and oxygen chemical signatures of water. Although scientists had long believed that water ice existed on Mars, this test provided firm proof by actually "tasting" the water—in the words of NASA investigators. Instruments on Phoenix also detected minerals known to form in the presence of liquid water, indicating that water flowed on the surface of Mars in the past.

In March, NASA released a series of photos taken by a camera on Phoenix that revealed small globs of an unknown substance clinging to one of the craft's landing struts. The globs appeared to grow and shrink in response to changing temperatures. Some researchers interpreted these globs as drops of liquid water.

Although low temperatures at the polar landing site would normally cause water to frozen, these researchers speculated that soil salts mixed with the water could have acted as a kind of antifreeze, lowering the freezing point of the water. The researchers theorized that this salty, sludgy water was puddled just below the surface, from where it was splashed up onto Phoenix by rocket jets as the craft rode down to a soft landing. Other scientists, how-

SPACE STATION'S SOLAR ARRAYS ALL IN PLACE

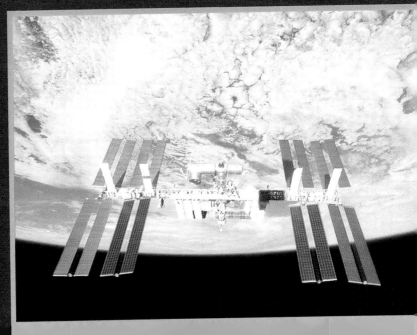

All four pairs of solar array panels are seen in this view of the International Space Station (ISS), photographed by the crew of the space shuttle Discovery in March 2009. Discovery and ISS astronauts installed the final pair to the orbiting outpost in March, doubling the amount of electric power available for the station's scientific experiments. Each array, measuring 73 meters (240 feet) in length, converts sunlight into electricity to power the station's life-support systems and communication equipment, as well as science experiments. The installation left the ISS virtually completed and ready to support a full crew of six.

SPACE TECHNOLOGY continued

ever, expressed doubts that the mysterious globs were liquid water.

Scientists said they expected to be analyzing the mountain of data provided by Phoenix's cameras and automated chemistry labs for many years. During this time, many additional robotic missions to Mars were also planned.

Ice geysers in Saturn system. Cassini was another NASA spacecraft that touched extraterrestrial water in 2008. The Cassini probe, which began orbiting Saturn in 2004, made its closest pass over Saturn's tiny frozen moon Enceladus in October 2008. The probe, traveling at a speed of about 64,400 kilometers (40,000 miles) per hour, blasted through ice geysers erupting from the moon's surface. Cassini scientists at the Jet Propulsion Laboratory in Pasadena, California, had previously discovered these plumes of ice crystals and water vapor erupting from crevices near the south pole of Enceladus. Some of the ice crystals are directed by gravity into the rings surrounding Saturn.

As Cassini passed through the plumes, the spacecraft's instruments gathered data about the ice particles and water vapor. Researchers said that analyses of the data would help them determine if the geysers are evidence of a liquid-water ocean beneath the surface of Enceladus. The discovery of a subsurface ocean on Enceladus would give scientists another place in our solar system to look for extraterrestrial life—in addition to Mars and Europa, a moon of Jupiter also believed to have an ocean of liquid water under an icy surface.

Messenger at Mercury. NASA's Messenger spacecraft flew within 200 kilometers (125 miles) of the surface of Mercury in October 2008. The close approach gave astronomers at the Johns Hopkins University Applied Physics Laboratory in Laurel, Maryland, their first look at about 30 percent of the planet's cratered surface. Photographs sent to Earth by Messenger during this fly-by showed *scarps* (steep slopes); ancient, dried lava flows; and extremely long, bright streaks of *ejecta* (material blown out of the ground by a meteorite impact) surrounding a crater near the north pole. Scientists said these ejecta streaks indicated that the crater was formed by a massive, relatively recent meteorite impact.

Messenger was scheduled to make another close fly-by of Mercury in September 2009. The probe was to enter orbit around the closest planet to the sun in 2011.

Kepler planet finder. In March 2009, NASA launched the Kepler planet-finder observatory into orbit around the sun on a Delta II rocket. Kepler, one of the most sophisticated scientific spacecraft ever built, carried a highly sensitive light meter and a special telescope with a field of view 30,000 times as broad as that of the Hubble Space Telescope. Astronomers planned to use Kepler to detect

SEARCHING FOR OTHER "EARTHS"

The Kepler observatory, seen in this artist's rendition, was launched by NASA into orbit around the sun in March 2009. Kepler, named after German astronomer Johannes Kepler (1571-1630), was the first telescopic instrument sensitive enough to detect the faint flickers of light caused by Earth-sized planets passing in front of distant sun-like stars as they orbit the stars. Astronomers hoped to use Kepler to find *extrasolar* (orbiting stars other than our sun) planets similar to Earth in the so-called "habitable zone" around stars. The habitable zone is the region around a star in which moderate temperatures allow the existence of liquid water—and, possibly, life—on planets.

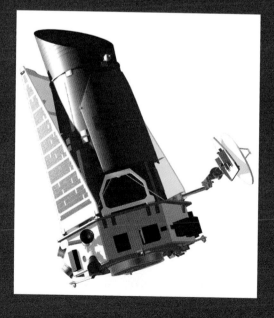

extremely faint flickers in the light from distant stars. Such flickers happen when planets orbiting the stars pass in front of the stars as seen from Earth.

Kepler was designed to find Earth-sized planets circling average-sized stars that are similar to our sun—particularly in the "habitable zone" around these stars. The habitable zone is the region around a star in which moderate temperatures would be conducive to the existence of liquid water and life on planets. Although previous astronomical searches had detected numerous stars with large planets around them, Kepler was the first observatory with the sensitivity and power needed to detect planets similar to Earth. Astronomers focused Kepler's initial search on stars that are from 30 to 1,000 light-years away in the direction of the Cygnus and Lyra constellations. (A light-year is the distance traveled in one year by a pulse of light, equal to about 9.46 trillion kilometers [5.88 trillion miles]).

Climate change satellites. Two satellites were launched in 2009 to gather data related to climate change on Earth. NASA's Orbiting Carbon Observatory (OCO), launched in February, was designed to map concentrations of carbon dioxide in Earth's atmosphere. Carbon dioxide is a so-called greenhouse gas, which traps heat near Earth's surface. Although carbon dioxide is necessary for life, many scientists believe that increasing concentrations of this gas from the burning of fossil fuels are contributing to global warming.

A windshield-like device needed to protect the OCO from friction with the atmosphere failed to separate after the craft passed through the atmosphere. The extra weight made the OCO so heavy that it could not reach orbit, and the craft fell into the ocean near Antarctica.

In March, the ESA launched the Gravity field and steady-state Ocean Circulation Explorer (GOCE) satellite into orbit from the Plesetsk Cosmodrome in Russia. The main mission of the GOCE satellite was to make precise measurements of Earth's gravitational field. Scientists planned to use these measurements as a reference model for analyzing changes in ocean level and circulation believed to be caused by climate change.

India and China touch the moon. In November 2008, India's first lunar spacecraft, Chandrayaan 1, entered a planned two-year orbit around the moon. Although Chandrayaan 1 was built in India and launched from India's space facility on the Bay of Bengal, a

ICE GEYSERS AROUND SATURN

A series of ice geysers erupt into space (below) from crevices, or fractures (bottom), in the surface of the south polar region of Enceladus, a small, inner moon of Saturn. The NASA spacecraft Cassini, in orbit around Saturn since 2004, analyzed the makeup of these geysers as the craft traveled through them in October 2008. According to NASA scientists, the geysers consist of plumes of ice crystals and water vapor, possibly originating in an ocean of liquid water that lies beneath the frozen surface of Enceladus. The gravity of Saturn captures some of these erupting ice crystals and directs them into the famous rings that surround the giant planet.

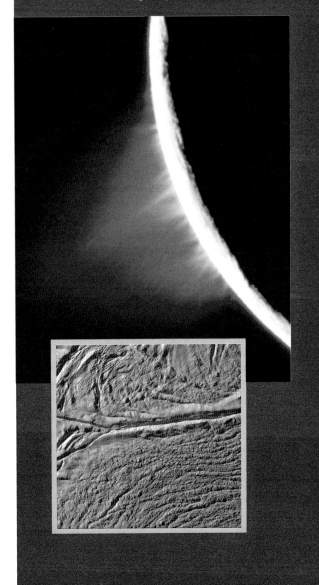

SPACE TECHNOLOGY continued

number of other nations placed scientific instruments on board the probe to gather data about the moon. Bulgaria, Germany, Sweden, the United Kingdom, and the United States added a total of six instruments to the five instruments supplied by India.

Among the instruments on Chandrayaan 1 was an experimental radar device from the United States for peering into the permanently dark craters at the moon's poles. Scientists believe that water-ice delivered long ago by comet impacts may be preserved in these craters. In addition, India's High Energy X-ray Spectrometer was to search for the chemical signatures of ice in the polar craters. Some scientists believe that lunar crater ice could serve as a source of water and rocket fuel during future exploration of the moon by astronauts.

Chandrayaan 1 released a small probe in November to deliberately crash into the lunar surface. Engineers designed this crash as preparation for a future mission in which India planned to land a roving vehicle on the moon.

In March 2009, China also sent a probe, Chang'e 1 (which had been orbiting the moon since November 2007), into a controlled crash on the moon's surface. The lunar missions of India and China were clear signs that both of these nations planned to have growing roles in the future international exploration of the moon. ■ Frank Morring, Jr.
See also **ASTRONOMY.**

NASA'S FERMI GAMMA-RAY SPACE TELESCOPE

The deepest and best-resolved view of high-energy gamma rays in the sky is captured in an image representing 87 days of observations by NASA's Fermi Gamma-ray Space Telescope. Released in March 2009, the image reveals how the universe would appear to human beings, if we could detect radiation 150 million times as energetic as visible light. The telescope, launched in June 2008, was designed to help scientists identify sources of gamma rays from distant galaxies, as well as from objects within our own galaxy and solar system.

Milky Way center

WORLD BOOK SUPPLEMENT

Eight new or revised articles reprinted from the
2009 edition of *The World Book Encyclopedia*

The Arctic landscape is mostly dry and treeless. In this photograph, an Inuit stone marker overlooks a glacier valley on Baffin Island, Canada. Mosses and lichens grow on the rocks.

© Robert Huberman, SuperStock

Arctic wildlife are adapted for living in cold, harsh conditions. Caribou, shown in this photograph, migrate vast distances to find food in the winter, sometimes traveling thousands of miles.

© All Canada Photos/Alamy Images

Arctic is the northernmost region of Earth. It surrounds the North Pole and includes the northern areas of North America, Europe, and Asia. Some parts of the Arctic are freezing, barren landscapes that cannot support much life. During winter, the sun never rises above the horizon in much of the Arctic. But during the brief Arctic summer, the sun never sets, and life flourishes in some places. The word *Arctic* comes from *Arktos* (bear), the ancient Greek name for a constellation that appears in the northern sky.

The southernmost parts of the Arctic border a vast band of evergreen forests called the *taiga*. Farther north, trees cannot grow, and the landscape consists of dry, frozen plains called the *tundra*. Herds of caribou migrate seasonally between the tundra and the taiga. In the rocky, windswept lands north of the tundra, few plants can survive. Arctic lands encircle the Arctic Ocean, which remains mostly frozen all year. The North Pole lies in the Arctic Ocean.

Despite the challenging environment, people have found ways to adapt to life in the Arctic since ancient times. The *indigenous* (native) peoples of the Arctic include the Inuit (sometimes called Eskimos) of North America and the Sami of Europe. English, Dutch, and Russian explorers arrived in the Arctic later.

Underground, the Arctic is rich in minerals, natural gas, and petroleum. Today, global demand for petroleum and gas drives much Arctic exploration.

This article will discuss the Arctic's land, climate, and natural resources; the traditional ways of life of Arctic peoples; and the history of Arctic exploration. The final section of the article deals with challenges facing the region today.

Land and climate

Scientists and governments define the Arctic in several different ways. Politically and culturally, the Arctic can be defined as the lands north of the taiga. Defined this way, it includes the northern parts of Alaska and Canada; northern Scandinavia (Norway and Sweden); northern Finland; and Russia's Siberia region. It also includes Greenland and most of Iceland.

Another common definition limits the Arctic to the region north of the Arctic Circle, an imaginary line that circles the globe at 66°33′ north latitude. The Arctic Circle marks the edge of an area where the sun stays above the horizon one or more full days each year, a phenomenon known as the *midnight sun*.

Many scientists define the Arctic as the northern region with an average July temperature lower than 50 °F (10 °C). The boundary of this region is called the 50 °F (10 °C) July *isotherm*. An isotherm is an imaginary line defined by a common temperature. Under this definition, the Arctic includes some lands south of the Arctic Circle, but not some lands north of the Arctic Circle.

Climate. The Arctic climate is cold because the area receives relatively little energy from sunlight. In winter, the sun never rises during the day in some places. Even when the sun is shining, the sunlight is less direct and thus less intense than that farther south. Without sunlight, winter temperatures may drop below −76 °F (−60 °C). But in the constant sunlight of summer, temperatures in some regions can rise above 86 °F (30 °C).

The Arctic is a dry region. Most of the Arctic receives only 2 to 10 inches (5 to 25 centimeters) of precipitation each year, much of which falls as snow. Some parts of the Arctic are as dry as many deserts in other regions.

Land regions. The Arctic can be divided into three land regions: (1) the polar deserts, (2) the tundra, and (3) the subarctic.

Polar deserts make up the northernmost lands on Earth. Like warmer deserts, they receive little precipitation and have thin, rocky soil. Strong, cold winds blow frequently in the polar deserts. Few plants can survive the extreme conditions, but *lichens*—algae and fungi that live together—grow on the rocky surfaces (see Lichen).

The tundra lies south of the polar deserts. The tundra receives more precipitation than the polar deserts and is therefore more favorable for plant growth. In addition to mosses and lichens, grasses and other flowering plants grow in the tundra. Shrubs also grow there, but trees cannot survive in the tundra.

The subarctic includes lands south of the 50 °F (10 °C) July isotherm and thus is excluded from some definitions of the Arctic. The subarctic climate is warmer and less dry than that of the tundra and so can support trees. The subarctic includes the northern fringes of the taiga.

Environment and natural resources

The Arctic includes vast areas of wilderness largely untouched by industry and development. Other areas have long served as an important source of food and raw materials.

Soil conditions in the Arctic are shaped by the presence of *permafrost*, a layer of permanently frozen soil beneath the ground. Only the top layer of soil, called the *active layer*, thaws during summer. In some areas, the active layer can extend about 10 feet (300 centimeters) deep. In other areas, the top layer may only thaw to a depth of 8 to 12 inches (20 to 30 centimeters).

Despite the dry climate, Arctic soils tend to be moist because the permafrost prevents drainage. But plants grow slowly because cold temperatures slow biological processes in the soil, limiting the availability of nutrients.

Plant life in the Arctic is limited by the cold and the short growing season. In the polar deserts, mosses and lichens dominate. The tundra supports a variety of grasses and such shrubs as dwarf birch, Labrador tea, lingonberry, and willow. In the subarctic, birch, larch, and spruce trees may dominate the landscape.

Arctic plants have adapted to the harsh climate and soil conditions in several ways. Some plants have extensive root systems. They use the extra roots to better absorb scarce nutrients from the soil. Because the growing season in the Arctic is only 6 to 12 weeks long, most Arctic plants are *perennials*—that is, they take several years to complete their life cycle. Some plants can keep their delicate leaves and flower buds alive under the cover of winter snow. When the snow melts, these structures quickly develop to take full advantage of the short growing season. Some Arctic plants can even sprout from seeds under the snow.

Animal life in the Arctic depends on cycles of plant life for food. In general, food for animals is abundant in the summer and scarce in the winter. During the growing season, such *herbivores* (plant-eating animals) as lemmings, hares, and caribou flourish. The large population of herbivores in the summer, in turn, supports such predators as snowy owls, Arctic foxes, and wolves.

Both herbivores and predators respond to the changing availability of food in a variety of ways. Some Arctic animals simply leave during the winter. Arctic birds migrate in large numbers to warmer regions in the south. Caribou migrate overland from the tundra to the taiga, where more plants grow during the winter. Some groups of caribou travel more than 3,000 miles (4,800 kilometers) in their migrations.

Other animals survive the winter by living off fat they build up during the summer. Musk oxen restrict their activity in the winter to conserve energy. Their thick, warm undercoats help insulate against the cold. Such predators as foxes, lynxes, and wolves also grow thick fur coats in the winter. Smaller hunters, such as weasels, spend their time under the snow, which reduces their exposure to the cold winds above. They also hunt for lemmings, voles, and other prey beneath the snow. Ground squirrels and bears move into underground dens during the winter and enter a sleeplike state.

Many of the world's most important fishing waters lie around the edge of the Arctic. Indigenous people also hunt seals and whales in Arctic waters.

Minerals, oil, and natural gas are abundant in the Arctic, and mining ranks as an important industrial activity throughout the region. Coal deposits are found in

The Arctic

Scientists define the boundaries of the Arctic in several ways. The *tree line* is the northern limit of tree growth. The climatic boundary of the Arctic is the 50 °F (10 °C) July isotherm. This imaginary line connects areas where the average July temperature is 50 °F (10 °C). Both lines are shown on this map.

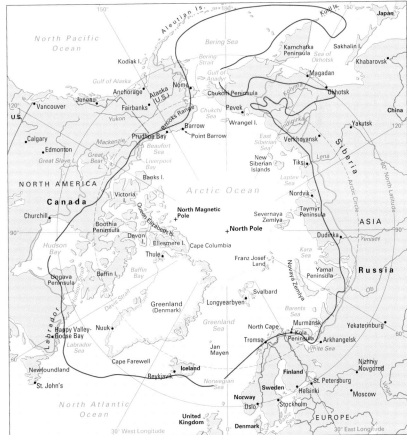

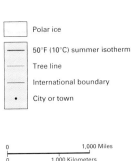

Polar ice

50°F (10°C) summer isotherm

Tree line

International boundary

• City or town

0   1,000 Miles

0   1,000 Kilometers

WORLD BOOK map

Housing in the Arctic consists mostly of modern buildings specially adapted to the extreme cold. In this photograph, for example, heated corridors hold the pipes that carry water and sewage to and from homes. A layer of permanently frozen soil, called *permafrost,* prevents pipes and home foundations from being dug into the ground.

© John Sylvester, Alamy Images

Alaska, Siberia, Canada, and Greenland, as well as on Svalbard, a group of Norwegian islands. Subarctic areas of Alaska and Canada support large mining operations for such minerals as copper, gold, lead, silver, and zinc. Several areas in the Canadian Arctic have active diamond mines. The Arctic has large reserves of oil and natural gas, most of them in Russia. Production of oil and gas forms a major part of the economy of Alaska, Norway, and Russia.

Arctic peoples

In the past, indigenous Arctic peoples lived in small, widely scattered groups. The peoples were often isolated from one another and spoke many different languages. Development and modern technology have lessened the isolation of Arctic life for many groups.

Groups. Siberia is home to a large number of indigenous groups. More than 20 separate groups live scattered along northern Siberia's coastline and rivers. They speak many languages, most of which are from the Uralic and Altaic language family. Several of their languages are not related to any language family.

The Arctic coastlines of Alaska, Canada, and Greenland are inhabited by several groups of Inuit and Yuit. They speak languages from the Eskimo-Aleut family. Some American Indian groups also live in the North American Arctic. They speak languages from the Athabaskan family.

The Sami people live in Norway, Sweden, Finland, and the Kola Peninsula in northwest Russia. They speak several dialects of the Sami language, which is related to Finnish and Estonian.

Traditional ways of life. Before modernization, most Arctic peoples were *hunter-gatherers*—that is, they survived by hunting animals and gathering plant materials from the wild. They were *seminomadic,* moving from place to place to find food. Their diet consisted of fish, game, roots, and berries. Before firearms, Arctic peoples used a variety of devices to hunt, such as snares, traps, harpoons, spears, and bows and arrows. In the winter, they rode sleds pulled by dogs or reindeer.

In winter, many Arctic peoples lived together in small communities. They built underground winter houses made of stone or sod. In summer, smaller bands moved about in search of game. Each band consisted of an *ex-*

tended family—parents, married children and their offspring, and other relatives. Portable tents made of animal skin served as summer housing.

Most Arctic clothing was made of caribou or reindeer fur. The hollow hairs acted as a good insulation against the cold air. People sewed the skins together using sinew and bone needles before thread and steel needles were available. For decoration, they sewed various skins together in decorative patterns. Later, they added trade beads and colored threads to their outfits.

The beliefs of indigenous Arctic people held that animals had spirits that must be respected. Most communities had *shamans,* men or women who were responsible for communicating with the spirit world.

Arctic exploration

The first written account of the Arctic comes from Pytheas, a Greek who sailed to the Far North around 325 B.C. The Inuit first settled much of the Arctic about 1,000 years ago, around the same time that a Scandinavian people called the Vikings began to explore there. About A.D. 982, the Viking explorer Erik the Red reached Greenland, where he made the earliest known European contact with the Inuit. Erik and other Vikings established colonies in Greenland. However, the colonies did not survive past the 1400's.

Search for the Northwest Passage. In 1497, King Henry VII of England dispatched the Italian explorer John Cabot to northeastern North America. Cabot hoped to find a quick passage to eastern Asia by sailing west through North America—a "Northwest Passage." At the time, Europeans did not realize the size of the North American continent and the extent to which it blocked their path. Though Cabot believed he had reached Asia, in actuality he probably landed in Newfoundland.

Europeans continued to explore the Arctic. In the 1570's, the English navigator Martin Frobisher sailed around Greenland to Baffin Island, where he had several hostile meetings with the Inuit. In 1590, the Dutch explorer Willem Barents reached the far northern islands of Svalbard and Novaya Zemlya, which later became whaling centers. In the early 1600's, the English explorer Henry Hudson sailed farther north than any European explorer before him. He helped to establish the North American fur trade.

In 1648, the Russian explorer Semyon Dezhnev sailed

through what is now known as the Bering Strait. Vitus Bering, the Danish navigator for whom the strait is named, made several voyages between 1725 and 1742, exploring the strait and southeastern Alaska. He encountered the Aleuts when he landed on the Shumagin Islands. In 1778, the British navigator James Cook explored North America's northwestern coast, continuing the search for the Northwest Passage. He passed through the Bering Strait and on to Cape Prince of Wales.

In the early 1800's, the British Navy sent several expeditions to try to find the Northwest Passage, despite centuries of exploration without success. William Edward Parry, a British naval officer, led three expeditions and went farther north than any previous explorer.

In 1845, the British Navy launched the most ambitious—and ultimately the most disastrous—Northwest Passage expedition. Its leader was John Franklin, who had previously led two Arctic expeditions. In 1847, Franklin's ships became icebound, and he and his crew died of starvation. Search parties charted much of the remaining stretches of Arctic coast while looking for his stranded expedition. The first explorer to actually sail through the Northwest Passage was the Norwegian adventurer Roald Amundsen in 1906.

Race to the pole. During the 1860's, attention turned to reaching the North Pole. To get there, explorers had to cross the treacherous, frozen Arctic Ocean.

After numerous attempts, the American explorer

Robert E. Peary claimed to be the first person to reach the pole in 1909. That same week, the American physician Frederick A. Cook claimed that he had reached the pole a year before Peary, in 1908. Peary disputed Cook's claim, and the controversy over who actually first reached the pole continues today.

The Arctic today

The Arctic, once protected by its remoteness and harsh climate, faces many challenges today. Modernization has upset traditional Arctic ways of life, and many indigenous peoples have struggled to preserve their culture. Further, a warming climate threatens the landscape and environment of the region.

Modernization. Today, the Arctic is governed by Canada, Denmark, Finland, Iceland, Greenland, Russia, and the United States. These countries have worked to develop the region, largely for its natural resources. As a result, the lifestyles of most indigenous peoples have changed dramatically. Many Arctic people speak English or another European language instead of their native language, and many Arctic languages are in danger of being forgotten. Many Arctic peoples have converted from their traditional religions to Christianity.

Most indigenous peoples have settled towns and cities and use modern technology. Many live in *prefabricated* housing, housing built in sections at a factory and assembled at the building site. Arctic hunters drive snowmobiles

Arctic exploration

Europeans began widespread exploration of the Arctic during the 1500's. This map shows the routes taken by some of the most important Arctic explorers since then.

——— Frobisher (Britain) 1576

– – – Barents (Netherlands) 1596-97

------ Bering (Netherlands) 1728-29

——— Franklin (Britain) 1845-47

– – – McClure (Britain) 1850-54

------ Nordenskjöld (Sweden) 1878-79

—·—· Nansen (Norway) 1893-96

——— Amundsen (Norway) 1903-06

– – – Peary (U.S.) 1908-09

------ Nobile (Italy) 1926

—··—·· U.S.S. Nautilus 1958

WORLD BOOK map

and four-wheeled all-terrain vehicles. The modern Arctic diet includes fewer traditional foods and more imported goods, such as frozen meals, soft drinks, and candy.

The removal of minerals, natural gas, and petroleum from Arctic lands has damaged hunting and fishing in many areas. Rapid modernization has also led to serious social problems among indigenous people, such as alcoholism, drug use, domestic violence, and suicide.

Climate change. The Arctic climate has warmed significantly in the past few decades, causing the ranges of various Arctic plants to shift northward. Shrubs have become dominant in some areas of the tundra, crowding out mosses and lichens. Along with plants, a number of animals have extended their ranges northward. Warming has also changed the life cycle of certain animals. An example is the spruce bark beetle, which attacks spruce trees. The beetle, which once took two years to complete its life cycle in Arctic areas, now completes it in a single year in some parts of the Arctic.

The warming climate results in less of the Arctic Ocean freezing each year. Less sea ice may benefit human activities, such as shipping and pumping petroleum from the sea floor. But many animals depend on the sea ice. Seals and walruses climb onto the ice to rest. Polar bears, who hunt on the ice, are especially threatened by its rapid disappearance.

The warming climate may also harm human settlement in the Arctic. Warmer air causes more frequent storms, which endanger coastal settlements. The thawing of permafrost can cause roads and buildings to buckle and collapse.

In 2007, scientists from dozens of nations launched a study of the Arctic and Antarctic called the International Polar Year 2007-2008. The investigation involved more than 200 research projects, with a focus on how climate change affects the polar regions and their inhabitants.

Knut Kielland and Molly Lee

Arctic Ocean is the body of icy water covering Earth's northernmost regions. It ranks as the smallest of the world's oceans, touching only the northern shores of Asia, Europe, and North America. The North Pole lies near the center of the Arctic Ocean.

People define the boundaries of the Arctic Ocean differently for different purposes. For oceanographers, the ocean's limits include: (1) the Bering Strait, between Alaska and Siberia; (2) the northern limits of the Canadian islands; (3) Fram Strait, between Greenland and Svalbard; and (4) the opening to the Barents Sea, between Svalbard and Norway. Defined this way, the Arctic Ocean covers about 3,680,000 square miles (9,530,000 square kilometers). Its widest part, between Alaska and Norway, measures about 2,630 miles (4,235 kilometers) across. The narrowest stretch separates Greenland and the Taymyr Peninsula of Russia. These areas lie about 1,200 miles (1,930 kilometers) apart.

The Arctic Ocean is bitterly cold. At its surface, thick chunks of floating ice form a treacherous, shifting landscape. During the winter, the sun does not rise for weeks over the Arctic Ocean. In the summer, the sun remains above the horizon for several weeks, and some of the ice melts.

The Greek explorer Pytheas sailed near the Arctic Ocean in the late 300's B.C. He reported that a frozen sea

William Cromie

An Arctic research station operated by United States scientists stands on this drifting mass of sea ice. The man in the foreground is untangling wire to build a radio antenna.

lay a six-day voyage north of Britain. The name *Arctic* comes from *Arktos* (bear), the ancient Greek name for a constellation that appears in the northern sky.

Groups of islands divide the coastal waters of the Arctic Ocean into seven seas. These seas, from Greenland eastward, are (1) the Barents Sea; (2) the Kara Sea; (3) the Laptev Sea; (4) the East Siberian Sea; (5) the Chukchi Sea; (6) the Beaufort Sea; and (7) the Lincoln Sea.

Far northern lands extend into the Arctic Ocean. They include most of Greenland and parts of Norway, Russia, and Canada, as well as Alaska. For more information on the land and people of the Arctic region.

Climate

In January, surface water temperatures in the Arctic Ocean drop to as low as about 28 °F (-2 °C), the freezing point of seawater. In summer, the waters warm to only a few degrees above freezing—and only in limited areas.

A high-pressure dome of cold, dry air generally covers the Arctic region. It prevents moist, warmer air from the south from reaching the central Arctic Ocean. As a result, rain and snowfall tend to be light over the Arctic Ocean. However, fog commonly forms over coastal waters in the summer, when humid, warm air from the land blows out over the ocean.

Arctic weather varies dramatically. In winter, violent storms form rapidly and unexpectedly in some areas. Such storms are sometimes called *Arctic hurricanes*.

Since the late 1900's, the patterns of air pressure that drive Arctic weather have been changing. The changes result from a combination of natural cycles and *global warm-*

Facts in brief

Area: About 3,680,000 mi² (9,530,000 km²).
Greatest distance: About 2,630 mi² (4,235 km²), between Alaska and Norway.
Average depth: 4,465 ft (1,361 m).
Greatest depth: 18,399 ft (5,608 m), Molloy Hole, northwest of Svalbard.
Surface temperature: *Lowest,* 28 °F (-2 °C), in January. *Highest,* 29 °F (-1.5 °C), in July.

ing. Global warming is an average increase in Earth's surface temperaure, thought to be caused in part by human activities (see **Global warming**). Scientists have linked changing air pressure patterns to other changes, such as increases in the frequency of storms and the strength of waves. These changes, in turn, contribute to increased erosion along lengthy stretches of Arctic coastline.

Ice

Much of the Arctic Ocean is covered in a thick layer of floating ice. Most of the ice is *sea ice* or frozen seawater. The rest is *glacial ice,* which breaks off from glaciers along the coasts of Arctic lands.

Sea ice. Seawater freezes at a lower temperature than does fresh water because seawater has a higher salt content. When sea ice forms on the ocean surface, much of the salt sinks into the water below.

In winter, the cover of sea ice spreads beyond the Arctic Ocean's boundaries. But in the summer, the sea ice melts to less than half the ocean's area. The ice that remains in the Arctic Ocean throughout the summer is typically 3 to 12 feet (1 to 4 meters) thick. The ice sometimes piles up into ridges and becomes thicker.

Arctic sea ice is constantly on the move. Winds and currents push the floating ice at speeds of up to about a mile or a couple kilometers per day. On the North American side of the ocean, the ice tends to drift in a clockwise motion called the Beaufort Gyre. On the European side, it flows along a path from the New Siberian Islands toward Fram Strait, called the Transpolar Drift.

Because sea ice is always moving, there are always areas of open water throughout the ice cover, called *leads.* Leads range from extremely thin cracks to huge breaks in the ice as wide as rivers.

Some areas of the ice cover tend to have thin ice or open water in the same place each winter. These areas, called *polynias,* serve as seasonal homes to many living things in the Arctic Ocean.

Glacial ice, unlike sea ice, is frozen fresh water from glaciers on land. Chunks of glacial ice break off along the coasts of Greenland, northern Canada, Svalbard, and other lands to form *icebergs.* Some icebergs become part of the Arctic sea ice cover. Many other icebergs float into the North Atlantic Ocean, where they eventually melt in the warm waters of the Gulf Stream.

Icebergs can be extremely dangerous to ships. Some icebergs are so large and thick that they are called *ice islands.* Scientists have even been able to set up research stations on some ice islands.

Disappearance of ice. The Arctic Ocean's summer sea ice cover has decreased by about 10 percent each decade since 1978, when satellite measurements were first gathered. Global warming may be contributing to this trend in a number of ways. For example, more sea ice may melt each year as a result of warming air temperatures over Siberia and North America. The ice cover may also be affected by changing weather and ocean circulation patterns related to global warming.

Declining sea ice cover could accelerate warming across the planet. White snow and ice reflect the sun's heat back into space, in much the same way that white clothing helps people stay cool in the summer sun. Darker areas of open water, on the other hand, absorb the sun's heat in much the same way dark clothing does. Thus, the more the ice melts, the more heat Earth absorbs. The heat can, in turn, cause even more ice to melt, creating a dangerous, escalating cycle.

Ocean life

Despite its icy cover, the Arctic Ocean supports a diversity of wildlife. Seals and whales feed on fish and tiny floating organisms called *plankton.* Large numbers of diatoms, a type of plantlike *phytoplankton,* thrive near the surface of waters along the edges of the sea ice. Some whales eat huge amounts of shrimplike *zooplankton* called *krill.*

Shellfish serve as an important source of food for walruses, bearded seals, and sperm whales. Halibut and other bottom-dwelling fish are plentiful in shallow seas along the ocean's coasts.

Polar bears live on top of the sea ice. They use it as a platform from which to hunt seals in the water below.

The ocean floor

The floor of the Arctic Ocean includes a shallow area along the coasts—called the *continental shelf*—and a central area called the *deep basin.* The Arctic Ocean's average depth is 4,465 feet (1,361 meters).

The continental shelf is a gently sloping band of underwater land at the edges of the continents. In the Arctic Ocean, it is mostly less than 500 feet (150 meters) deep. North of Greenland and North America, it extends about 45 to 120 miles (70 to 200 kilometers) from shore. Off the Russian coast, it extends much farther into the ocean—up to 1,000 miles (1,600 kilometers) from shore.

The deep basin. Several underwater ridges crisscross the deep basin of the Arctic Ocean. These ridges

Floating ice covers much of the Arctic Ocean's surface. Most of the ice is *sea ice* (frozen seawater) that drifts with the currents. The rest is freshwater *glacial ice,* which breaks off from glaciers along the coasts of Arctic lands. Chunks of glacial ice form *icebergs,* seen in the distance in this photo.

divide the deep basin into several smaller basins.

The Lomonosov Ridge, the tallest of the dividing ridges, rises about 10,000 feet (3,000 meters) from the surrounding floor. It extends about 1,100 miles (1,800 kilometers), stretching from a point near Ellesmere Island to an area north of the New Siberian Islands. The Lomonosov Ridge divides the deep basin into two main areas—the Canadian Basin and the Eurasian Basin. The Canadian Basin has an average depth of 12,500 feet (3,800 meters). The Eurasian Basin has an average depth of 13,800 feet (4,200 meters).

Several other ridges run parallel to the Lomonosov Ridge. On the Canadian side, the Alpha Ridge and the Mendeleyev Ridge form a ridge system that stretches

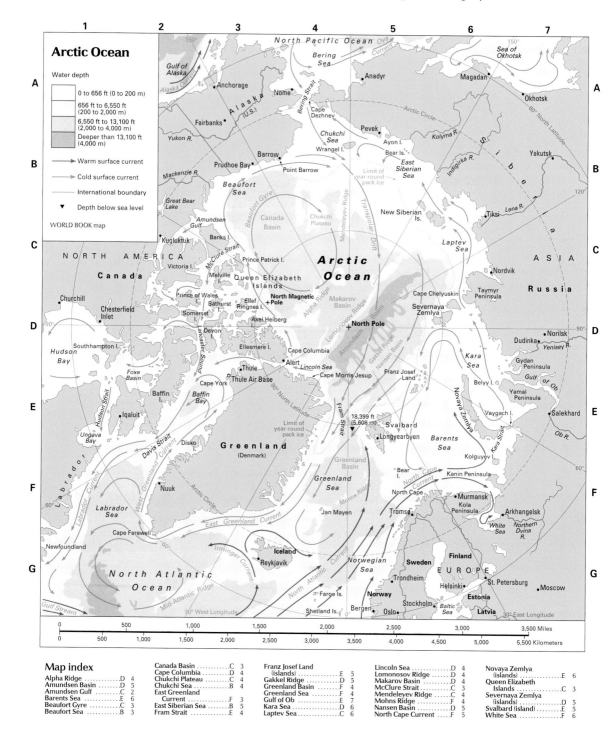

Map index

NASA

The disappearance of sea ice poses a threat to the wildlife of the Arctic Ocean. These satellite photographs show the extent of summer sea ice in 1979 *(left)* and 2005 *(right)*. The ice covering has decreased as a result of *global warming,* an increase in the average temperature at Earth's surface.

from north of Ellesmere Island to the East Siberian Sea. The ridge system separates the Canadian Basin into two smaller parts—the Canada Basin and the Makarov Basin.

In the European Basin, the Nansen-Gakkel Ridge stretches from the tip of Greenland toward the Laptev Sea. It separates the Amundsen Basin from the Nansen Basin. The Amundsen Basin includes the deepest areas of the Arctic Ocean, dropping in places to more than 18,000 feet (5,500 meters) below the ocean surface.

Waters

Water constantly flows into, out of, and around the Arctic Ocean, pushed along by currents and winds. In addition, about 10 percent of Earth's river water flows into the Arctic Ocean.

Currents. The North Atlantic Current brings a large amount of relatively warm, salty water from the Atlantic Ocean into the Arctic Ocean. The rest of the seawater flowing into the Arctic Ocean comes from the Pacific Ocean. This water is colder and less salty.

Ice and water flow out of the Arctic Ocean through the Fram Strait and along the East Greenland Current. Some of this water flows all the way around Greenland into Baffin Bay. There, it circles in a counterclockwise motion before flowing south. It is joined by water flowing out of the Arctic Ocean through passages between Canadian islands, where it forms the Labrador Current of the northwestern Atlantic Ocean.

Water masses. The Arctic Ocean's waters are not uniform in temperature or salt content. As in other oceans, the different layers of the water form distinct *water masses* with unique properties.

The Arctic Ocean's surface waters tend to be less salty than those of other oceans. Rivers and precipitation bring much fresh water to the ocean's surface. Also, the formation of sea ice causes much salt to sink to lower levels. The surface waters circulate in a pattern similar to that of sea ice, following the Beaufort Gyre and the Transpolar Drift. These motions vary somewhat, depending on wind patterns. The surface waters extend down to about 80 to 250 feet (25 to 75 meters) of depth.

Below the surface waters lies a near-freezing, nutrient-rich mass of Pacific water. This layer reaches about 500 feet (150 meters) deep and is generally found only in basins in the ocean's Canadian side.

A warmer mass of Atlantic water lies deeper, reaching 2,625 feet (800 meters) below the surface. This water enters the Arctic Ocean from the Fram Strait, where it

starts out several degrees above freezing. It circulates in the smaller basins in counterclockwise patterns.

The deepest water mass, called Arctic bottom water, is saltier and colder than the Atlantic water mass. The Arctic bottom water is slightly warmer and saltier in the Canadian Basin than in it is in the Eurasian Basin. Little is known about how the Arctic bottom water circulates.

Tides. The Arctic Ocean has smaller tides overall than the other oceans do, probably due to its small size and nearly landlocked geography. Most of the tides in the Arctic Ocean rise and fall less than 1 foot (0.3 meter).

The Arctic Ocean and people

The Arctic Ocean has long provided fishing waters and hunting platforms for Arctic peoples. For many centuries, Europeans tried to find a sea route through the Arctic Ocean, referred to as the Northwest Passage. The ocean continues to provide many natural resources. But it also faces threats from pollution and global warming.

Use. The Arctic Ocean provides a water route to distant Arctic ports. It enables ships to deliver fuel, manufactured goods, and other products to Arctic settlements and carry back such goods as fish, fur, and lumber. Special *icebreaker* ships clear routes for these ships, and aircraft help guide them through the ice.

Major petroleum deposits lie off the north coast of Russia and Alaska, and oil wells operate in these areas. The continental shelf near Canada and Russia is also believed to hold large reserves of oil and natural gas.

Russian and Nordic fishing crews catch such fish as cod and halibut in the Barents and Kara seas. Arctic people from several nations hunt whales in the ocean.

Threats. Pollution is limited in the Arctic Ocean because there is little development in the region. But the disposal of wastes from military bases in the Arctic has resulted in some local pollution, as has oil production on the Alaskan shelf. Air pollution sometimes drifts over the region from factories in China, Russia, the United States, and other northern countries. This pollution contributes to the *Arctic haze* sometimes reported by airplane pilots. Some toxic chemicals used in low latitudes end up in the Arctic because they repeatedly evaporate, redepositing in colder areas. These chemicals tend to accumulate in animal fat, reaching higher concentrations in animals high on the food chain.

Global warming causes the Arctic Ocean's sea ice to decrease. The ice's disappearance threatens polar bears and other animals that depend on it. Kelly K. Falkner

Brain

Brain is the organ that serves as the body's control center. The brain constantly receives information from the senses about conditions both inside and outside the body. It rapidly analyzes this information and sends out signals that control the body's muscles and glands. The brain also stores information from past experiences, making learning and remembering possible. In addition, the brain is the organ of the mind. It is the source of all thoughts, moods, and emotions.

Human beings have the most highly developed brain of any living creature. The human brain enables people to use language, solve difficult problems, and create works of art.

The human brain appears as a grayish-pink, jellylike ball with many ridges and grooves on its surface. An adult brain weighs an average of about 3 pounds (1.4 kilograms). It includes about 100 billion nerve cells, called *neurons.* The neurons are linked by as many as 50 trillion connections called *synapses (sih NAP seez).* The neurons produce and transmit *nerve impulses,* electrical and chemical signals that are sent from cell to cell along distinct pathways.

Scientists in various fields work together to study the structure, function, and chemical composition of the brain. This study is called *neuroscience* or *neurobiology.* Neuroscience is rapidly increasing our understanding of the brain. But much remains to be learned.

The human brain develops in complexity over time. Most of the brain's neurons are formed before birth. But many connections between neurons develop after birth. The human brain does not reach its full size until about 6 years of age. Some parts of the brain do not fully mature until after the teenage years.

Proper brain development depends on good nutrition and a stimulating environment early in life, when the brain is growing. Even in adulthood, however, the brain's structure is not completely fixed. The brain is always forming new connections between neurons, enabling people to form new memories and learn new skills throughout life.

Although the brain never stops making new connections, its ability to form new connections declines with age. The brain also loses neurons over time. Neurons die as people age, and most of these neurons are not replaced. Once the brain has reached adult size, it begins to shrink gradually. This shrinking is part of the normal aging process. But in some diseases, such as Alzheimer's disease, the brain shrinks faster than normal. In people with Alzheimer's, the ability to form new memories declines sharply. Eventually, other vital brain functions are lost.

The brain requires vast quantities of oxygen and food, which are supplied by a network of blood vessels. The human brain makes up only about 2 percent of the body's weight, but it accounts for about 20 percent of the oxygen used by the body at rest. The brain can go without oxygen for only three to five minutes before neurons begin to die, resulting in serious damage.

The brain's neurons work together with the millions of other neurons that make up the rest of the *nervous system.* Some of these other neurons form the nerves that connect the brain to various parts of the body. Many nerves connect to the brain through the *spinal cord.* The

Interesting facts about the brain

The brain of an unborn baby occupies a surprisingly large portion of the body. But, after birth, the brain grows less compared to other parts of the body.

About 100 billion neurons are found in the human brain. Almost half of these are in the cerebellum.

The cerebral cortex of an average adult human includes about 20 billion neurons.

Roughly 1 neuron dies every second in an adult. This amounts to about 85,000 neurons per day.

About 5 ounces (150 milliliters) of liquid bathe the human brain and spinal cord. This *cerebrospinal fluid* is replaced at a rate of about four times per day. The old fluid is recycled into the blood.

The left side of your brain controls movements on the right side of your body, and the right side of your brain controls movements on the left side of your body.

The brain itself has no receptors for pain and does not "feel" pain. But the membranes surrounding the brain are sensitive to pain.

People with brain damage may lead normal lives with more than half of the cerebral cortex missing, if the damage occurred early in life.

The brain of an elephant is 16,000 times larger than the brain of a mouse and contains about 800 times more neurons.

About 15 watts of energy is consumed by the average human brain. This amount is about 16 percent of the body's total energy use.

About 20 percent of the human body's oxygen supply is needed by the brain, though it makes up only about 2 percent of total body weight.

A neuron's electrical impulse lasts about 0.001 second and may travel down an axon faster than 100 meters per second (220 miles per hour).

The brain of Albert Einstein, the great physicist, was found to be average in overall size. But one study reported that a portion thought to be related to mathematical ability was about 15 percent larger than average. Some scientists think this difference may explain Einstein's genius.

spinal cord is a thick cable of neurons that extends from the base of the brain, through the neck, to about two-thirds of the way down the backbone. In addition, 12 pairs of nerves called *cranial nerves* connect the brain directly with certain parts of the body.

This article will discuss the parts of the brain, differences in individual brains, how the body protects the brain, how scientists study the brain, how the brain works, how neurons work, and the brains of other animals. For more information about the nervous system and the brain's place in it.

The parts of the brain

The human brain has three main divisions: (1) the cerebrum *(suh REE bruhm),* (2) the cerebellum *(SEHR uh BEHL uhm),* and (3) the brain stem. These structures consist of neurons and other specialized cells that support and care for them.

The cerebrum, also called the *forebrain,* controls thought and many kinds of learning. It is the largest and most complex part of the brain. The cerebrum makes up about 85 percent of the human brain's total volume. Some regions of the cerebrum are involved in analyzing complex sensory information. Other parts of the cerebrum control fine movements. Still other areas help regulate breathing, blood pressure, heartbeat, hunger, thirst, urination, and sexual urges.

A large groove divides the cerebrum into halves called the *left cerebral hemisphere* and the *right cerebral hemisphere*. A large bundle of nerve fibers connects the hemispheres.

Each hemisphere of the cerebrum is divided into four lobes. The lobes are (1) the frontal lobe, at the front of the brain; (2) the temporal lobe, at the brain's lower side; (3) the parietal *(puh RY uh tuhl)* lobe, in the middle; and (4) the occipital *(ahk SIHP uh tuhl)* lobe, at the rear.

The outer portion of the cerebrum is called the *cerebral cortex*. The cerebral cortex is heavily folded, resulting in a surface with many ridges and grooves. The folds greatly increase the surface area of the cortex, enabling a large number of neurons to be held within the limited space of the skull. The neurons of the cortex are arranged in layers that vary in thickness. Because the neurons appear gray in color, the nerve tissue that makes up the cerebral cortex is often called *gray matter*.

Just beneath the gray matter, there are a large number of nerve fibers called *axons (AK sahnz)*. The axons connect neurons in the different parts of the cortex with one another. They also connect neurons in the cortex with those in other parts of the brain. The axons have a coating of fatty material called *myelin (MY uh lihn)*. Myelin insulates the axons and speeds the transmission of nerve impulses along them. Myelin is white, and tightly packed axons covered with myelin form the brain's *white matter*. White matter makes up nearly half of the cerebrum.

Just beneath the cerebrum, at the upper end of the brain stem, are two structures called the *thalamus* and the *striatum*. The thalamus receives nerve impulses from other parts of the nervous system and sends them to appropriate areas of the cerebral cortex. The striatum receives nerve inputs from the cerebrum and transmits impulses back to it. The striatum also has some important connections to the brain stem.

The cerebellum is the part of the brain most responsible for balance, posture, and the coordination of movement. It makes up about 10 percent of the human brain's total volume.

The cerebellum lies toward the back of the brain, below the occipital lobe of the cerebrum. Like the cerebrum, the cerebellum is heavily folded. It also has a right and a left hemisphere.

Scientists understand the workings of neurons in the cerebellum more thoroughly than those in any other major region of the brain. The cerebellum sends signals to the muscles to coordinate movements. When movements are not accurate, the cerebellum receives error signals, which it then uses to adjust motor commands.

People who suffer damage to the cerebellum have difficulty maintaining their balance and reaching for objects. Excessive drinking of alcohol can damage the cerebellum and several other regions of the brain.

The brain stem controls heart rhythm and breathing. It also passes signals between the cerebrum and cerebellum and between the rest of the brain and the body. For example, the brain stem receives information from all the senses except for smell. It sends this information on to the cerebrum through the thalamus. The brain stem likewise receives sensory inputs and signals from the cerebrum, which it passes on to the spinal cord and to muscles in the head.

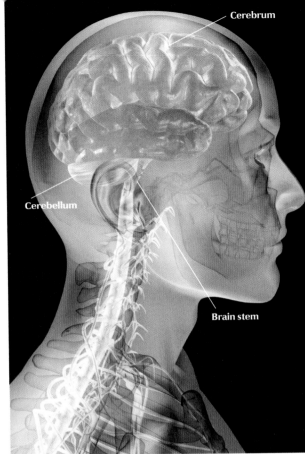

© 3D4Medical.com/Getty Images

The human brain is the organ of the mind. This computer-generated false-color image shows the brain in its natural position in the head. The brain has three main regions: (1) the cerebrum, (2) the cerebellum, and (3) the brain stem.

The brain stem is a stalklike structure underneath the cerebellum. Deep within it lies a network of nerve fibers called the *reticular (rih TIHK yuh luhr) formation*. The reticular formation helps regulate and maintain *arousal* (readiness). Sensory messages that pass through the brain stem stimulate the reticular formation. The reticular formation, in turn, stimulates alertness and activity throughout the cerebral cortex.

Brain cells. The human brain has from 10 billion to 100 billion neurons. The neurons connect with one another in complex networks. Neurons are more complex than most other cells of the body. They also vary in size and shape. For more information on neurons, see the section *How neurons work* later in this article.

Neurons make up much of the brain. But they are outnumbered by another kind of cell, called *glial (GLY uhl) cells*. There are several types. One type regulates the rate at which blood flows through various regions of the brain, helping to supply neurons with nutrients and energy. Another type of glial cell rids the brain of injured and diseased neurons by engulfing and digesting them. These cells increase in number when the brain is damaged by disease or injury. Still other glial cells produce the myelin sheaths that insulate some axons.

Glial cells continue to multiply into adulthood, replacing those that die over time. Neurons, in contrast, do not typically multiply. Most of a person's neurons are formed before birth. In only a few regions of the brain do neurons continue to multiply into adulthood. Thousands of neurons die and are removed from the brain each day. However, scientists have found that neurons in one region of the brain associated with learning and memory are continually replaced.

Differences in individual brains

Individual brains can differ significantly in overall size and in organization. Some differences appear to be consistent between the sexes.

In overall size. Human brains vary most noticeably in overall size. Although the average human brain weighs about 3 pounds (1.4 kilograms), it is not uncommon for a brain to weigh as little as 2.5 pounds (1.1 kilograms) or as much as 3.5 pounds (1.6 kilograms).

Most variation in brain size can be accounted for by variations in body size. People with larger bodies tend to have larger brains. Human females, for example, tend to have smaller bodies compared to males. Brains of adult human females weigh an average of about 0.22 pound (100 grams) less than brains of males. This size difference, however, does not produce a significant difference in intelligence between the sexes.

In organization. The brain's internal organization also differs between individuals. For example, in most people, the language circuits of the brain are mainly in the left cerebral hemisphere. In a small number of people, however, the language circuits are mainly in the right hemisphere. Among still other people, the two hemispheres participate almost equally in language.

Particular regions of the brain can vary in size, even among individuals of the same overall brain size. For example, scientists have observed that some areas of the cerebral cortex are larger in musicians than in other people. The cortex of a violinist, for instance, may be enlarged in regions associated with the sensation of touch from the fingers. In such cases, differences in individual experience shape differences in the brain's organization.

Neuroscientists know that both experience and genes affect brain organization. But it is difficult to distinguish the role of genes from other factors. It is clear, however, that people can perform similarly on many tasks despite differences in brain organization. This fact suggests that brains organized in different ways may perform equally well.

Between the sexes. In some animals, there are clear differences between the brains of males and females. Among some songbirds, for example, males sing, but females do not. The region of the brain associated with singing is much larger and more developed in the males.

Studies have revealed more subtle differences between the brains of human males and females. For example, studies show that some brain functions are less *lateralized* in females—that is, they are less strongly associated with a particular cerebral hemisphere. Some patterns of brain activity also differ between males and females, particularly in tasks not related to language. For example, an experiment showed that a part of the right hemisphere becomes more active in men who watch an exciting video. In women watching the same video, the corresponding part of the left hemisphere became more active.

Overall, neuroscientists have observed only a few clear differences in brain structure between human males and females. Researchers are not sure if these differences show that men and women think differently. Some evidence suggests that the sexes may have different mental strengths. Psychological testing consistently shows that men, on average, perform better than women on spatial tasks, such as visualizing objects in three dimensions. Women, on the other hand, do better than men on tests involving writing, reading, and vocabulary. But the average difference in both abilities is small. Many men do better at language tests than the average woman, and many women have better spatial skills than the average man.

How the body protects the brain

The brain ranks among the most vital parts of the body and the most sensitive to damage. For this reason, it needs protection both from injury and from harmful substances in the rest of the body.

From injury. The hard, thick bones of the skull shield the brain from blows that might injure it. In addition, the brain and spinal cord are protected by membranes called *meninges (muh NIHN jeez).* The outermost membrane is the tough *dura mater,* which lines the inner surface of the skull. A thinner membrane, called the *arachnoid mater,* lies just beneath the dura mater. The delicate *pia mater* directly covers the brain, following the folds of the brain's surface. The pia mater contains the vessels that carry blood to and from the cerebral cortex. A clear liquid called *cerebrospinal (SEHR uh broh SPY nuhl) fluid* surrounds the entire surface of the brain and spinal cord, flowing between the meninges. Cerebrospinal fluid serves as a cushion between the soft tissues of the brain and the hard bones of the skull. It also removes wastes produced by brain cells.

A blow to the head can cause the brain to move violently within these cushioning layers, hitting the inside of the skull. Such a blow may cause an injury called a *concussion.* A concussion typically results in a temporary loss of consciousness, followed by a brief memory loss. If the injury is severe, more extensive memory loss or permanent brain damage can occur.

Although the meninges protect the brain from blows, they can become infected. Infections of the meninges, called *meningitis* or *encephalitis,* often cause serious illness. Symptoms of such illness include headaches, nausea, and sensitivity to light. Physicians can treat the illness with antibiotics or antiviral drugs, but the infections may be fatal.

Some parts of the brain are more vulnerable to damage than others. Damage to the cerebral cortex generally causes fewer serious problems than similar damage to the brain stem. In the cerebral cortex, undamaged neurons can often take over the functions of the damaged cells. Neurons in the brain stem, in contrast, are not so easily replaced.

Because the brain stem controls many of the basic functions necessary for life, most injuries to the brain stem are serious. A stroke or injury that damages the brain stem, for example, can cause a rare neurological disorder called *locked-in syndrome.* Locked-in syndrome is characterized by the complete paralysis of voluntary muscles, except in some cases for the muscles that control eye movement. More serious brain stem injuries usually prove fatal.

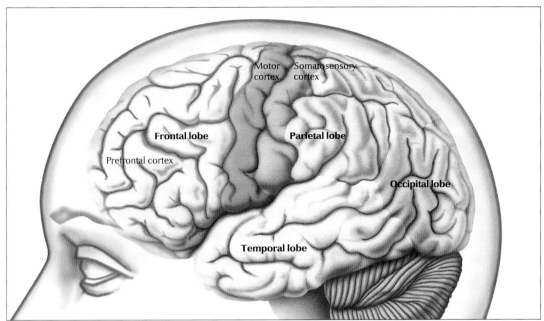

The cerebrum appears wrinkled because its outer portion, a layer of nerve cells called the *cerebral cortex,* is deeply folded. The cerebrum is divided into left and right hemispheres. Each hemisphere is divided into four lobes by *fissures* (deep grooves) in the cortex. This diagram shows the left hemisphere. Labels indicate the four lobes and some important divisions of the cerebral cortex.

From harmful substances. Nutrients and other substances in the blood reach body tissues through tiny blood vessels called *capillaries.* The cells in the wall of a capillary have spaces between them, making it easy for large molecules to pass through. In capillaries that service the brain, however, the cells of the wall are packed more tightly. The packing restricts the passage of certain substances from the blood to the brain cells, a protective effect referred to as the *blood-brain barrier.* The blood-brain barrier keeps most large molecules from entering the brain. Such large molecules include most of the substances that are poisonous to neurons.

Despite the protection offered by the blood-brain barrier, the brain needs some kinds of large molecules for nutrition. Special molecules must actively pump these nutrients into the brain.

The blood-brain barrier also helps keep out harmful bacteria. As a result, the brain rarely gets infected. Some viruses, however, are small enough to pass through the barrier and infect the brain. When this occurs, the blood-brain barrier can actually hinder the body's ability to fight the disease. It does this by blocking the passage of cells from the body's immune system.

Scientific study of the brain

Neuroscientists have learned much about the brain's structure, function, and organization through laboratory studies of animals, such as rats and monkeys. Importantly, such studies have shown that rodent and monkey brains are similar to human brains in many ways. Therefore, much of the knowledge from animal studies can be applied to human brains. However, the studies also show that human brains are unique in some important

ways. For example, the brain regions involved in making complex decisions are much larger in human beings than in other animals. Human brains were traditionally studied only after removal from the bodies of dead people. Today, scientists can study the brain using imaging technology, experiments with wires called *electrodes,* and genetic techniques.

Imaging. Modern medical technology can produce detailed images of the living human brain. For example, a special kind of X ray called a *computed tomography* (CT) scan can reveal brain tumors or bleeding in the brain. Two other scanning techniques also enable scientists to study healthy, living brains at work. They are *positron emission tomography* (PET) and *functional magnetic resonance imaging* (fMRI). Both techniques produce images similar to X rays. These images show which parts of the brain are active while a person does a particular mental or physical task.

Electrode experiments. Neuroscientists can also study the brain by placing electrodes on the scalp. These wires pick up electrical signals produced by neurons in the cerebral cortex. The signals can be recorded to produce an *electroencephalogram* (EEG).

Occasionally, physicians may insert fine electrodes directly into a person's brain in preparation for brain surgery. The insertion can be done while the patient is awake because the brain tissue cannot feel pain directly. The electrodes can then be used to record the activity of neurons while the patient performs a task. They can also be used to stimulate parts of the brain while the patient reports any feelings experienced. Such experiments help scientists learn about human brain function.

Genetics. Genes carry instructions for the development of the entire body, including the brain. These instructions are complex, and slight changes in the genes, called *mutations,* can produce drastic changes in the body. Genetic mutations can lead to serious defects in the structure and functioning of the brain. But scientists have also learned about the brain from studying such mutations. For example, scientists have discovered genetic mutations in mice that produce a condition identical to Alzheimer's disease. Scientists can use this knowledge to understand how such diseases occur in human beings, enabling the development of new treatments.

How the brain works

Scientific studies have revealed much about the workings of the human brain. These studies provide insight into how the brain: (1) senses the environment, (2) controls movement, (3) regulates bodily processes, (4) remembers and imagines events, (5) regulates emotions, (6) controls attention and consciousness, (7) makes decisions, and (8) produces language.

Sensing the environment. Various parts of the body send sensory messages to the brain in the form of nerve impulses. These messages are received and interpreted primarily in the cerebral cortex. For example, the back of the eye contains cells that detect light. These cells stimulate nerve fibers that join at the back of the eye to form the *optic nerve.* The optic nerve carries signals from the light-sensing cells to certain regions of the cerebral cortex. The cortex interprets the signals as visual images.

Cells in other parts of the body specialize in detecting pain, smell, sound, taste, temperature, and touch. Some sense blood pressure and blood chemistry. Others de-

tect the stretching and tension of muscles. All of these sensory cells send nerve impulses along nerves to the brain or spinal cord. Through the nerves, the brain receives an enormous amount of information about environment inside and outside the body.

Within the brain, sensory information flows from neuron to neuron along multiple pathways. Some of these pathways go to the brain stem. There, sensory information is used to adjust basic functions, such as heart rate, breathing, and posture. Other neuron pathways go to the cerebellum, which helps to fine-tune adjustments made by the brain stem. Many pathways carry sensory information to the cerebrum, where it is used to control more complex behaviors.

Messages related to bodily sensations, such as touch and temperature, are received and interpreted in an area of the cerebrum called the *somatosensory (SOH muh tuh SEHN suhr ee) cortex.* The somatosensory cortex lies near the front of the parietal lobe in each hemisphere. Different areas of the cortex process information from different parts of the body, with information from neighboring body parts usually processed in neighboring areas of the cortex. Certain parts of the body have more sensory cells than other areas. More neurons are required to process information from these sensitive parts. For example, about half of the neurons in the somatosensory cortex process sensory impulses from the hands and face. These sensitive areas have the highest density of touch sensors.

The same sensory information can follow multiple neuron pathways within the cerebrum, each dedicated to a different purpose. Neuroscientists learned this fact by studying patients who suffered brain damage. Upon looking at a photograph of an object, for example, some brain-damaged patients can tell a person where the object is, but they cannot tell the person what the object is. This fact suggests that the two tasks involve different neuron pathways.

Even though various types of sensory information are processed in different parts of the cerebrum, we experience the world as a unified whole. Neuroscientists have wondered how this is possible. Most of them think that connections between neurons in different areas of the cerebrum coordinate patterns of nerve impulses in the brain. The connections enable the cerebrum to combine the impulses into a unified perception of the environment. Support for this view comes from studies of patients who have had their *corpus callosum (KAWR puhs kuh LOH suhm)* cut for medical reasons. The corpus callosum is a large bundle of nerve fibers that connects the cerebral hemispheres. Patients who have had theirs cut sometimes act as if they had two separate minds. For example, a patient's hands—each of which is controlled by a different hemisphere—might struggle against each other.

Controlling movement. Some reflex actions do not involve the brain. If a person touches a hot stove, for example, pain impulses flash to the spinal cord. The spinal cord immediately sends back a message to withdraw the hand. However, the brain also receives information about such pain and plays a major role in controlling our conscious movements.

Certain neurons in the brain stem and spinal cord send command signals to muscles. These neurons are

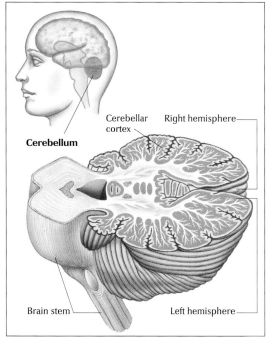

Cerebellar cortex   Right hemisphere

Cerebellum

Brain stem   Left hemisphere

WORLD BOOK diagram by Colin Bidgood and Barbara Cousins

The cerebellum is at the back of the brain, partly covered by the overlying cerebrum. The cerebellum plays a major role in controlling movements. Its outer portion, called the *cerebellar cortex,* is even more highly folded than the cerebral cortex.

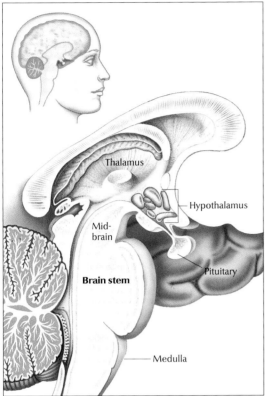

Thalamus

Hypothalamus

Mid-
brain

Pituitary

Brain stem

Medulla

WORLD BOOK diagram by Colin Bidgood and Barbara Cousins

The brain stem links the brain's largest section, the *cerebrum,* with the spinal cord. The brain stem's lower portion is called the *medulla.* Its upper portion forms the *midbrain.* Above the brain stem are the *thalamus* and *hypothalamus,* parts of the cerebrum.

called *motor neurons.* Motor neurons receive commands from multiple sources in the brain. One source is a region of the cerebral cortex called the *motor cortex.* The motor cortex lies at the rear of the frontal lobe, just in front of the somatosensory cortex. The motor cortex controls mainly the muscles of the arms, legs, mouth, and face. Damage to the motor cortex can interfere with the ability to handle objects or talk. However, some lost abilities may return as other brain regions take over for damaged areas.

Neurons in the motor cortex work with brain stem neurons to control some involuntary movements, such as quick eye or head movements. They also help control the muscles of the hips and back, which play a role in maintaining posture and balance. The motions controlled by the cerebral cortex are tightly coordinated with those controlled by the brain stem.

When the neuron pathways from the brain to the spinal cord are damaged, most voluntary movements of the body cease. Movements of the eyes and face, however, are generally not affected by spinal cord damage. Their motor neurons originate in the brain stem rather than the spinal cord. Some simple reflexes also remain.

Regulating body processes. The brain controls not only visible movements but also movements deep inside the body. Such movements include the beating of the heart, the expansion or tightening of blood vessels,

and the contraction of muscles in the intestines. In addition, the brain controls the secretion of hormones, tears, sweat, saliva, and digestive juices. All of these functions are vital for survival and good health, but they all happen without much awareness or voluntary control.

Many basic body processes are coordinated by a small structure called the *hypothalamus (HY puh THAL uh muhs).* The hypothalamus is one of the smallest regions within the cerebrum, but it helps regulate many of the most vital body functions. The hypothalamus helps control the *autonomic nervous system,* which regulates such automatic functions as breathing, blood pressure, heartbeat, hunger, thirst, urination, and sexual urges. The hypothalamus also controls the pituitary gland, the so-called "master gland" of the *endocrine* (hormone-producing) system.

The hypothalamus helps maintain a stable internal environment by receiving information about the condition of the body and sending out commands. For example, certain neurons detect changes in the level of water in the body's tissues. They relay this information to the hypothalamus. The hypothalamus helps create the sensation of thirst and causes the person to look for something to drink. Other neurons in the hypothalamus sense when the blood is running low on nutrients. These neurons send out commands that promote eating and the search for food. Still other neurons sense when the stomach is full and signal when it is time to stop eating.

The brain responds to the body's changing needs during increased activity and in emergencies. At these times, it can send signals to speed up the heartbeat, increase blood pressure, send additional blood to the muscles, and enlarge the pupils of the eyes to take in more light. This *fight-or-flight response* prepares an individual to either attack or run away. After the need has passed, other brain regions instruct heart rate, breathing, and blood flow to return to normal.

Memory and imagination. Neuroscientists once thought that different brain regions controlled memory, imagination, and experience. But they now understand that these processes involve overlapping brain regions.

One brain structure important to the formation of memories is the *hippocampus,* part of the cerebrum. Many neuroscientists believe that memory formation involves the neuron pathways from various parts of the cerebral cortex that connect to the hippocampus. Scientists think the pathways create small networks of neurons called *cell assemblies,* which store memories.

When a new memory is triggered, a cell assembly in the hippocampus is activated along with corresponding neurons elsewhere in the cerebral cortex. When a memory has been triggered repeatedly, the activated neurons in the cerebral cortex gradually become linked to one another, changing the original cell assembly. Eventually, the memory will become independent of the hippocampus and will be stored primarily in other areas of the cerebral cortex. When part of a cell assembly is stimulated, it can cause the entire assembly to become active. Thus, a sensory signal, such as a familiar smell, can trigger a whole related memory.

People who suffer damage to the hippocampus develop *anterograde amnesia,* the inability to form new long-term memories. But these people retain at least some old memories. People with Alzheimer's disease—which

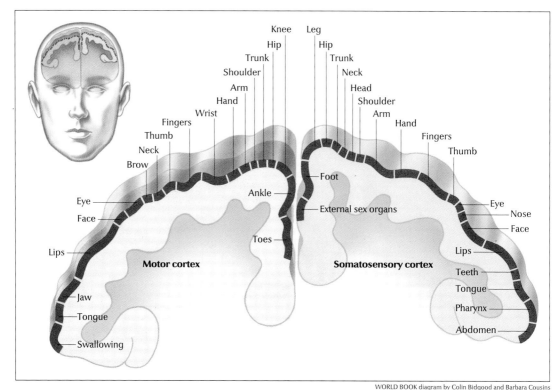

WORLD BOOK diagram by Colin Bidgood and Barbara Cousins

Regions of the motor and somatosensory cortexes are linked to specific parts of the body. The motor cortex is involved in the control of movement. Its largest areas correspond to the parts of the body that make the most complex voluntary movements. The somatosensory cortex receives sensory information from the body. Its largest areas correspond to the most sensitive body parts.

destroys the neurons of the hippocampus and the cerebral cortex—tend to lose their old memories. This type of loss is called *retrograde amnesia*. Interestingly, the oldest memories are usually the last ones to be lost.

Neuroscientists have found that remembering an event activates many of the same regions of the cerebral cortex that were active when the event occurred. In addition, simply imagining an action or event also activates many of the same brain regions that would be active if it actually happened.

Even dreaming can activate most of the same brain regions that are activated by real waking experience. When the dream includes body movements, however, the neuron pathways that send commands to the muscles are blocked. This prevents people from harming themselves by moving while dreaming.

Regulating emotions. Strong emotions involve both physical responses and our understanding of what caused them. For example, a person's heartbeat may increase in response to either joy or fear. Memories of recent events help the brain determine which emotion is being experienced.

Fear is a strong emotion that causes most animals to run, attack, or hold completely still. The body's reaction to fear is largely controlled by a part of the brain called the *amygdala (uh MIHG duh luh)*. The amygdala sits deep within the temporal lobe. When a rat smells a cat, for example, the smell activates a pathway from the nose to the amygdala, and from there to the hypothalamus.

The hypothalamus triggers the fight-or-flight response. Many fears are learned through bad experiences. Learned fears involve not only the amygdala but also brain regions such as the hippocampus.

The emotion of happiness includes the release of certain chemicals into the blood. These chemicals, called *endorphins,* are carried to the brain. Endorphins are chemically similar to opioid drugs, such as morphine or heroin. Neuroscientists do not know exactly how endorphins work. But scientists have observed that a small region of the midbrain called the *ventral tegmental area,* along with a small region of the forebrain called the *nucleus accumbens* are sensitive to opioids. In laboratory experiments with animals, the direct application of opioids to these areas causes the animals to act happy. Natural happiness also activates the same regions.

In addition to fear and happiness, people may feel anger, surprise, disgust, or more complex emotions. People can also suppress emotions. The ability to control emotional behavior is regulated by neuron pathways that originate in the *prefrontal cortex,* a part of the frontal lobe. These pathways connect to the amygdala. When the associated part of the prefrontal cortex is damaged, patients become more likely to have emotional outbursts. They may also become depressed because they cannot control their unpleasant feelings.

Attention and consciousness. The concepts of attention, awareness, and consciousness are difficult to define. This fact makes it difficult to study the brain mechanisms behind these conditions. However, neuroscientists have observed certain changes in brain activity that correlate with falling asleep, dreaming, waking up, or becoming unusually alert. Many of these changes in activity are caused by groups of cells in the brain stem. One region of the brain stem that plays an important role in attention and consciousness is the *locus ceruleus (LOH kuhs sih ROO lee uhs)*. The neurons in this location are relatively inactive during deep sleep and active while a person is awake. When something unexpected grabs your attention, neurons in the locus ceruleus generate a sudden burst of signals. This burst of activity helps the brain's sensory pathways to process information more efficiently.

When people focus their attention on a specific location in space, they often move their head and eyes so that they are looking directly at the location. People also sometimes direct their attention to a particular region of space without moving their head or eyes, called *covert attention*. Neuroscientists have found that covert attention involves some of the same neuron pathways as head and eye movement.

Neuroscientists have learned much about the mechanisms of attention from studies of certain patients. These patients suffer damage to the lower part of the right parietal lobe. Such patients often exhibit *hemispatial neglect*—that is, they tend to ignore whatever happens to be on their left side. Damage to the left side of the brain is sometimes associated with neglect of the right side of the body. This, however, is less common.

People often direct their attention to particular objects unconsciously. For example, when you take a walk down a familiar path, your brain pays attention to obstacles even though your conscious mind may be preoccupied with different thoughts. Indeed, only a small fraction of what goes on in the brain ever reaches consciousness. Neuroscientists know almost nothing about what causes some brain processes to erupt into consciousness while other processes remain hidden.

One of the most remarkable aspects of consciousness is the ability to be aware of oneself. People develop such self-awareness during the first two or three years of life. There is evidence that some apes also have self-awareness. Chimpanzees, for example, can recognize themselves in a mirror. But monkeys cannot. Other intelligent animals, including dolphins and elephants, show some signs of self-awareness. However, the brain mechanisms behind self-awareness remain almost entirely unknown because they are almost impossible to study in animals.

Making decisions. People make many different kinds of decisions, both conscious and unconscious. One simple form of decision involves choosing between opposite courses of action. When faced with an unfamiliar object, for example, a person might decide to approach it or move away from it. Within the brain, this kind of decision is usually handled by having the pathway involved in one action *inhibit* (block) the pathway for the other action, or vice versa. This kind of *reciprocal inhibition* keeps conflicting pathways from becoming active at the same time.

A region of the brain called the *striatum (stry AY tuhm)* appears to play a major role in decision making. The striatum is deep within the cerebrum. It receives impulses from many different regions of the brain. It sends impulses to areas in the brain stem and cerebrum that control movements. The striatum can use information from the rest of the brain to influence which movements should take place. It normally inhibits activity in its target regions, but it can temporarily cancel the inhibition. When the inhibition is removed, neurons in the motor cortex or brain stem send out motor commands. Thus, the striatum effectively decides which movements are allowed and which remain inhibited.

The striatum normally helps select the most appropriate motor commands for action. But research shows what happens when the striatum fails to work properly. For example, in people with Parkinson disease, damage to a nearby part of the brain causes the striatum to inhibit the motor control regions too much. Motor movements are suppressed, and the patient finds it difficult to initiate any new movements. In contrast, people with Huntington's disease have a weakened striatum that cannot inhibit the motor control regions effectively. These

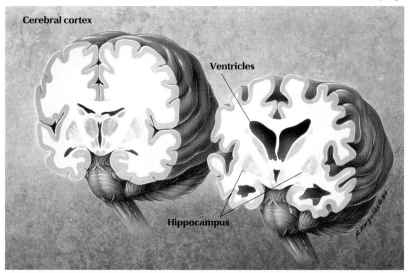

Cerebral cortex

Ventricles

Hippocampus

Alzheimer's disease causes shrinking in the brain. This illustration shows a normal human brain, *left*, next to the brain of a person with advanced Alzheimer's disease, *right*. Both brains are shown in cross section. Alzheimer's disease destroys neurons in areas of the brain called the *hippocampus* and the *cerebral cortex*. As a result, large areas of the brain shrink and fluid-filled *ventricles* (cavities) in the brain grow larger.

patients tend to perform inappropriate movements uncontrollably.

Neuroscientists believe that some neurons in the striatum are modified during learning. Most scientists agree that damage to the striatum interferes with the ability to learn new habits or skills. This kind of learning may seem to have little to do with making decisions. But it can be seen as the brain learning to decide what actions are appropriate.

More complicated decisions involve the prefrontal cortex. The prefrontal cortex is significantly larger in human beings than in chimpanzees and other intelligent animals. In the 1940's and 1950's, thousands of patients had their prefrontal cortex surgically cut as a therapeutic procedure for certain mental illnesses. This procedure, called a *prefrontal lobotomy,* may have helped a few patients, but it seriously damaged the mind of many other patients. In particular, it destroyed the patients' ability to make sound decisions and keep to long-term plans.

Language requires an enormous number of special abilities, all of which are controlled by the brain. Human speech requires the ability to perform intricate movements of the lips, tongue, and vocal cords. It also requires the ability to link words to the concepts or objects that they represent. In addition, people must be able to understand what others are saying.

Human language involves several different regions of the brain. In the late 1800's, scientists observed that damage to particular parts of the brain caused the same language disabilities in most patients. Damage to the left frontal lobe, in *Broca's area,* destroyed the ability to produce fluent speech. Damage to the upper back region of the temporal lobe, in *Wernicke's area,* caused difficulty understanding language. These areas are named for the French surgeon Pierre Paul Broca and the German neurologist Carl Wernicke. Broca's and Wernicke's areas play crucial roles in human language. But scientists have also found both areas in monkeys. Scientists do not fully understand the function of these areas in monkeys, but the regions seem to be activated by the vocalizations of other monkeys.

Neuroscientists have discovered other areas of the cerebral cortex that also contribute to language. These areas were discovered in experiments in which surgeons electrically stimulated different brain regions. Stimulating certain parts of the cerebral cortex disrupted speech in the patients. Brain imaging studies have shown that speaking or listening activates different areas of the cerebral cortex and some regions outside the cortex.

For most people, the left cerebral hemisphere is more important for controlling language than the right hemisphere. However, all the areas that control language in the left hemisphere also exist in the right hemisphere. Neuroscientists have observed that patients with damage in the language areas of the right hemisphere often sound robotlike and that their speech lacks the rhythm of normal human speech. This fact suggests that although the hemispheres are specialized for different language functions, they work together to produce speech.

How neurons work

All the brain's functions rely on the transmission of nerve impulses by neurons. A neuron consists of a round cell body with slender extensions called *dendrites* branching out from it. The dendrites grow narrower the farther they extend from the cell body. Most neurons also have a thin, tubelike axon. The axon may have a myelin coating or no coating at all. The axon extends far beyond the cell body. There, it branches and comes into contact with the dendrites of other neurons, forming synapses. A single neuron may form synapses with thousands of other nerve cells.

Action potentials. Neurons differ from other cells in their ability to transmit nerve impulses. A nerve impulse travels along a neuron as an electrical signal called an *action potential.*

Neurons generate action potentials by controlling the movement of *ions* (electrically charged particles) across their cell membranes. The ions move in and out of the neuron through pores called *ion channels.* When the neuron is at rest, the membrane maintains a low concentration of positively charged ions inside the neuron. When stimulated, the ion channels allow more positive ions to enter the neuron, which becomes electrically excited. Once the excitement reaches a certain level, more ion channels open and an action potential is generated. The action potential travels down the axon to a synapse.

Synapses. The action potential cannot be transmitted

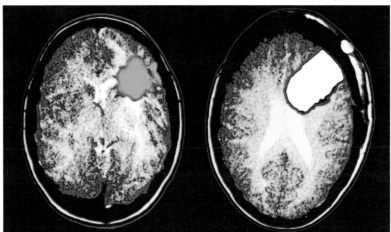

A scan of the brain using an X-ray technique called *computed tomography* (CT) can reveal brain tumors and other abnormalities. In the CT scan on the left, a patient's brain tumor appears as a green mass. A second CT scan, *right,* shows the brain after surgery. The tumor has been removed and the remaining space is filled with *cerebrospinal fluid,* a protective liquid produced by the body.

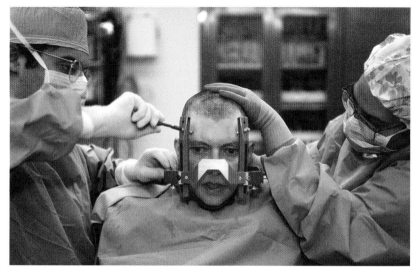

Brain surgery can be performed while the patient is awake because the brain has no pain receptors. In this photograph, doctors prepare a patient for brain surgery by securing her head in a frame.

© Joe McNally, Getty Images

electrically across the *synaptic gap,* the tiny space between the axon of one neuron and the dendrite of another. Instead, chemicals called *neurotransmitters* carry the impulse between neurons. When the action potential reaches the end of the axon, it triggers the release of neurotransmitter molecules from the cell. The molecules cross the synaptic gap to the dendrite of the next neuron. There, they attach themselves to receptor molecules on the dendrite, causing ion channels to open. If enough channels open, the second neuron will become electrically excited, generating its own action potential. In this manner, nerve impulses are transmitted from neuron to neuron. For more details about this process, see **Nervous system** (How neurons carry impulses).

Synapses vary in how efficiently they transmit impulses between neurons. Synapses that are more active tend to become stronger and transmit more reliably. Synapses that are inactive become weaker. Neuroscientists have also shown that when two neurons fire electrical impulses at the same time, the synapses that connect those neurons become stronger. This effect is called *Hebbian synaptic plasticity.* It is named for the Canadian neuroscientist Donald Hebb, who first described it in 1949. Neuroscientists believe Hebbian synaptic plasticity underlies a variety of complex processes in the brain, including the formation of memories.

Neurotransmitters. The human brain produces many kinds of chemicals that are used as neurotransmitters. The most common ones include acetylcholine, dopamine, norepinephrine, and serotonin. Neurotransmitters are not distributed evenly throughout the brain. Many are found exclusively or primarily in specific areas. For example, the bodies of neurons that contain dopamine are in the brain stem. The axons of these cells reach into other areas, including the frontal lobes of the cerebrum. This arrangement forms dopamine pathways that function in the regulation of emotions and in the control of complex movements.

Disorders of the brain

Injuries, diseases, and inherited disorders can damage the brain. However, the seriousness of brain damage depends chiefly on the area of the brain involved rather than on the cause of the damage. Disorders that destroy brain cells are especially serious because the body cannot replace the lost cells. In some cases, however, undamaged areas of the brain may eventually take over some functions formerly carried out by the damaged areas.

Modern instruments and techniques enable physicians to diagnose brain disorders earlier and more accurately than in the past. For example, an instrument called an *electroencephalograph* (EEG) measures the patterns of electrical activity produced by the brain. Differences from normal EEG patterns may indicate damage to the brain and help locate the area of the damage.

Another important technique is computed tomography (CT). It involves X-raying the brain in detail from many angles. A computer then analyzes the X-ray data and constructs a cross-sectional image of the brain on a TV screen. CT scans are especially useful for identifying cases of bleeding within the skull, which may cause headaches, nausea, and brain damage. Magnetic resonance imaging (MRI) uses magnetic fields and radio waves to produce three-dimensional images of the brain's internal structure. The images produced by MRI are more detailed than those obtained from CT scans. They are most often used to check for brain tumors.

Injuries are a leading cause of brain damage among people under 50 years of age. A blow to the head may cause temporary unconsciousness. People may recover from such blows (also known as *concussions)* without permanent damage. But a medical doctor should be consulted, especially if the injured person becomes nauseated or remains confused for more than one minute after the blow. Neuroscientists now understand that repeated blows to the head, as occur in some sports, may cause long-term brain damage and depression.

Stroke is the most common serious disorder of the brain. A stroke occurs when the blood supply to part of the brain is cut off. Nerve cells in the affected areas die, and the victim may lose the ability to carry out functions controlled by those areas. Many stroke victims suffer paralysis on one side of the body. Other symptoms in-

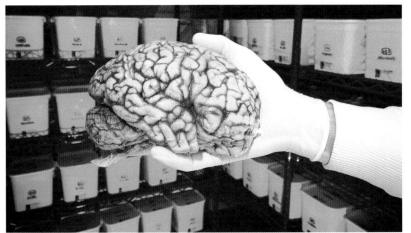

Studies of human brains removed from dead bodies have revealed much useful information. In this photograph, a researcher handles a brain kept in a facility called a *brain bank*. The bank preserves hundreds of donated brains from people with brain diseases and disorders, such as Alzheimer's disease and Parkinson disease. The brain bank also stores samples of normal brains for comparison.

© Joe McNally, Getty Images

clude difficulty in speaking or in understanding language. Most strokes result from damage to the blood vessels caused by *hypertension* (high blood pressure) or *arteriosclerosis* (hardening of the arteries). Some victims of massive strokes die, but many other stroke victims survive and recover at least partially.

Tumors are abnormal growths that can cause severe brain damage. The effects of a tumor depend on its size and location. A tumor may destroy brain cells in the area surrounding it. As the tumor grows, it also creates pressure, which may damage other areas of the brain or interfere with their normal function. Symptoms of a tumor include headache, seizures, unusual sleepiness, a change in personality, or disturbances in sense perception or speech.

Surgery cures some tumors. For cancerous tumors, physicians may combine surgery with drugs or radiation. One type of radiation, called *stereotactic radiosurgery*, is sometimes used as an alternative to traditional surgery. In stereotactic radiosurgery, doctors use computers and a CT scan or MRI to produce a three-dimensional image of the brain. Beams of radiation are then focused precisely on the target, which may be a tumor or a blood-vessel malformation. The individual beams are either too brief or too weak to harm areas of the brain in the path of the radiation. But their combined effect will destroy the target. These procedures are quick and painless and allow patients to resume moderate activity the same day.

Infectious diseases. A number of diseases caused by bacteria or viruses can damage the brain. The most common of these infectious diseases are encephalitis and meningitis, either of which may be caused by bacteria or viruses. Encephalitis is an inflammation of the brain. Meningitis is an inflammation of the meninges, the membranes that cover the brain and spinal cord. A virus disease called *poliomyelitis* attacks the brain and spinal cord. Vaccines to prevent polio were developed in the 1950's.

Genetic disorders. Our genes carry instructions for the development of our entire bodies, including the brain. These instructions are extremely complex, and so errors occasionally occur. These errors can lead to serious defects in the structure and functioning of the brain.

Myths about the human brain

Myth: Human beings only use about 10 percent of their brains. Neuroscientists are not certain how this common myth originated. However, studies have demonstrated that all areas of the brain are active, although not all of the time.

Myth: The left side of the brain is logical, while the right side is creative. In most people, brain regions responsible for language are in the left cerebral hemisphere, while the right cerebral hemisphere controls other tasks, such as spatial perception. However, neuroscientists do not think that logical thinking or creative ability can be neatly assigned to one hemisphere or the other.

Myth: The brain is a collection of centers that function independently. Damage to a specific brain region often has a specific behavioral effect, and brain imaging often shows activity in just one or two brain regions. However, all brain regions work with other regions of the brain to accomplish their functions.

Myth: Exposing babies to the music of Mozart will make them smarter. Research studies in the 1990's suggested that listening to music by the Austrian composer Wolfgang Amadeus Mozart improved scores on intelligence tests. Later studies have not confirmed this finding. However, experts agree that a stimulating environment encourages brain development in babies.

Myth: The brain stores highly detailed memories that can be played back in full. Research studies from the 1950's suggested that electrical stimulation of the cerebral cortex can trigger detailed memories. But later studies suggested that these *flashbacks* were not accurate memories—they were only mental images that seemed like memories.

Some infants have mental retardation at birth because genetic errors caused the brain to develop improperly during the mother's pregnancy. In Down syndrome, for example, an extra *chromosome* is present. Chromosomes are structures in the cell nucleus that contain the genes. The extra chromosome causes mental retardation as well as physical defects. Another disorder that causes mental retardation is *fragile X syndrome*. This disorder results from an abnormality on the X chromosome, one of the chromosomes that determine a person's sex.

Some children suffer severe brain damage after birth because of an inherited deficiency of an enzyme that the body needs to use foods properly. For example, a child who has *phenylketonuria* (PKU) lacks an enzyme needed to convert a certain *amino acid* (one of the building blocks of protein) into a form the body can use. This amino acid, *phenylalanine,* accumulates in the blood and damages developing brain tissues. A diet low in phenylalanine can prevent brain damage in people who have PKU.

Some genetic errors damage the brain only later in life. Huntington's disease, for example, usually strikes during middle age. The disease causes some areas of the cerebrum to wither away. Involuntary jerky movements are the main early symptoms of Huntington's disease. However, the disease eventually leads to incurable mental disintegration.

Scientists believe that genetic factors play an important role in most cases of Alzheimer's disease. This disease most commonly strikes after age 60. It is characterized by an increasingly severe loss of memory and other mental abilities. Most people with Alzheimer's disease eventually cannot care for themselves and become bedridden.

Heredity also plays a role in some types of mental illness. Many children of schizophrenics apparently inherit a tendency to develop schizophrenia. Studies have also revealed an inherited tendency to develop bipolar disorder. These tendencies may involve inherited defects in brain chemistry. Researchers continue to study these tendencies and how they interact with environmental conditions to produce mental illness.

Other brain disorders include (1) epilepsy, (2) multiple sclerosis (MS), (3) cerebral palsy, and (4) Parkinson disease.

Epilepsy. Victims of epilepsy suffer attacks called *seizures.* The seizures occur when many nerve cells in one area of the brain release abnormal bursts of impulses that tend to spread to other brain regions. A seizure may cause temporary uncontrolled muscle movements or unconsciousness. Defects in genes cause some cases of epilepsy, but the cause of most cases is not known. Physicians treat epilepsy with drugs that reduce the number of seizures or prevent them entirely.

Multiple sclerosis develops when axons in parts of the brain and spinal cord lose their myelin sheaths. As a result, the axons cannot carry nerve impulses properly. Symptoms vary depending on what brain areas are affected, but they may include double vision, loss of balance, and weakness in an arm or leg. A major cause of multiple sclerosis is that the body's own immune system attacks the myelin sheaths. No cure is yet known. Drugs can relieve some of the symptoms. Some of these drugs help slow the loss of myelin.

Cerebral palsy is a form of brain damage that develops before, during, or soon after birth. There are several types of cerebral palsy, all of which involve a loss of control over muscle movement. Mental retardation, seizures, and physical deformities may also be a part of cerebral palsy. The cause or causes of cerebral palsy remain unclear, but premature babies are especially likely to develop this defect.

Parkinson disease is characterized by slowness of movement, muscle rigidity, and trembling. It may also include problems with thinking, learning, memory, and mood. These conditions result mainly from the destruction of specific nerve pathways that use dopamine as a transmitter. Treatment with the drug L-dopa replaces the missing dopamine and so can relieve the symptoms of Parkinson disease, though it cannot cure the illness. Researchers continue to explore the possibility of replacing Parkinson patients' lost dopamine-producing cells with transplanted cells from other sources.

The brain in other animals

Many aspects of neuron structure and function are nearly identical for almost all animals. But the number of neurons and their arrangement varies widely. Most *invertebrates* (animals without backbones) do not have a well-developed brain. All *vertebrates* (animals with backbones) have a complex brain. The human brain is the most complex of all.

WORLD BOOK illustration by Barbara Cousins

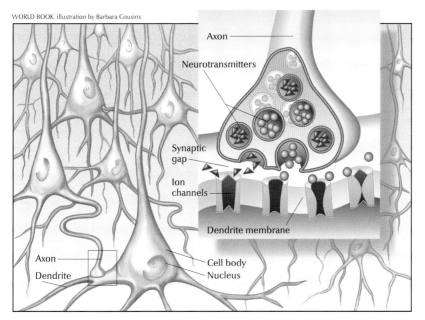

Axon

Neurotransmitters

Synaptic gap

Ion channels

Dendrite membrane

Axon

Dendrite

Cell body

Nucleus

Neurons, *background,* transmit nerve impulses within the brain. An impulse travels as an electrical signal down the *axon* to a connection called a *synapse.* At the synapse, *inset,* the neuron releases chemicals called *neurotransmitters.* The neurotransmitters cross the *synaptic gap* to reach the *dendrite* of the next neuron. There, they open *ion channels,* generating a new electrical signal. In this way, nerve impulses are passed from one neuron to the next.

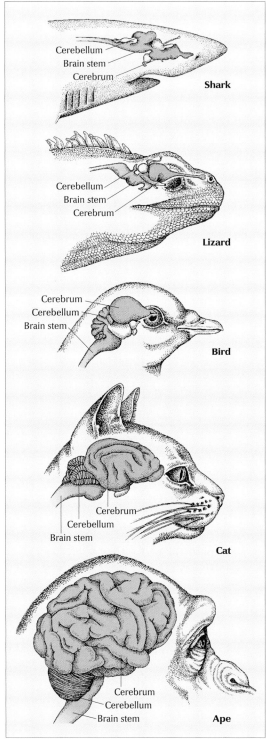

Cerebellum
Brain stem
Cerebrum
Shark

Cerebellum
Brain stem
Cerebrum
Lizard

Cerebrum
Cerebellum
Brain stem
Bird

Cerebrum
Cerebellum
Brain stem
Cat

Cerebrum
Cerebellum
Brain stem
Ape

WORLD BOOK illustrations by Patricia J. Wynne

Brains of some vertebrates show the progression of brain development as animals evolved over millions of years. Sharks and other fish have a relatively simple brain with a small, smooth cerebrum. The cerebrum is larger but still quite smooth in reptiles and birds. The most advanced mammals, such as cats and apes, have a large, wrinkled cerebrum with billions of neurons.

Invertebrates often lack a brain entirely. For example, jellyfish have a network of neurons distributed over the body, but these creatures lack a distinct brain. Other invertebrates have large clusters of neurons, called *ganglia,* that coordinate the activities of the body. These clusters can be considered a kind of brain.

Some invertebrates have brains that are surprisingly large in comparison to body size. The brain of a honey bee, for example, includes about 1 million neurons.

The octopus has the largest and most complex brain of any invertebrate. The neurons in the brain of an octopus may number up to about 300 million. The neurons are arranged differently from the neurons in a vertebrate brain, but they perform similar functions. For example, the optic lobe of an octopus's brain processes information from its eyes. Octopuses are also among the most intelligent invertebrates. In laboratory studies, they quickly learn to solve simple puzzles.

Among vertebrates, the brain has a cerebrum, cerebellum, and brain stem. The brain stem and the cerebellum are often similar in the different groups of vertebrates, although they may vary greatly in size. The cerebrum, however, varies enormously in size and structure among different groups of vertebrates. In mammals, for example, most of the cerebrum develops into a multilayered cerebral cortex. In reptiles and birds, no such cortex is found. Instead, the cerebrum of reptiles and birds contains large clusters of neurons that are not arranged in distinct layers. In more ancient groups of vertebrates, such as sharks and amphibians, the cerebrum usually makes up only a small part of the brain.

Among vertebrates, brains vary enormously in overall size. The brains of small fish can weigh a tiny fraction of an ounce. The brain of a blue whale, the largest animal, weighs a million times as much, about 15 pounds (7 kilograms). Brain size generally increases with body size, so larger animals tend to have larger brains. Larger-brained animals also tend to be more intelligent and have more complex behaviors. However, a large animal with a large brain is not necessarily more intelligent than a smaller animal with a smaller brain.

Different parts of the brain can vary in proportion among vertebrates. For example, squirrels and rats are both mammals and have brains of roughly equal size. But the main structures of the brain stem responsible for vision are about 10 times larger in squirrels than in rats. Such differences tend to reflect an animal's behavioral abilities and lifestyle. Squirrels, for example, are active during daylight and rely heavily on eyesight. Rats, on the other hand, are mainly active at night and tend to rely more on smell.

Some vertebrates have brains that are particularly large for their body size. These include several highly intelligent animals, such as whales, dolphins, chimpanzees, and human beings. Scientists have observed that many large-brained animals, including human beings, are highly social. These animals may need large brains to master complex social relationships. However, not all animals with large brains are social. For example, many species of owls have large brains compared to the size of their bodies. But owls do not have the complex social behaviors seen in other birds. Biologists believe that every species has evolved the kind and size of brain that suits its unique needs.   Georg F. Striedter

Emotion, for most people, is a feeling, such as happiness, anger, or fear, that is triggered by certain events or thoughts. Emotions can cause changes in the body or behavior without personal effort or control. An emotion can be pleasant or unpleasant. People often seek out such pleasant emotions as love and happiness. They often try to avoid feeling unpleasant emotions, such as fear and grief. These experiences lead people to believe that emotions are *innate* (inborn) responses.

However, not all scientists believe in the common sense view that emotions are automatic responses to a trigger, or that a certain class of emotions, such as fear, anger, sadness, happiness, and disgust, are innate. Through the ages, philosophers, scientists, and authors have debated the nature of emotion. Today, scientists have not agreed on a formal definition that adequately distinguishes the variety of emotions seen in human beings and other animals. They have, however, developed three approaches to explaining how emotions occur. These are: (1) the basic emotion approach, (2) the appraisal approach, and (3) the constructivist approach. All three approaches have some scientific evidence to support them.

The basic emotion approach to emotion is similar to most people's understanding of emotion. It began with Charles Darwin, the British scientist who developed the theory of natural selection, who later wrote *The Expression of the Emotions in Man and Animals* (1872). In this book, Darwin proposed that all mammals express internal mental states in a similar way, through body postures and facial behaviors, that he called *expressions.* Darwin considered human emotions to be little more than remaining traces of our evolutionary past.

Other psychologists expanded on Darwin's ideas. They described emotions as complex biological reflexes that are automatically triggered by events in the environment. Scientists who believe that emotions are biologically basic do not agree on how many emotions there are or what they are called. But, most agree that there are at least five basic emotions: (1) happiness, (2) anger, (3) sadness, (4) fear, and (5) disgust. They believe that each emotion issues from specific nerve networks in the brain. Thus, people are supposed to experience the same bodily sensations with a particular emotion, regardless of the situation that triggers it.

The appraisal approach to the understanding of emotions started with the work of the American psychologist David Irons in the 1890's. It was further developed by another American psychologist, Magda Arnold, in her landmark book *Emotion and Personality* (1960). According to this approach, emotions are not simply triggered by an event. Instead, they result from a person's meaningful interpretation, or *appraisal,* of an event or situation.

In some versions of the appraisal approach, an event triggers a *meaning analysis* (a series of appraisals) in the person's mind. The combination of these appraisals results in an emotional experience that can be unique to that person and situation. Generally, different combinations of appraisals produce a variety of different degrees of anger, sadness, fear, and other emotions. In other versions of this approach, appraisals merely describe the situations in which emotions take place. For example, anger may occur when people feel that their goals are being blocked or their standards are being violated.

The constructivist approach to understanding

emotion began when the American psychologist William James published his article "What Is an Emotion?" in 1884. James, along with the Danish physiologist Carl Lange, believed that emotions were physical states that are perceived or understood as telling a person something meaningful about the world. In 1962, the American psychologists Stanley Schachter and Jerome Singer proposed a popular constructionist view, where emotions are produced by two factors: (1) physical changes in a person's body and (2) the reason the person gives for those changes. For example, both pleasant and unpleasant events can trigger a person's heartbeat to increase. But memories and experience help the brain determine whether the person is experiencing fear or joy. Other scholars have since developed more complex constructivist theories of emotion.

Constructivist theories maintain that emotions are not basic elements in the mind. Instead, the mind constructs emotions by combining more basic psychological processes. This approach helps explain how the same emotion can be felt differently over time, among different people, and among different cultures.

Emotion and the brain. Research on people with brain injuries once suggested that specific locations in the brain control particular emotions, such as fear and disgust. But brain imaging studies suggest that there are no regions of the brain that are specific to emotion. Nerve connections in the brain that are involved in memory, thought, and perception, along with those that represent a person's physical state, are all routinely active when a person experiences an emotion.

Lisa Feldman Barrett

Extraterrestrial intelligence, EHKS *truh tuh REHS tree uhl,* is life originating beyond Earth that has such abilities as thinking and learning. Space probes have discovered no life—let alone intelligent life—on the other planets or the moons of our solar system. But many scientists think that intelligent life could exist on worlds around other stars. Beings that originate beyond Earth are often referred to as *extraterrestrials* or simply *aliens.*

Scientists think that intelligent life may exist on other worlds because the universe contains a vast number of stars and planets. Our own galaxy, the Milky Way, has hundreds of billions of stars. Many scientists think that from 10 percent to more than 50 percent of these stars may have planets, and so our galaxy alone could contain more than a trillion planets. Furthermore, the universe has more than 100 billion galaxies. Scientists expect that many planets do not have the conditions—such as liquid water—necessary to support life as we know it. But if even a tiny fraction of planets have the right conditions, the Milky Way still might contain millions of worlds with life, and perhaps some with intelligent life.

One effort to find extraterrestrial intelligence is called SETI, which stands for Search for Extraterrestrial Intelligence. SETI research involves looking in the vicinity of other stars for signals sent by extraterrestrials in the form of light or radio waves. In 1960, the American astronomer Frank Drake conducted the first SETI experiment. He used a radio telescope to try to detect signals coming from around two relatively nearby stars. During the 1990's and early 2000's, scientists used radio telescopes to hunt for signals coming from many hundreds of stars. Also in the 2000's, researchers began building the Allen Telescope Array in California, which was designed to conduct SETI studies of about 1 million stars.

In the late 1990's, astronomers also began searching for signals in the form of brief, bright flashes of visible light. Scientists think that an extraterrestrial intelligence might produce such flashes with powerful lasers. The flashes could briefly outshine the star near which they originate, but might last only billionths of a second or less. Natural sources are not known to produce such flashes. Astronomers have used visible-light telescopes and electronic equipment to try to detect such events.

Many people wonder whether intelligent extraterrestrial life could have come to Earth. Each year, thousands of people report seeing unidentified flying objects (UFO's). Some people believe that such objects could be spacecraft from other worlds. But scientists who study UFO reports have found that most sightings can be explained as ordinary things, such as airplanes or balloons, or as natural astronomical objects, such as meteors or bright stars. Scientists have no evidence that Earth has ever been visited by extraterrestrials. Seth Shostak

Global warming is an increase in the average temperature at Earth's surface. People often use the term *global warming* to refer specifically to the warming observed since the mid-1800's. Scientists estimate that Earth's average surface temperature rose by about 1.4 Fahrenheit degrees (0.76 Celsius degrees) from the mid-1800's to the early 2000's. Researchers have also found that most of the temperature increase occurred from the mid-1900's to the 2000's.

Natural processes have caused Earth's climate to change in the distant past. But scientists have found strong evidence that human activities have caused most of the warming observed since the mid-1900's.

Scientists predict that Earth's average surface temperature will rise an additional 2.0 to 11.5 Fahrenheit degrees (1.1 to 6.4 Celsius degrees) by 2100. They also predict that, if warming continues unchecked, rising temperatures will have a damaging impact on human society and the natural environment. For example, global warming could melt enough of the ice on land near Earth's poles to significantly raise sea level. It could also lead to more widespread droughts and raise the risk of extinction for many plant and animal species.

Researchers have developed a number of ways to limit global warming. But because the warming is a global problem, many strategies require the cooperation of a diversity of nations, each with its own interests. Nevertheless, many countries are taking action individually and by international agreement to limit future warming.

This article discusses the causes and the impact of global warming, ways to limit global warming, and government action on global warming. The final section describes how scientists study global warming.

Causes of global warming

Global surface temperatures have risen chiefly because of a process called the *greenhouse effect*. In the greenhouse effect, certain gases in the atmosphere trap heat from the sun, acting much like the glass roof and walls of a greenhouse (see **Greenhouse effect**). The heat-trapping gases are called *greenhouse gases*. They include methane (CH_4), nitrous oxide (N_2O), ozone (O_3), and a number of industrial gases. But the gas that has produced the most warming is carbon dioxide (CO_2).

Natural concentrations of greenhouse gases in the atmosphere help keep the planet warm enough to support life. Levels of greenhouse gases in the atmosphere have varied greatly at different times in Earth's history, but they held relatively stable for several thousand years before industry began to grow rapidly in the 1800's.

Since the mid-1800's, however, modern industry has caused significant increases in *emissions* (releases) of greenhouse gases. The increase in CO_2 levels comes chiefly from the burning of *fossil fuels* (coal, oil, and natural gas) to produce energy and for transportation. Fossil fuels contain carbon, and burning them creates carbon dioxide. CO_2 levels also rise due to the clearing of land. Trees and other green plants remove CO_2 from the air during *photosynthesis*—the process they use to produce their food. Thus, as land is cleared and forests are cut down, more CO_2 remains in the atmosphere.

Not all human activities contribute to global warming. Some things that people do actually have a cooling influence on Earth's surface. For example, many *aerosols* (suspensions of tiny particles) enter the atmosphere from automobile exhaust and factory smoke. The aerosols encourage the formation of clouds. Both aerosols and clouds reflect the sun's heat back into space, exerting a cooling influence on Earth's surface. But researchers estimate that overall, human activities have caused far more warming than cooling.

Scientists have also compared the influences of various human activities on Earth's climate with the influences of certain natural processes. They estimated the strength of these influences in the 2000's relative to their values in the mid-1700's, before the rapid growth of industry. They found that, in the 2000's, human activities—mainly greenhouse gas emissions—produced more than 10 times the warming influence of the only significant natural process—changes in the sun's energy output.

Impact of global warming

Researchers have linked global warming to a number of potentially damaging effects on living things and their *ecosystems*. An ecosystem consists of a community of organisms along with its physical environment. Global warming is also raising sea level. In addition, it is rapidly affecting the Arctic region. Global warming may also alter weather patterns and affect human health around the world. Scientists project that these effects will intensify and spread with further warming.

Effect on plant and animal life. Global warming affects many plants and animals by causing seasonal changes in temperature to occur at slightly different times of the year. In many parts of the world, for example, warm spring weather has come earlier in the year. As a result, events that occur in the spring—such as flowering, egg laying, migration, and the growth of new leaves—have also begun earlier for many species. For example, lilac bushes have flowered earlier in the spring across much of the United States. Butterflies have appeared earlier in the United Kingdom.

Rising temperatures have also forced many animals to move to cooler areas. In general, these animals move to

About 1940
2006
(left) Glacier National Park Archives, (right) U.S. Geological Survey, photograph by Karen Holtzer

The retreat of a mountain glacier can provide visible evidence of global warming. These photographs show two late-summer views of Grinnell Glacier in Glacier National Park, Montana. In the photo taken around 1940, *left,* Upper Grinnell Lake had only begun to form at the glacier's end. By 2006, *right,* melting ice had caused the lake to swell in size. Researchers predict that warming will melt all of the park's glaciers by 2030.

higher latitudes—that is, toward Earth's poles—or to higher elevations. For example, white storks are nesting higher in the mountains in Poland. In Australia, the large bats called *flying foxes* have migrated toward cooler conditions in the south. Scientists are particularly concerned about organisms that have difficulty spreading to new places, such as many land animals and plants.

The faster global warming occurs, the more difficult it will become for many species to adapt. Scientists project that 20 to 30 percent of known plant and animal species would likely face a higher risk of extinction if the average temperature rose more than an additional 2.7 to 4.5 Fahrenheit degrees (1.5 to 2.5 Celsius degrees).

Rise in sea level. Average sea level rose about 7 inches (17 centimeters) over the 1900's, and global warming contributed to the rise. Part of the increase occurred because water expands as it warms. Rising temperatures also melt ice on land, which then flows into the oceans. Rising sea level has already contributed to coastal flooding, erosion, and the loss of wetlands.

Researchers project that further warming could cause sea level to rise another 7 to 23 inches (18 to 59 centimeters) by 2100. However, the projections do not include possible contributions from the melting of major ice sheets in Greenland and Antarctica. Increases in the rates at which the sheets are melting could lead to a significant additional rise in sea level.

Rapid change in the Arctic. Temperatures in the Arctic have increased about twice as fast as the global average. Due to the rapid warming, the area of the Arctic covered by sea ice in the summer has dropped significantly since the late 1970's, when satellite record-keeping began. The melting of sea ice has little effect on sea level because the ice already floats on the ocean. But the loss of sea ice threatens many Arctic species, including polar bears, which hunt on the ice, and seals, which give birth on it.

Harm to ocean life. Warming seas have damaged marine ecosystems, particularly coral reefs. High ocean temperatures can cause *coral bleaching.* In this process, corals lose the colorful algae that live inside them and provide them with food. If temperatures remain too

high, the corals turn white and die. Scientists project that only about 2 to 5 Fahrenheit degrees (1 to 3 Celsius degrees) of further warming of the ocean surface could eventually cause the death of many of the world's coral reefs. This fact is of particular concern because the reefs provide a habitat for huge numbers of ocean species.

Changing weather patterns. Researchers predict that global warming will lead to more extreme weather. Warming could increase the frequency of heavy rain and snowfall events. It could also cause more frequent and intense heat waves, more floods, and more widespread droughts. These impacts could strain water supplies, damage crops, and harm ecosystems.

Threats to human health. More frequent and intense hot days and heat waves can contribute to heat-related death and illness. Scientists also project more deaths and diseases caused by storms, floods, droughts, and fires. On the other hand, higher temperatures can reduce cold-related deaths. However, researchers predict that the harmful effects of rising temperatures on human health will outweigh the benefits.

Ways to limit global warming

To limit global warming, emissions of greenhouse gases must slow to a rate that allows atmospheric levels to stabilize. But emissions are instead rising rapidly. In addition, because the climate system changes slowly, there is a delay between an increase in greenhouse gas levels and the full temperature rise from that increase. As a result, some warming will continue even if greenhouse gas levels stabilize. Scientists project that even if concentrations had stopped rising and stayed at their 2000 level, an additional warming of 1 Fahrenheit degree (0.6 Celsius degree) would occur in this century.

Scientists have studied several ways to limit global warming. The most obvious method is to limit CO_2 emissions. Another method, called *carbon sequestration (SEE kwehs TRAY shuhn),* involves preventing CO_2 from entering the atmosphere or removing CO_2 already there. A third method, *geoengineering,* involves altering the environment in ways that may counteract warming.

Limiting CO$_2$ emissions chiefly involves burning less fossil fuels. This can be done by: (1) using alternative energy sources, (2) using fossil fuels more efficiently, and (3) practicing personal energy conservation.

Alternative energy sources that do not emit CO$_2$ include the wind, sunlight, nuclear energy, and Earth's internal heat. Devices known as *wind turbines* can convert wind energy to electric energy. *Solar cells* can convert sunlight to electric energy. *Geothermal* energy systems extract energy from steam or water heated deep underground. Many alternative sources of energy cost more to use than do fossil fuels. However, increased research and use is reducing the cost of alternative sources.

Increased fuel efficiency. CO$_2$ emissions could be greatly reduced if automobiles and trucks used fuel more efficiently. Researchers are developing devices to replace fuel-burning engines or to make them more efficient. Fuel-saving cars known as *hybrids* have already entered the market. A hybrid combines the components of a battery-driven electric car with a small gasoline engine. Scientists are also studying the use of *biofuels* from crops or other plant material as a replacement for gasoline and other fuels. Future cars may use *fuel cells,* devices that convert chemical energy to electric energy.

Personal energy conservation saves energy, reducing the need to burn fossil fuels. For example, you can turn off and unplug computers, televisions, and other electronic devices when you are not using them. You can also turn off lights when you are not in a room and replace traditional incandescent light bulbs with compact fluorescent bulbs, which use less energy. Outside the home, you can cut emissions by driving less and instead walking or biking. If you must drive, you can carpool or combine multiple errands in one trip. Public transportation may also help reduce emissions in some areas.

Carbon sequestration requires a place to store unwanted CO$_2$. It could be stored (1) underground or underwater or (2) in living plants.

Underground or underwater sequestration would involve injecting industrial emissions of CO$_2$ into underground rock formations or into the ocean. Suitable rock formations include natural petroleum reservoirs from which most of the oil or gas has been removed. Pumping CO$_2$ into such a reservoir would have the added benefit of making it easier to remove the remaining oil or gas. But CO$_2$ injected in this way could escape due to an earthquake or other disruption. Some scientists think that CO$_2$ could also be stored in layers of *basalt,* a type of volcanic rock. The basalt could chemically convert the CO$_2$ gas into solid salts that would be unlikely to escape.

CO$_2$ readily dissolves in water, and the oceans naturally store much of the gas. Scientists are examining the possibility of sequestering carbon by pumping CO$_2$ directly into the deep sea. However, they must carefully study the effects on ocean life. For example, water and CO$_2$ combine to form carbonic acid, which would increase the acidity of the water.

Sequestration in living plants. Green plants absorb CO$_2$ from the atmosphere as they grow, using the carbon for photosynthesis. Creating or enhancing ecosys-

© Hyungwon Kang, Reuters/Landov

Protesters concerned about global warming gather near the United States Capitol in Washington, D.C. The protesters' formation spells out "80 percent by 2050," calling on the U.S. government to reduce the country's carbon dioxide (CO$_2$) emissions by that amount.

tems with abundant plant life, such as forests and even cropland, could therefore remove much carbon dioxide from the atmosphere. However, future generations would have to preserve the ecosystems to prevent the carbon from reentering the atmosphere as CO_2.

Geoengineering involves making large-scale changes to the environment to limit global warming. One approach would be to inject aerosols into the atmosphere to reflect sunlight and so cool the planet. Another scheme would involve adding iron to the oceans to promote the growth of *phytoplankton*, tiny marine organisms that capture CO_2 for use in photosynthesis. Another proposal is to put trillions of tiny screens in orbit around Earth to deflect some of the sun's rays.

Such proposals carry unknown risks and challenges. For example, injecting aerosols into the atmosphere could increase *acid rain*—rain and other precipitation polluted by certain acids. Acid rain can kill fish in lakes and streams. Adding large amounts of iron to the sea could harm marine environments. Putting sun screens into space would be extremely expensive, and the screens would need to be maintained far into the future.

Government action on global warming

In an effort to limit global warming, many national and other governments have developed policies to reduce emissions of greenhouse gases. Most countries have agreed to the Kyoto Protocol, an international treaty aimed at cutting emissions.

The Kyoto Protocol requires *developed* (relatively wealthy) countries to restrict their emissions of CO_2 and five other greenhouse gases. Different nations have different yearly emissions targets for the period from 2008 to 2012. As a whole, the developed countries must reduce their emissions to a yearly average of about 95 percent of their 1990 emissions. The protocol does not place restrictions on *developing* (less wealthy) countries.

Delegates from around the world adopted the Kyoto Protocol as a preliminary document in 1997 in Kyoto, Japan. To enter into force, the protocol had to be *ratified* (formally approved) by at least 55 countries. The countries that approved also had to account for at least 55 percent of the CO_2 emissions of all developed countries in 1990. Most nations eventually agreed to the protocol, and it went into effect in 2005. However, the United States refused to ratify the treaty.

The Kyoto Protocol alone will do little to stop global warming. It limits emissions for only a short period and to levels that will not stop the increase in greenhouse gas concentrations. But the protocol establishes a basis for future measures. Delegates at an international climate conference in Bali in 2007 began negotiating a new agreement, for the period beyond 2012.

Types of policies. The Kyoto Protocol is a *cap-and-trade* system. It requires each developed country to *cap*, or limit, its emissions to a certain target. Nations that reduce their emissions below their targets can *trade*, or sell, *emissions credits* to other countries. Such credits can be used to offset emissions. Cap-and-trade policies can also be used to control emissions within one country or within a single industry.

A related approach enables groups and individuals to earn and sell credits called *carbon offsets*. Such a credit is similar to an emissions credit, but it is not earned by

Studying the causes of global warming

This graph shows the change in Earth's surface temperature during the 1900's, with zero marking the average temperature from 1901 to 1950. Scientists calculate how different factors affect temperature using computerized models called *climate simulations*. Only simulations that include both natural processes and human activities can account for the rapid warming from the mid-1900's to the early 2000's. This finding serves as strong evidence that human activities are the main cause of the recent warming.

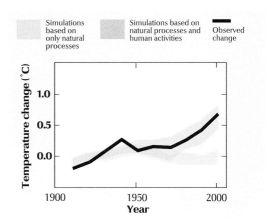

Adapted from Working Group I Report *Climate Change 2007: The Physical Science Basis*, Cambridge University Press for the Intergovernmental Panel on Climate Change, page 11, figure SPM-4. © Intergovernmental Panel on Climate Change. Reproduced with permission.

cutting one's own emissions. Instead, it is earned by undertaking other projects that help limit greenhouse gas levels overall. Carbon offsets often form part of cap-and-trade systems. Under the Kyoto Protocol, for example, developed countries can receive credit for investing in projects that reduce emissions in developing nations. Many companies now invest in emissions reduction projects to generate credits. They sell these credits to individuals and businesses that use them to offset emissions from such activities as air travel and power usage.

Another approach to limiting emissions is to impose a *carbon tax*, a tax on emissions of greenhouse gases. Such a tax can encourage companies to find ways to reduce emissions—ways that cost less than paying the tax.

Other measures. Some states, provinces, and countries have set goals that are more long-term than the Kyoto Protocol. For example, California has passed laws intended to reduce its total greenhouse gas emissions to 1990 levels by 2020, and the state proposed an 80-percent drop below 1990 levels by 2050. British Columbia has set a goal to cut emissions to 10 percent below 1990 levels, or 33 percent below 2007 levels, by 2020. The United Kingdom has proposed a 60-percent drop below 1990 levels, for CO_2 emissions specifically, by 2050.

How scientists study global warming

Climatologists (scientists who study climate) use information from many sources to analyze global warming. The most reliable climate information comes from standardized measurements using weather instruments. But records based on reliable instruments date back only to the mid to late 1800's. Such records cannot show variations in climate that occurred long ago, before people began to measure with such instruments.

To look farther back, climatologists analyze other

types of evidence. Such evidence includes growth rings in trees, *cores* (cylindrical samples) of ice drilled from Antarctica and Greenland, and cores of sediment from ocean or lake beds. Tree growth rings, for example, can show when the weather was favorable for trees to grow rapidly. Ice cores hold tiny bubbles of air trapped when the ice formed. The bubbles can be analyzed to determine ancient greenhouse gas concentrations.

Evidence from these sources indicates that Earth is likely the warmest it has been in at least 1,300 years. It also shows that the temperature increase of the 1900's was the largest rise in more than 1,000 to 2,000 years. Data from ice cores also show that the levels of CO_2 and other greenhouse gases in the atmosphere are higher than they have been in at least the past 650,000 years.

Climatologists use computers to analyze past climate change and project future changes. First, scientists program a computer with a set of mathematical equations known as a *climate model.* The equations describe how various factors, such as the amount of CO_2 in the atmosphere, affect temperature. Next, the scientists enter data representing how those factors change over time. The computer then runs the model, describing how the climate conditions would vary. Such a representation is known as a *climate simulation.*

A complete understanding of global warming cannot be gained through simple observation. Its study relies on the scientific analysis of evidence and on climate simulations. This fact has enabled critics to dispute that warming has occurred or that it was caused by human activities. To help establish a scientific *consensus* (general agreement) on these issues, the United Nations established the Intergovernmental Panel on Climate Change (IPCC). The IPCC is a panel of scientists and governmental officials from more than 100 nations. It released several scientific reports during the 1990's and 2000's.

The IPCC conducted climate simulations as part of its studies of global warming. Its climatologists used different sets of simulations to model the warming of roughly the past 100 years. One set took into account both natural processes and human activities. Another set took into account only natural processes. The scientists then compared the temperatures produced by the simulations with temperatures recorded by thermometers. Only the set based on both natural processes and human activities produced results that corresponded closely to the actual temperature records, especially to the period of rapid warming since the mid-1900's. The results provided strong evidence that both natural processes and human activities have affected Earth's climate and that human activities are the primary driver of the recent warming.

The IPCC also carried out simulations to predict the effects of natural and human influences on temperatures until 2100. The simulations showed that there can be no "quick fix" to global warming. Even if all emissions of greenhouse gases were to cease immediately, the temperature would continue to rise because of the greenhouse gases already in the atmosphere. However, the rate of emissions reductions will determine the severity of global warming and how difficult it will be to deal with its impacts. The IPCC, along with former United States Vice President Al Gore, won the 2007 Nobel Peace Prize for increasing public awareness of global warming.   Michael D. Mastrandrea

Mountain

Mountain is a landform that stands much higher than the surrounding terrain. Mountains generally are larger than hills, but features that people call *hills* in one place may be higher than features called *mountains* elsewhere. For example, the Black Hills of South Dakota and Wyoming stand higher above their surroundings than do the Ouachita Mountains of Arkansas and Oklahoma.

Mountains typically have steep slopes and sharp or slightly rounded peaks or ridges. Many geologists consider an elevated area to be a mountain if it includes two or more zones of climate and plant life at different altitudes. In general, the climate becomes cooler and wetter with increasing elevation. In most parts of the world, a mountain must rise about 2,000 feet (600 meters) above its surroundings to include two climate zones.

A mountain may stand as an isolated peak, such as a lone volcano, or it may form part of a mountain range. A group of mountain ranges forms a mountain system. The Pacific Mountain System, for example, includes the Cascade Range, the Olympic Mountains, the Sierra Nevada, and several other mountain ranges along the west coast of North America.

Mountains occur in the ocean as well as on land. Many islands are the exposed peaks of mountains that rise from the ocean floor. The world's longest mountain system—the Mid-Atlantic Ridge—lies almost totally underwater. It stretches more than 10,000 miles (16,000 kilometers) from the North Atlantic Ocean nearly to Antarctica. Some of the ridge's highest peaks form such islands as Iceland and the Azores.

The height of a mountain is usually expressed in terms of the elevation of its peak above sea level. The world's highest mountain, Mount Everest, on the border of Tibet and Nepal, rises 29,035 feet (8,850 meters) above sea level. A mountain's height can also be described in

A mountain range is shaped over millions of years by forces of lifting and erosion. The Andes Mountains in South America, shown in this aerial photograph, developed largely from volcanic eruptions that occurred over the last 65 million years.

terms of its *relief,* the overall rise from its base to its peak. Mauna Kea, a volcano on the island of Hawaii, has the world's largest relief. The volcano rises a total of 33,480 feet (10,205 meters) from its base on the floor of the Pacific Ocean to its peak 13,796 feet (4,205 meters) above the ocean surface—a relief of more than 6 miles (10 kilometers).

Other rocky worlds in our solar system also have mountains, some of which stand much taller than the highest mountains on Earth. Olympus Mons, an ancient volcano on the planet Mars, ranks as the tallest known mountain in the solar system. It rises about 16 miles (25 kilometers) above the surrounding plain, nearly three times the height of Mount Everest.

The importance of mountains

Mountain ranges are important because they affect the climate and water flow of surrounding regions. Mountains also provide a home for plants and animals and a source of such natural resources as lumber and minerals. Mountain ranges influence a variety of human activities, shaping patterns of transportation, communication, and settlement.

In affecting climate. Mountain ranges strongly affect air movements and precipitation patterns. At higher altitudes, air pressure decreases, causing the temperature of the air to drop. Cold air cannot hold as much moisture as warm air can. As a result, when warm, moist air moves up one side of a mountain—known as the *windward* side—the air cools, and the water vapor it holds condenses into water droplets. Much of the water then falls on the windward slope as rain or snow.

By the time air passes the crest of a mountain, it has lost most of its moisture. For this reason, the side of the mountain away from the wind, called the *leeward* side, is drier than the windward side. The dry area beyond the leeward side of a mountain range is called a *rain shadow.* Many of the world's deserts lie in rain shadows.

In maintaining water flow. Because so much precipitation falls on mountain slopes, many rivers have their headwaters in mountain regions. The Rio Grande and the Colorado River, for example, receive nearly all their water from mountains. Much of the snow in high mountains melts only during the summer. Thus, mountains act as reservoirs, feeding streams and rivers even during periods of summer drought.

As a home for plants and animals. Because mountains include diverse conditions at different elevations, they provide environments suitable to many kinds of plant and animal life. Few living things survive in the bitter cold of snow-capped mountain peaks. However, a variety of insects and other small animals, such as chinchillas and pikas, make their home just below the snowfields. A few sure-footed large animals, such as mountain goats and sheep, also live in these areas. These animals feed on shrubs, mosses, and other plants that grow above the *timber line,* the line above which the cold and wind prevents the growth of trees. Below the timber line, many mountains have large forests filled

Gary J. Axen, the contributor of this article, is Associate Professor of Geology at New Mexico Institute of Mining and Technology.

with a wide range of plant and animal life.

As a wealth of natural resources. Much of the world's mineral resources come from mountainous areas. Mountains are formed by such geological processes as volcanic eruptions and earthquakes. These processes may bring valuable minerals near the surface, where they can be mined.

Through their effects on climate and water flow, mountains influence the availability of water over vast areas. Because of their steep slopes and abundant flowing water, mountainous areas also make suitable locations for building hydroelectric power plants, which convert the energy of moving water into electric power. Mountainous Norway, for example, produces nearly all its electric power in this way.

Some regions, including many areas of the western United States, are too dry to support trees except in the cooler, wetter climate of the mountains. The lumber industry in such regions depends on timber grown in mountainous areas. Many animals valued by the fur industry or by hunters also live in the mountains.

As an influence on human activities. In many parts of the world, mountains have long served as barriers, hindering transportation, settlement, communication, and military invasion. The isolation of mountain communities can contribute to the development of a great diversity of culture. In Switzerland's Alps, for example, relatively isolated groups living in the same region speak hundreds of *dialects* (variations) of four different languages.

Mountains also serve as important recreation areas. Each year, millions of people vacation in mountainous regions to camp, hike, ski, climb, or kayak, or just to enjoy fresh air and spectacular views.

How different types of mountains form

Mountains are created by tremendous forces in Earth operating over a period of about 1 million to 100 million years. Earth scientists have developed a theory called *plate tectonics* that explains the formation of mountains and other geological features. According to this theory, Earth's outer shell consists of about 30 rigid pieces of various sizes called *tectonic plates*. The surfaces of these plates make up the continents—called *continental crust*—and the ocean basins—called *oceanic crust*. The plates are in slow, continuous motion. Most mountain building occurs along the boundaries between plates.

Geologists classify mountains into two major families: *volcanic mountains,* formed by the eruption of molten rock and its build-up as it cools, and *tectonic mountains,* built by geological forces that change the shape of, or *deform,* Earth's crust. Both families consist of a number of different types of mountains. In addition, a single mountain system may develop from both volcanic and tectonic processes. For example, the Andes Mountains in South America contain some peaks created by volcanic eruptions and others formed by tectonic activity.

Volcanic mountains, such as Washington's Mount Rainier and Japan's Mount Fuji, form when molten rock from deep within Earth erupts and piles up on the surface. As a result, volcanic mountains consist chiefly of *igneous rocks,* such as basalt and rhyolite, which are formed when molten material cools and solidifies. Igneous rocks are one of the three major types of rocks. The

other types, *sedimentary rocks* and *metamorphic rocks,* can be found in mountains formed by other processes.

Volcanic mountain building takes place in regions where molten rock rises up from Earth's *mantle,* the hot, rocky layer beneath Earth's crust. Most such activity occurs along the boundaries of tectonic plates, at *mid-ocean ridges* and *subduction zones.* Other volcanic mountain building occurs above *hot spots.*

At mid-ocean ridges. Mid-ocean ridges form beneath the ocean in areas where two plates separate. Molten rock from Earth's interior wells up between the plates, creating a submerged mountain range. The Mid-Atlantic Ridge formed in this way. As the molten rock cools and the plates continue to move apart, the solidified material becomes new ocean floor. Geologists estimate the total length of all of Earth's mid-ocean ridges to be from 30,000 to 50,000 miles (50,000 to 80,000 kilometers).

At subduction zones. Subduction zones are regions where two plates collide. At these boundaries, the oceanic edge of one plate is thrust beneath the edge of the other plate in a process called *subduction.* The sinking plate contains water that soaked into the rock and became chemically bound into minerals as the plate formed and moved beneath the ocean. As the plate subducts, it carries this water down into the mantle. There, the heated minerals release the water. The water rises into the overlying mantle, where it lowers the melting temperature of the rock. Melted rock then rises through the overlying plate, creating volcanic eruptions.

If continental crust lies atop this region, subduction zone mountain ranges can form along the continent's edge. Such mountain ranges include the Cascade Range in North America and the volcanoes of the Andes Mountains. If the edges of both plates are oceanic, mountain-building activity at the subduction zone may form a chain of islands called an *island arc.* Such island arcs include the Aleutian Islands of Alaska and the Mariana Islands in the Pacific Ocean.

Above a hot spot. Geologists believe that some mountain-building activity occurs above deep hot spots in the mantle. These hot spots contain partially molten rock that rises from deep inside Earth. From these locations, hot rock continues to rise through the mantle and the overlying plate, finally erupting as a volcano.

Over millions of years, as a plate moves over a hot spot, and as the hot spot itself moves within the mantle, eruptions create a trail of volcanic mountains. The Hawaiian Islands formed in this manner as the movements of the Pacific Plate and an underlying hot spot traced out a chain of volcanoes, a process that continues today.

Tectonic mountains, such as the Alps in Europe and the Sierra Nevada in California, result from geological forces that raise or fold Earth's crust or otherwise change its shape. Some tectonic mountains form when plates collide or pull apart. Others develop from the lifting and wearing down of regions of the crust. Most tectonic mountains fit into one of four types: (1) fold-thrust mountains, (2) fault-block mountains, (3) dome mountains, and (4) erosion mountains.

Fold-thrust mountains, such as the Alps, the Appalachian Mountains of the eastern United States, and the Himalaya, form when two plates collide head-on. During the collision, the plates' edges fold or crumple, and some layers of rock may be thrust over other layers. Fold-thrust mountains consist mainly of sedimentary rocks, such as limestone and shale. Sedimentary rocks form when *sediments* (particles of older rock or plant and animal remains) settle to the bottom of a body of water and harden.

The thickest deposits of sedimentary rock generally accumulate along the edges of continents. As one plate subducts beneath another, any continents riding on the two plates collide. The accumulated layers of rock—and any previously formed volcanic mountains—crumple together, causing the rock layers to wrinkle up like a tablecloth that is pushed across a table. The resulting folds may range in character from gentle, wavelike patterns to sharp, complex folds. The compression may also produce extensive *thrust faults,* fractures in the rock layers in which one layer is pushed up and over another.

Much of the Appalachian Mountains consists of gently folded rock. Europe's Alps, however, are so sharply folded that a person climbing in some areas may cross the same layer of rock several times during a single ascent. The first time the layer appears right side up, the next time upside down, then right side up again, and so on. In such intensely folded and faulted mountains, some rocks are pushed down so far that they are subjected to great pressure and temperature. The heat and pressure transform the sediments into such metamorphic rocks as schist and gneiss. Some of the rock may melt and then rise up into the overlying rocks, creating veins of granite and other igneous rocks.

Fault-block mountains form where a plate is pulling apart or *rifting.* The stretching of Earth's crust produces fractures called *normal faults.* Huge blocks of crust become tilted or pushed up along these faults, while neighboring regions drop down to form basins. Fault-block mountains include the Sierra Nevada, the Teton Range in Wyoming, the Wasatch Range in Utah, and the Harz Mountains in Germany. Most such mountains occur where a block is tilted up along one side of a single fault. But some blocks are pushed up between two separate faults.

The uplifted blocks rapidly wear down, and the debris from this erosion accumulates at the base of the mountain, filling nearby basins. Most of the isolated mountains of the Basin and Range Province, in the southwestern United States and northern Mexico, are fault-block mountains separated by broad plains filled with such debris.

Both fault-block and fold-thrust mountains can also form along *strike-slip faults,* areas near plate boundaries where blocks of rock slide past each other horizontally, often producing earthquakes. The Peninsular Ranges in southern California and Baja California—which are fault-block mountains—and New Zealand's Southern Alps—a fold-thrust range—both developed on strike-slip faults.

Dome mountains, such as the Black Hills of South Dakota and the Adirondack Mountains of New York, form where geological forces lift Earth's crust into the shape of a broad bulge or dome. Because the dome rises above its surroundings, it becomes vulnerable to increased erosion. The layers of sedimentary rock covering the dome erode, exposing underlying igneous and metamorphic rock. This harder underlying rock erodes irregularly, forming peaks and valleys.

Erosion mountains. A few mountains, such as the Catskill Mountains in New York, result from the erosion of a thick, flat pile of sedimentary rock. Such mountains are all that remains of a plateau that has been eroded away by rivers or glaciers.

Forces that shape mountains

Mountains may appear solid and enduring, but geological and climatic processes gradually and continuously alter a mountain's height and shape. These forces can work together over millions of years to sculpt beautiful mountain landscapes, such as gently sloping ranges or soaring, rugged peaks. The processes that shape mountains include: (1) isostasy (pronounced *eye SAHS tuh see)* and uplift, (2) plate flexing, and (3) erosion.

Isostasy and uplift. The elevation of a mountain is closely tied to the rise and fall of the underlying tectonic plate through a mechanism called *isostasy.* The rigid plates float on the *asthenosphere*—a hot, soft layer of Earth's mantle—in much the same way that a wooden block will float on water. In the case of a wooden block, the water exerts an upward force of *buoyancy* that balances the downward force of gravity, causing the block to float. Floating freely, the block tends to rise or fall in the water until the buoyancy force exactly equals its weight. Likewise, the plates float on the molten rock of the asthenosphere, tending to rise or fall until they reach a condition of balance between weight and buoy-

Fold-thrust mountains form where slabs of crust collide, folding rock layers and producing *thrust faults,* breaks where a section of rock is forced over another.

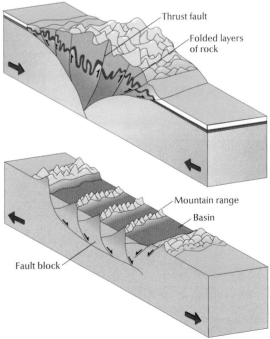

WORLD BOOK illustration by Matt Carrington

Fault-block mountains develop as crust is pulled apart, creating fractures called *faults.* Blocks of crust tilt along the faults, forming ranges separated by basins.

ancy called *isostatic equilibrium.*

An object's elevation at isostatic equilibrium depends in part on its density. For example, a block of light wood, such as balsa wood, will float higher on the water than will an identical block of heavy wood, such as oak. Similarly, a continental region of a plate, which is less dense than an oceanic region, will float higher above the asthenosphere, helping the continents to rise above the ocean basins.

The height at which an object floats also depends on its thickness. A thick wooden block will float higher above the water than will a thin wooden block made of the same material. Mountain-building processes generally involve the build-up of mass and thickness—the mountains—over a certain area of plate. Without the effects of isostasy, the additional mass might cause that area to sink entirely, canceling any change in elevation. With isostasy, the thickening can actually produce a buoyant, upward influence called *uplift.* Most mountain ranges have buoyant *crustal roots* beneath them that cause the underlying plate to bulge into the asthenosphere. These roots provide the uplift that enables the mountains to tower above the surrounding terrain.

Plate flexing. Although isostasy prevents mountains from sinking entirely, the load exerted by large mountains can cause the plates to flex downward significantly, lowering the height of the mountains in turn. The Hawaiian Islands, for example, have flexed the Pacific Plate downward by about 1 to 3 miles (2 to 5 kilometers). The weight of the Himalaya, along with the forces of compression as the Indian subcontinent collides with Asia, has bent the northern edge of the Indian Plate down by about 12 miles (20 kilometers).

For a given load, stronger plates flex less than weaker plates. As a result, the strength of the plate that a mountain rides on limits the height the mountain can reach.

Erosion by water and ice constantly wears away uplifted terrain. In warm, wet climates, or at low elevations, rivers can carve hills and gorges into the land. At higher elevations, glaciers can form, cutting jagged peaks and deep valleys as they move down the rock. As elevation increases, erosion by glaciers intensifies, imposing another limit on the height that a mountain can reach.

Erosion gradually lowers the average elevation of an uplifted region. But as erosion removes material, the underlying plate will rise over time, maintaining isostatic equilibrium.

Major mountain systems on Earth

Many of Earth's mountain systems are still geologically active, but others have ceased building and are slowly eroding down to plains. Some systems consist of both volcanic and tectonic mountains and may include multiple types from either family. Individual ranges may even include more than one type of mountain. The Front Range of the Rocky Mountains in Colorado, for example, initially consisted of fold-thrust mountains. Later, geological forces pushed up large blocks of Earth's crust in the range, creating fault-block mountains.

The Appalachian Mountains extend from Alabama to the Gaspé Peninsula in Canada—a distance of about 1,500 miles (2,400 kilometers). They consist mainly of folded and faulted sedimentary and metamorphic rock layers. Many scientists think the Appalachian Mountains were formed by three collisions of the North American Plate with the Eurasian and African plates and much smaller "microplates," beginning about 435 million years ago. The last collision, between the North American and African plates, occurred about 250 million years ago. Since then, the continents have rifted apart, and the Atlantic Ocean has formed due to spreading along the Mid-Atlantic Ridge, leaving Europe and Africa far from North America. As a result, geological activity stopped in the Appalachians, and they are now simply eroding.

The Rocky Mountains stretch for about 3,300 miles (5,300 kilometers) from New Mexico into Alaska. The Rockies include fold-thrust, fault-block, and volcanic mountains. They began to form about 100 million years ago and some areas were lifted again in the past 25 million years, but mountain building seems to have ended since then. See **Rocky Mountains.**

The Pacific Mountain System consists of two parallel chains of mountains that run for about 2,500 miles (4,000 kilometers) from southern California to Alaska. One chain, the Coast Ranges, includes the Olympic Mountains of Washington, many islands off the coast of British Columbia, and part of Alaska's coast and coastal islands. The Coast Ranges consist chiefly of fold-thrust mountains composed in large part of marine sediments and volcanic rocks. The North American Plate scraped these materials from the oceanic crust of other plates that subducted beneath it. The other chain in the Pacific system includes the Sierra Nevada of California, the Cascade Range of Oregon and Washington, and the Coast Mountains of British Columbia. Both chains began forming about 240 million years ago and have been further uplifted within the past 63 million years. Many of these mountains continue to grow.

The Andes Mountains stretch along the west coast of South America for about 4,500 miles (7,200 kilometers). They consist largely of igneous rocks formed by volcanic eruptions within the past 65 million years. The volcanic activity resulted from the subduction of the Nazca Plate beneath the South American Plate. The Nazca Plate underlies the Pacific Ocean west of South Amer-

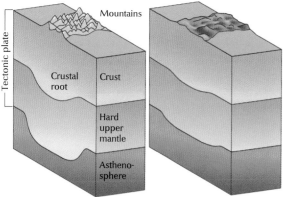

WORLD BOOK illustration by Matt Carrington

Crustal roots help lift many mountains above their surroundings. The buoyant root, *left,* causes a bulge in the underlying plate, which floats on the soft *asthenosphere.* As erosion wears down the mountains, *right,* the root also thins but continues to support the mountains.

© phdpsx/Shutterstock

The Teton Range, part of the Rocky Mountains, soars above the Snake River in Wyoming. The Snake and many other rivers begin high in the Rockies.

ica. Mountain building continues in the Andes. The Andes form part of the *Ring of Fire,* as does the Pacific Mountain System and the mountains of Antarctica. The ring is a belt of subduction zones that encircles the Pacific and includes most of the world's volcanoes. The mountains of Antarctica include an extension of the Andes called the Antarctic Peninsula.

The Tethyan Mountain System (pronounced *TEH thee uhn)* extends for well over 7,000 miles (11,000 kilometers) across Africa, Europe, and Asia. It includes the Atlas Mountains of northwestern Africa, the Alps and the Carpathian Mountains in Europe, and the Caucasus Mountains between Europe and Asia. In Asia, it continues through the Zagros and Alborz mountains, the Pamirs, the Karakoram Range, and the Himalaya.

The mountains of the Tethyan system consist largely of highly deformed sedimentary and igneous rocks that have been folded and faulted within the past 80 million years. Earth scientists consider the system to be a result of the African, Arabian, and Indian plates colliding into the Eurasian Plate. Earthquakes occur frequently along the Tethyan system, indicating that mountain building is still taking place.

Mountains on other planets or moons

Many other bodies in the solar system have mountains on their surfaces. All of the other inner, rocky planets—Mercury, Venus, and Mars—feature mountains, as does Earth's moon. In addition, mountains appear on several moons of the outer, gas-giant planets.

On Venus, six mountainous areas cover more than one-third of the planet's surface. The tallest mountain range, called Maxwell Montes, reaches a peak 7 miles (11 kilometers) in height. Scientists believe that the mountains of Venus formed by the folding and faulting of the planet's surface. However, because Venus has no water, its mountains lack the erosion-carved features found on Earth's mountains.

On Io, a large moon of Jupiter, the surface is dotted with fault-block mountains and volcanic mountains. Scientists think the fault-block mountains formed when regions of the crust sank toward Io's center and became compressed. In addition, built-up internal heat in these regions may have caused the overlying crust to expand. These processes fractured the crust, producing faults and mountains. Io's mountains soar to 55,000 feet (17,000 meters) tall, nearly twice the height of Mount Everest.

On Titan, the largest moon of Saturn, mountain ranges occur south of Titan's equator. The biggest known range runs for about 90 miles (150 kilometers) and measures about 1 mile (1.5 kilometers) tall. Scientists think the mountains formed from material that welled up as Titan's tectonic plates pulled apart, similar to the way mid-ocean ridges formed on Earth. White material, believed to be methane snow, tops the mountain peaks.

Studying mountains

Geologists and geographers study mountains to learn important and useful knowledge about Earth. Planetary scientists may also study mountains on other planets or moons to learn similar information about these bodies.

Why scientists study mountains. Analyzing the structure, composition, and distribution of a planet's mountains yields information about the geological forces that shape the planet. It also provides clues about the makeup of the planet's interior. Because mountains are formed by major geological events, geologists study them to learn about the planet's history.

The study of Earth's mountains is necessary in the ongoing search for useful mineral resources. Knowledge of mountain geology helps engineers design and build mountain roads, railroad beds, tunnels, and dams.

Measuring mountains. Accurately determining the location and height of mountains ranks as a particularly important challenge for geographers and mapmakers. To do this, they often use aerial photography, in which an airborne camera takes a series of overlapping photographs of an area. Mapmakers then use a process called *photogrammetry* to create maps from the photographs.

For Earth, high-flying aircraft and artificial satellites provide accurate data about location and altitude by means of instruments called *altimeters*. Some altimeters send radio signals or laser light down to the surface and receive the waves after they have been reflected from the ground. These altimeters compute the distance to the surface based on the speed of the waves and the time they took to travel to the ground and back.

Space probes carrying altimeters have measured mountains on other planets and on moons. In the late 1990's and early 2000's, for example, the Mars Global Surveyor spacecraft used a laser altimeter to help map that planet's surface.

Mountains can also be measured using the Global Positioning System. The system's artificial satellites, orbiting Earth, send radio signals to special receivers, which

Mountains of the world

Some famous mountains

| Name | Height above sea level | | Location | Interesting facts |
	In feet	In meters		
Aconcagua	22,835	6,960	Andes in Argentina	Highest peak in the Western Hemisphere
Annapurna I	26,504	8,078	Himalaya in Nepal	Highest mountain climbed until 1953
Aoraki/Mount Cook	12,316	3,754	Southern Alps in New Zealand	Highest peak in New Zealand
Chimborazo	20,702	6,310	Andes in Ecuador	For many years thought to be the highest mountain in the Western Hemisphere
Cotopaxi	19,347	5,897	Andes in Ecuador	One of the world's highest active volcanoes
Ixtacihuatl	17,343	5,286	Plateau of Mexico	Aztec name for *white woman*
Jungfrau	13,642	4,158	Alps in Switzerland	Electric railroad partway up the mountain
K2, or Mount Godwin Austen, or Dapsang	28,250	8,611	Karakoram, or Mustagh, in Kashmir	Second highest mountain in the world
Kilimanjaro	19,340	5,895	Isolated peak in Tanzania	Highest mountain in Africa
Lassen Peak	10,457	3,187	Cascade in California	One of the few active U.S. volcanoes
Matterhorn	14,692	4,478	Alps on Switzerland-Italy border	Favorite for daring mountain climbers
Mauna Kea	13,796	4,205	Island of Hawaii	World's greatest rise from base to peak
Mauna Loa	13,677	4,169	Island of Hawaii	World's largest volcano
Mont Blanc	15,771	4,807	Alps on France-Italy-Switzerland border	Highest mountain in the Alps
Mount Ararat	16,946	5,165	Eastern Plateau in Turkey	Noah's Ark supposed to have rested on Ararat
Mount Elbrus	18,510	5,642	Caucasus in Russia	Highest mountain in Europe
Mount Etna	10,902	3,323	Island of Sicily	Volcano known to have erupted over 260 times
Mount Everest	29,035	8,850	Himalaya on Nepal-Tibet border	Highest mountain in the world; first scaled in 1953
Mount Fuji	12,388	3,776	Island of Honshu in Japan	Considered sacred by many Japanese
Mount Hood	11,239	3,426	Cascade in Oregon	Inactive volcano with many glaciers
Mount Kanchenjunga, or Kinchinjunga	28,208	8,598	Himalaya on Nepal-India border	Third highest mountain in the world
Mount Kenya	17,058	5,199	Central Kenya	Base straddles the equator
Mount Kosciuszko	7,310	2,228	Australian Alps	Highest peak in Australia
Mount Logan	19,551	5,959	St. Elias Range in Canada	Highest peak in Canada
Mount Makalu	27,824	8,481	Himalaya on Nepal-Tibet border	Fourth highest mountain in the world
Mount McKinley	20,320	6,194	Alaska Range in Alaska	Highest peak in North America
Mount Olympus	9,570	2,917	Greece	Considered home of the gods by early Greeks
Mount Rainier	14,410	4,392	Cascade in Washington	Highest peak in Washington
Mount St. Helens	8,364	2,549	Cascade in Washington	One of the few active U.S. volcanoes
Mount Shasta	14,162	4,317	Cascade in California	Famous for its twin peaks
Mount Whitney	14,494	4,418	Sierra Nevada in California	Highest mountain in California
Pico de Orizaba	18,410	5,610	Plateau of Mexico	Highest peak in Mexico
Pikes Peak	14,110	4,301	Front Range in Colorado	Most famous of the Rocky Mountains
Popocatépetl	17,887	5,452	Plateau of Mexico	Aztec name for *smoking mountain*
Vesuvius	4,190	1,277	Italy	Only active volcano on the mainland of Europe

Sources: Rand McNally & Company; U.S. Geological Survey.

Major mountains of the Western Hemisphere

WORLD BOOK illustration by Robert Addison

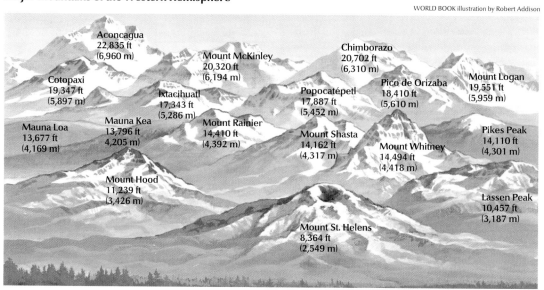

Aconcagua
22,835 ft
(6,960 m)

Mount McKinley
20,320 ft
(6,194 m)

Chimborazo
20,702 ft
(6,310 m)

Mount Logan
19,551 ft
(5,959 m)

Cotopaxi
19,347 ft
(5,897 m)

Ixtacihuatl
17,343 ft
(5,286 m)

Popocatépetl
17,887 ft
(5,452 m)

Pico de Orizaba
18,410 ft
(5,610 m)

Mauna Loa
13,677 ft
(4,169 m)

Mauna Kea
13,796 ft
(4,205 m)

Mount Rainier
14,410 ft
(4,392 m)

Mount Shasta
14,162 ft
(4,317 m)

Mount Whitney
14,494 ft
(4,418 m)

Pikes Peak
14,110 ft
(4,301 m)

Mount Hood
11,239 ft
(3,426 m)

Mount St. Helens
8,364 ft
(2,549 m)

Lassen Peak
10,457 ft
(3,187 m)

Location of the mountains

This map shows the location of the mountains featured in the table *Some famous mountains* and the illustrations *Major mountains of the Eastern Hemisphere* and *Major mountains of the Western Hemisphere*. Those illustrations show how the mountains compare in height.

WORLD BOOK map

Arctic Ocean
Mount McKinley
Mount Logan
NORTH AMERICA
Mount St. Helens
Mount Rainier
Mount Shasta
Mount Hood
Lassen Peak
Pikes Peak
Mount Whitney
Mauna Kea
Mauna Loa
Ixtacihuatl
Popocatépetl
Pico de Orizaba
Cotopaxi
Chimborazo
SOUTH AMERICA
Pacific Ocean
Atlantic Ocean
Aconcagua
EUROPE
Jungfrau
Mont Blanc
Matterhorn
Vesuvius
Mount Etna
Mount Olympus
Mount Elbrus
Mount Ararat
ASIA
K2
Annapurna
Mount Makalu
Mount Everest
Mount Kanchenjunga
Mount Fuji
Pacific Ocean
AFRICA
Mount Kenya
Kilimanjaro
Indian Ocean
Equator
AUSTRALIA
Mount Kosciuszko
Aoraki/Mount Cook
ANTARCTICA

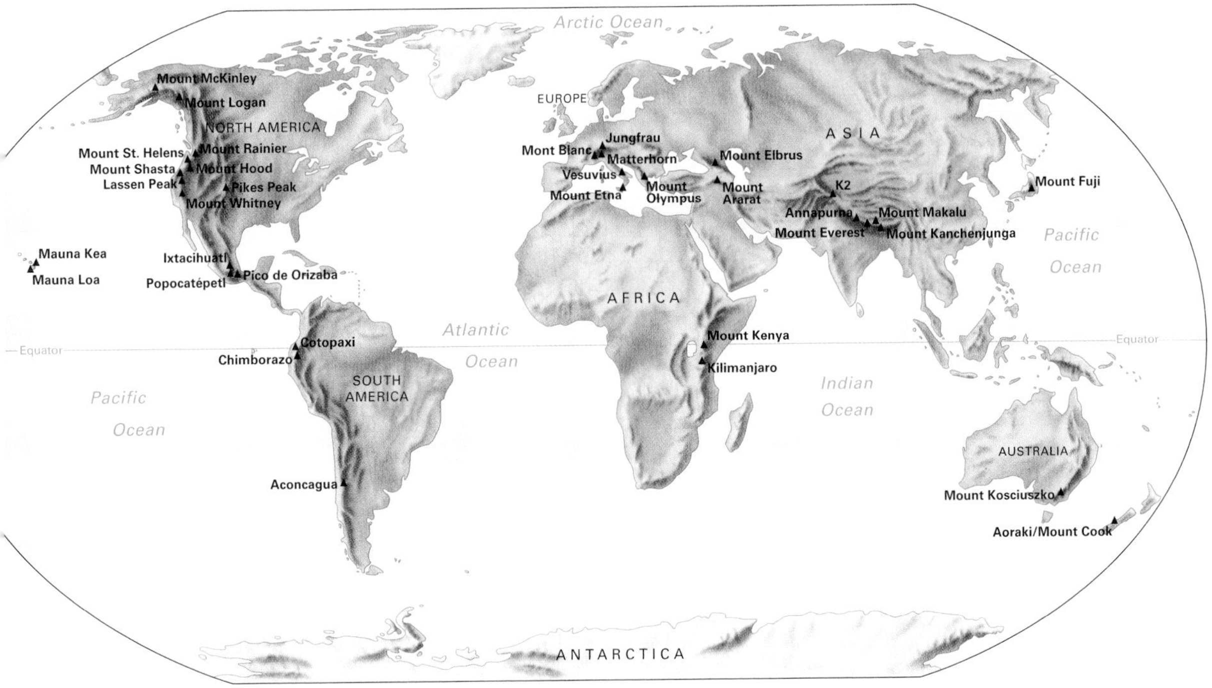

Major mountains of the Eastern Hemisphere

WORLD BOOK illustration by Robert Addison

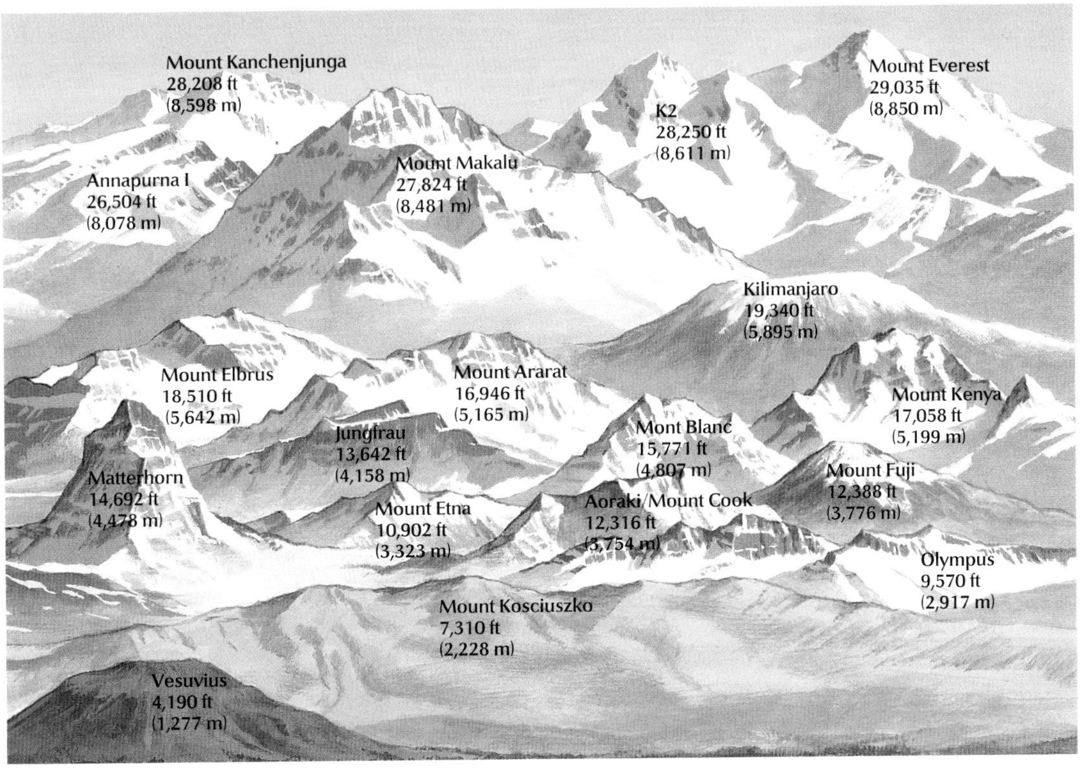

Mount Kanchenjunga
28,208 ft
(8,598 m)
K2
28,250 ft
(8,611 m)
Mount Everest
29,035 ft
(8,850 m)
Annapurna I
26,504 ft
(8,078 m)
Mount Makalu
27,824 ft
(8,481 m)
Kilimanjaro
19,340 ft
(5,895 m)
Mount Elbrus
18,510 ft
(5,642 m)
Mount Ararat
16,946 ft
(5,165 m)
Mount Kenya
17,058 ft
(5,199 m)
Jungfrau
13,642 ft
(4,158 m)
Mont Blanc
15,771 ft
(4,807 m)
Matterhorn
14,692 ft
(4,478 m)
Mount Fuji
12,388 ft
(3,776 m)
Mount Etna
10,902 ft
(3,323 m)
Aoraki/Mount Cook
12,316 ft
(3,754 m)
Olympus
9,570 ft
(2,917 m)
Mount Kosciuszko
7,310 ft
(2,228 m)
Vesuvius
4,190 ft
(1,277 m)

NASA/Jet Propulsion Laboratory

Sapas Mons, a volcanic mountain on Venus, lies surrounded by lava flows. This image was stretched vertically to show details of the broadly sloping mountain.

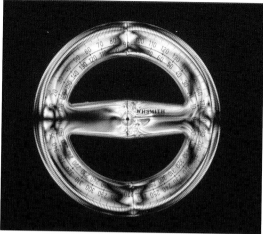

© Andrew Lambert Photography/Photo Researchers

Polarizing filters reveal weak areas in the plastic of a protractor, seen where the light appears most distorted in this photograph. People use such filters to study the structure of materials.

can be placed on mountains. The receivers then transmit information to stations below, where computers determine the mountain's altitude. Mountain surveyors measure mountains using a technique called *laser ranging,* in which laser beams are bounced off objects to determine their distance.   Gary J. Axen

Polarized light consists of light waves that vibrate in simple, regular patterns. In most of the light that we see, such as light from the sun or a lamp, the waves vibrate in many different directions. Such light is said to be *unpolarized.* If the vibrations stay in the same direction or form the same shape for a long time, the light is said to be polarized. Special filters that polarize light aid in the study of light and serve as tools in many industries. Polarized light also finds use in consumer products.

Understanding polarized light. To understand the behavior of a light wave, imagine a rope tied to something stationary at one end. If you shake the loose end of the rope, the rope *oscillates* (moves back and forth), causing a wave to travel along its length. If you shake the rope up and down, it will oscillate vertically. If you shake side to side, the rope will oscillate horizontally. The rope can oscillate in directions *perpendicular* (at right angles) to the direction in which the wave travels.

Light waves travel in much the same way as waves in the rope. But light waves are carried by *electric fields* and *magnetic fields,* electric and magnetic influences acting throughout regions of space (see **Light** [Electromagnetic waves]). Just like the rope, electric and magnetic fields can oscillate in directions perpendicular to the direction in which light waves travel.

The simplest type of polarized light is *linearly polarized* light, also called *plane polarized* light. In such light, the electric field oscillates in a single direction. The direction of this oscillation determines the direction of polarization. If the electric field oscillates only up and down, the light is said to be *vertically polarized.* In *horizontally polarized* light, the electric field only oscillates from side to side.

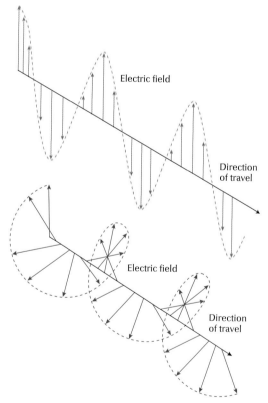

WORLD BOOK diagram

Polarized light is made up of waves that vibrate in regular patterns. A wave consists in part of an electric influence called an *electric field.* The electric field *oscillates* (moves back and forth) as shown by the arrows, tracing out a shape as the wave travels. Vertically polarized light, *top,* oscillates up and down. In circularly polarized light, *bottom,* the oscillations rotate in a circle.

INDEX

How to use the index

This index covers the contents of the 2008, 2009, and 2010 editions.

Each entry gives the edition year and the page number or page numbers—for example, **Antimatter**. This means that information on this topic may be found on page 238 in the 2010 edition.

The indications (il.) and (ils.) mean that the topic appears only in an illustration or illustrations and not in the main text of a page or the facing page. For example, there are pictures of ants on 66 and 70 of the 2010 edition.

A page number in italics means that there is an article on this topic on the page or pages indicated. For example, there is an Update article on **Archaeology** on pages 158-163 of the 2010 edition. The page numbers in roman type indicate additional references to this topic in other articles in the volumes covered.

An entry followed by *WBE* refers to a new or revised *World Book Encyclopedia* article in the supplement section, as in **Arctic Ocean.** This means that there is a *World Book Encyclopedia* article on pages 274-277 of the 2010 edition.

The "see" and "see also" cross-references refer the reader to other entries in the index. For example, information on **Astronauts** will be found under the heading **Space technology**, and additional astronomy topics will be found under the "see also" references for **Astronomy**.

When there are many references to a topic, they are grouped alphabetically by clue words under the main topic. For example, the clue words under **Automobiles** group some of the references to that topic under subtopics.

ACKNOWLEDGMENTS

The publishers gratefully acknowledge the courtesy of the following artists, photographers, publishers, institutions, agencies, and corporations for the illustrations in this volume. Credits are listed from top to bottom and from left to right on their respective pages. All entries marked with an asterisk (*) denote illustrations created exclusively for this yearbook. All maps, charts, and diagrams were staff-prepared unless otherwise noted.

6	Jacques Desclioitres, MODIS Land Rapid Response Team, NASA/GSFC
7	Dale Debolt*
8	Zina Deretsky, National Science Foundation; NASA/JPL-Caltech
9	University of Wisconsin, Madison
10	Chandler Wilkerson, Institute for Molecular Design, University of Houston
12	© George Steinmetz, Corbis
16	AP/Wide World; © Daniel H. Sandweiss
17	© Walter Hupiu, EPA/Landov
18	© Daniel H. Sandweiss
19	AP/Wide World; © EPA/Peruvian National Institute of Culture/Landov
20	AP/Wide World; © Daniel H. Sandweiss
22	WORLD BOOK illustration by Bob Hersey
24	© Pilar Olivares, Reuters/Landov; © George Steinmetz
26	NASA/JPL-Caltech
28	WORLD BOOK illustration by Steven Karp
30	© Ann Ronan Picture Library/HIP/The Image Works
31	NASA/JHUAPL/SwRI
33	NASA/JPL-Caltech
34	NASA/ESA/A. Feild (STScI)
37	© Detlev Van Ravenswaay, SPL/Photo Researchers
38	© Don Dixon
40	© Steve Haddock, MBARI
41	© Deeble & Stone, OSF/Animals Animals; © Steve Haddock, MBARI; © Steve Haddock, MBARI
43	© Mark Harmel, Photo Researchers
44	AP/Wide World
45	© Steve Haddock, MBARI
46	© Steve Haddock, MBARI; © MBARI
47	© Steve Haddock, MBARI; © MBARI
48	Janet R. Voight; Claudia E. Mills; Claudia E. Mills; Ronald J. Larson
49	Dan E. Nilsson; © Paul A. Sutherland, SeaPics
50	© Steve Haddock, MBARI
51	© Steve Haddock, MBARI; © MBARI
52	© Steve Haddock, MBARI
53	Keith M. Bayha; © Ken Lucas, Visuals Unlimited
54-61	Conservation International
62	Zina Deretsky, National Science Foundation
65	Kalliopi Monoyios, University of Chicago
67	Beth Romey, University of Chicago
68	© Singh/Custom Medical Stock Photo
71	Library of the College of Physicians of Philadelphia
72-73	Christine Gralapp*
77	© TH Foto-Werbung/Photo Researchers
80	© Clem Spalding, Southwest Foundation for Biomedical Research
84	© Mark Garlick, Photo Researchers
87	WORLD BOOK illustration by Barbara Cousins
88	NASA/D. Padgett, IPAC & Caltech/ W. Brandner, IPAC/K. Stapelfeldt, JPL
89	© Mark Garlick, Photo Researchers
90	AP/Wide World; © Marli Miller, Visuals Unlimited
92-93	WORLD BOOK illustration by George D. Fryer, Bernard Thornton Artists
94	NASA/JPL-Caltech/P.S. Teixeira, Center for Astrophysics
95	WORLD BOOK illustration by Barbara Cousins; NASA/JSC Astrobiology Institute
96	University of Washington; Verena C. Wimmer et al., Southern Illinois University
97	© Mitsuaki Iwago, Minden Pictures
98	NASA
100	© PhotoAlto/SuperStock
102	WORLD BOOK illustration by Barbara Cousins
104	© Meyer/Custom Medical Stock Photo
105	WORLD BOOK chart by Bill and Judie Anderson
108-109	© SuperStock
110	© Phanie/Photo Researchers; © Chris Priest, SPL/Photo Researchers; © Uniphoto
112	Oak Ridge National Laboratory
114	© Roger Powell, Foto Natura/Minden Pictures; © NanoSphere/Schoeller Switzerland AG
115	U.S. Department of Energy
116	Paul Perrault*
117	© E. H. Sykes, P. Han, & B. A. Mantooth, Weiss Group/ Penn State University